R. Marvin M'Innis
1968

An Introduction to
A MATHEMATICAL TREATMENT
OF ECONOMICS

An Introduction to
A MATHEMATICAL TREATMENT OF ECONOMICS

G. C. Archibald and Richard G. Lipsey

WEIDENFELD AND NICOLSON
5 Winsley Street London W1

ACKNOWLEDGEMENTS

We wish to thank all our students, past and present, who have endured the course on which this book is based, and contributed to its development by their co-operation and comments. We also thank many colleagues for innumerable external effects, and in particular Mr P.T.Geary of the University of Essex and Mr A.H.Vanags of Queen Mary College, London, for reading the manuscript. The former also made substantial improvements based on his own teaching experience, and the latter also rescued the index at a critical moment.

G.C.A.
R.G.L.

Made and printed in Great Britain by
William Clowes and Sons, Limited
London and Beccles

CONTENTS

CHAPTER 1

INTRODUCTION

1.1

We want to explain as clearly as we possibly can to whom this book is addressed, what the reader may hope to get out of it, and how best to use it. The 'What' requires that we explain why it is worth tackling economics mathematically at all. 'To Whom' comes first.

To Whom

This book is addressed to two distinct groups of students. The first group consists of those who have completed no more than O-level mathematics, who may have disliked it, and have almost certainly forgotten much of it, but who have already completed an introductory course in economics at a standard of one of the basic text-books such as Lipsey's *Introduction to Positive Economics*,[1] and who are going on in economics. The second group consists of students who have taken A-level mathematics, and are possibly taking a first-year university course in mathematics, who are currently studying introductory economic theory, and who wish to follow a more formal and rigorous treatment of some of the theory than they can find in the standard introductory text-books.

Let us consider first the students with only O-level mathematics, since it was with them in mind that the material for this book was first assembled. Indeed this book began several years ago as a course of lectures given at the London School of Economics to second-year students who satisfied the following criteria:

(i) they had done no mathematics since O-level;

(ii) they had taken the standard first-year course in economics, common to all first-year social science students, together with introductory courses in politics, economic history, etc.;

(iii) they had elected to specialise in economics.

Thus we address ourselves in the first place to those students who have not

---

[1] R. G. Lipsey, *An Introduction to Positive Economics*, Second Edition, Weidenfeld and Nicolson, London, 1966.

gone beyond O-level mathematics but who have done enough economics to be persuaded that it is a subject they wish to take seriously. We assert now, and argue later, that to become a professional economist nowadays it is necessary to have some mathematical equipment; and while mathematics is not necessary to take an honours degree in economics at most British universities, some notion of mathematical methods is indispensable to get the best out of the subject. We further assert, and hope that this book will demonstrate, that economics is so inherently mathematical a subject that anyone who has taken a 'principles' course and acquitted himself creditably has already demonstrated his capacity to do mathematical economics: what he lacks is some technical equipment which we hope to give him. He probably also lacks mathematical self-confidence; but this is easily remedied by success. Indeed, we hope that increasing success will persuade some readers that it is easier to learn economics when one has more powerful mathematical tools at one's command than those of plane geometry and verbal reasoning.

We must assume that the reader who belongs to this class is prepared to make some substantial investment in learning the necessary mathematical techniques. We also assume that he is, more or less concurrently, taking intermediate courses in both macro- and micro-theory: we sometimes use material which is beyond the normal principles course, but none which may not be found in a good second-year course. On the other hand, the sections in which the economics goes beyond a first-year course occur later in the book, and a student can read this book with no more preparation than a good introductory course in economics, provided he is prepared to invest time in learning additional economics as well as additional mathematics. The reason that we introduce, and use, more material than is to be found in a principles course is that this is a book about economics. The mathematical content is intended to help the economist who was mathematically maltreated at school, and to equip him with a few basic tools of wide utility. To demonstrate their utility, as well as to afford the opportunity for exercise, we do economics; and the bulk of this book falls into the sequence of a chapter of technique followed by one of application. We emphasise that this is a book about economics in which we explain some mathematical tools.

The second group to which this book is addressed consists of students who have already progressed well beyond O-level mathematics and who are impatient to see their tools applied to the basic economics that they are currently learning. Many students with a background in mathematics (and possibly also in science) who study elementary economics realise quickly that the subject has a structure that can be expressed in mathematical terms. Such students often become impatient to see the subject handled in a more rigorous fashion than is usual in elementary courses. If you are one of these students you should find that the present book goes some way towards satisfying your needs.

How readers in both of the groups described above should use this book is discussed under a later heading in this introduction.

1.2 What is a Mathematical Approach to Economics and Why Should it be Studied?

We have already stated that economics is so mathematical a subject that the student who has taken a principles course has done some 'mathematical economics', and demonstrated his capacity to do it. That a principles course is 'mathematical' may seem a surprising statement. But consider a sample of the ideas in a principles course, and their mathematical expression:

(i) 'general equilibrium', or 'everything depends on everything else': this suggests a very large number of relationships that must, somehow, fit together, i.e., a set of 'simultaneous equations'.

(ii) 'quantity demanded depends on price': an application of the fundamental mathematical notion of a functional relationship;

(iii) 'the equilibrium price is that at which quantity demanded equals quantity supplied': this refers to the solution of a system of two simultaneous equations in two unknowns, price and quantity;

(iv) 'consumption depends upon the level of income': another example of a functional relationship;

(v) 'profit maximisation': this assumption, and all the associated paraphernalia of marginal cost, marginal revenue, etc., is obviously an application of the mathematical notion of maximisation, whether we handle it in words, diagrams, or algebra;

(vi) 'marginal concepts': all marginal concepts such as marginal cost, revenue, utility, product, propensity to consume, save, import, etc., etc., are in fact first derivatives of the relevant functions going under other names;

(vii) 'the production frontier', or any other frontier, and the search for 'optimal points': this involves an application of the mathematical theory of 'constrained maxima'.

This list could easily be extended, but we hope we have made our point: the familiar, basic ideas of economics usually turn out to be particular cases of problems that are handled in mathematics; and if one is interested in the particular cases it seems natural to enquire into the general mathematics, in the hope of finding illumination and/or useful technical apparatus. Consideration of this list, however, suggests something more fundamental, that *there is no dichotomy between 'economics' and 'mathematical economics'.*

This we also wish to assert; and we believe that it will become obvious to anyone who persists with this book, if indeed it is not obvious already. Nevertheless, there clearly is some distinction between 'economics' and 'mathematical economics', and if the distinction is not the reflection of a real dichotomy of subject matter, we may ask of what it is a reflection. The answer is that the distinction is mainly a quantitative one: it is a matter simply of how much mathematical technique a particular problem demands. It reflects also a personal choice, since some economists know more mathematics than others, and are interested in problems the solution of which require more mathematics. As one might expect, there is also division of labour between the more and the less mathematically inclined; but division of labour is a matter of costs and convenience, and reflects no fundamental difference in what is divided.

It is common for the 'more mathematical' economist to be interested in questions which do not appear to other people to be of much practical significance: he may be interested in the 'generality', or 'rigour', or 'elegance' of proofs of propositions which we take for granted, as well as in solving technical problems that are too complicated for those with less equipment. The concepts of mathematics are intriguing, and the goals of the really 'mathematical' economist are worthwhile. We wish to stress at the very outset that this is not a 'rigorous' book: our goals are immediate and practical, and we have not scrupled to employ the easiest routes. This book aims accordingly at a much less ambitious level of mathematics than would satisfy the genuine mathematical economist; but it may also be a stage on the way and help the reader to appreciate what else may be done. There is no non-mathematical economics, only more and less; and we are concerned here with that amount which, we believe, any economist can learn and put to immediate use.

We have now explained the prior knowledge that we expect of the reader, and the relationship between this book and a principles course. The next question is naturally 'where will you be at the end?' To answer this, we must explain the aims of this book. We have already noticed that it is commonly possible to take an honours degree in economics at a British university with little or no mathematics beyond O-level. The situation is, however, changing rapidly, and economics departments now frequently require some more mathematics. For the student who has only O-level this is not easily acquired: normal university mathematics courses are closed to him, and some special provision is called for. In most economics departments, however, it is possible for the student who has A-level mathematics to continue his mathematics, and then to take mathematical economics as part of his undergraduate work. The mathematical economics course is then generally inaccessible to the student who has only O-level. The result is that the gap between those who did and those who did not take A-level mathematics generally widens while they are at university. If it is the case, as we think, that some mathematical equipment is nowadays essential to the professional economist, it does not seem right that there should be an 'arts stream' of economists who, because of the choice they made at school, should be permanently excluded from courses in which they may acquire professional equipment. Thus we hope that the student who perseveres with this book will subsequently be able to do some or all of the following:

(i) Take, if he wishes (and university regulations permit), a course in mathematical economics which would normally be closed to him;

(ii) Take, if he wishes (and regulations permit), his university's first-year mathematics course during his third year (in calculus, he will find himself far ahead of A-level students in some topics, and behind in others; linear algebra, which is the other main ingredient of most first-year mathematics courses, is not usually taught at school);

(iii) Read an elementary text in mathematical statistics, which requires some calculus, instead of having to depend exclusively on 'cook books';

(iv) Read most of R. G. D. Allen's *Mathematical Analysis for Economists* with comfort, and much of it for revision, and be equipped to tackle his *Mathematical Economics*,[1] which constitutes an entire 'second course' of about a year;

(v) Read during his third year many of the journal articles which are usually put on the reading list, but employ too much mathematical argument to be mastered by the student who has not gone beyond O-level.

All this suggests that the present volume is to be regarded only as a stepping stone to more advanced mathematical work. We hope that many people will use it in just this way; but we also think that, even if the student reads no further in 'mathematical' economics, he will still be rewarded by his increased technical power and ability to read literature which, although not advertised as 'mathematical', certainly employs calculus methods. We also hope that all readers will find some of the economic analysis in this book of genuine interest in itself.

1.3 Some Common Fallacies

Those readers who have already completed a 'principles' course, and who have been at all persuaded by the argument that even a principles course involves mathematical ideas, probably do not need to be convinced of the possibility of 'mathematical social science'.[2] Nevertheless, there are so

[1] Both published by Macmillan, London, the first originally in 1938, the second in 1956.

[2] For the possibility and nature of social 'science' in the first place, see Lipsey, *Introduction to Positive Economics*, *op. cit.*, Chapter 1.

many mistaken ideas in common circulation that it may be worth making a few points.

The argument most commonly encountered is that economics is a social science, and that human affairs are too complex to be adequately represented in mathematical models, which are necessarily crude oversimplifications. A little reflection suggests that this is a perverse argument. Suppose that we have to deal, as we do in the social sciences, with a complicated system of inter-relationships between many individuals and institutions, pursuing different goals and impinging on each other in different ways. Suppose also that, guided by our knowledge of human beings, and of institutions and of history, we feel that we can formulate some hypotheses about some, at least, of the behavioural relations of the system. If the way in which the system would then work were clear to us, we should not need mathematics: it is precisely because the logical relations between all the 'bits' that we can hypothesise are too complex to be perceived by unaided intuition that we require analytical methods to help us elucidate the properties of what was, in the first place, our own creation.

The more complex we believe society to be, the more we need the sort of help that mathematics can give us. It is consistent, although in our view mistaken, to believe that the world is so simple that mathematics can be dispensed with and verbal argument used instead. It is utterly self-contradictory to believe that the real world is so complex that mathematical methods are inadequate and verbal reasoning more effective.

Mathematics was not invented by accident, or merely to annoy: mathematical methods were invented precisely because the human imagination can perceive, and invent, problems that the unaided imagination cannot solve. Once the problem is solved, of course, it is generally possible to explain the properties of the solution in a manner which is intuitively acceptable, and that is why a principles course can be ostensibly non-mathematical. It is, however, inconsistent to accept the fundamental notions of a principles course and to denounce 'mathematical economics' as an oversimplification of human affairs. Indeed, just because mathematics is a very powerful tool for making logical deductions from a set of assumptions about behaviour, it forces us to make fewer simplifications of reality than we would have to make if we were to rely on verbal reasoning alone. We shall, of course, always simplify because of the amount we do not know, and our limited ability to handle complex problems. The limitation, however, is not a virtue: it is one thing to simplify because we wish to, in order to omit irrelevant detail and expose the structure of a problem; it is quite another thing to simplify merely because we are technically incompetent.

In fact, of course, any theory is some sort of 'simplification' of human affairs, and we shall discuss later the role of theory (*any* sort of theory, whether ostensibly mathematical or not) in social science. Let us now, however, continue with our discussion of ill-founded objections. Probably the next most frequently encountered objection is that mathematics lends a spurious accuracy to economic analysis, spurious because there is always an unknown or unpredictable element in human conduct, accuracy because it is in the nature of mathematics to be 'accurate'. This is the argument of the man who knows nothing whatever about either mathematics or mathematical economics, but believes the former to be glorified arithmetic and the latter to be a sort of super book-keeping. As for the 'accuracy' of mathematics, we shall discover again and again in this book that its great power and beauty lies in its generality: with the help of mathematical analysis, we are able to make deductions of the form 'if this works like this, and that like that, the result must be such and such' without knowing – or caring – what an arithmetic example might look like. Consider how frequently one argues like this in a 'non-mathematical' principles course: 'If the demand curve slopes down, then an increase in supply will lead to a reduction in price' is a simple mathematical deduction, about the excessive 'accuracy' of which no-one is likely to complain!

Frequently, however, one does want numbers: if, for example, economics is to serve the ends of macro-policy makers, then it is imperative to have numbers. We want answers to such questions as 'how much additional unemployment will be caused next winter if we now reduce the rate of government spending by £100 million per annum?' It is hard to see how one can get a better answer than 'some' by any non-mathematical means whatever. If we want a quantitative answer, the alternative to using an 'econometric model' is crystal-gazing, or reliance on the intuition of the wise man. This is fine when the wise man is right; but what happens when he is wrong? All we learn is that he is not wise enough, which is nothing like as useful as finding that we have made a remediable error in our analysis of the economy. Indeed, even when he is right, his uses are limited: to listen to him, we must have faith, and there is more than one prophet! It is more satisfactory to judge an answer reached by logical means, which anyone may evaluate for himself – if he is prepared to learn how. As for the criticism that a numerical answer, provided from a 'model' of the economy, has a misleading and spurious appearance of accuracy, its accuracy, spurious or otherwise, is a statistical matter. Economic statisticians, or econometricians as they are called, have at their disposal a substantial toolkit for working out the confidence that should be attached to their numbers. They will produce results qualified by such remarks as 'with a 95% chance of being within 10% either way'. The rules of this game are beyond the scope of this book, but it is simply not the case that the modern econometrician gives you a unique right answer, and says 'take it or leave it': the subject

is a good deal more sophisticated than most of its critics. Indeed if we wish
to allow for a degree of uncertainty, error, free will or call-it-what-you-may,
we can build it into our theoretical formulations and then use mathematical
analysis to determine both our predictions and their probable range of
error. The techniques required are sophisticated, and their understanding
requires training in statistics. We can see, however, that if we confine ourselves to verbal reasoning we shall have to be satisfied with vague non-
quantitative qualifications, the effect of which we shall be unable to assess
in anything but the most general fashion.

There is still, of course, the extreme 'anti' position of the man who argues
that the essential unpredictability of human conduct is such that we de-
lude ourselves when we pretend that even an answer qualified by 'with a
95% chance of being 10% either way' is anything but bogus. This position
is basically that *anything* can happen, from which it follows that social
science is really impossible. The man who argues like this often feels that
he is in some way defending human liberty and dignity, that free will is
being 'got at' or denigrated when the social scientist ventures to predict
behaviour, and that the defence of liberty depends not upon political action
but upon the obstinate assertion of hopeless disorder and blessed contrari-
ness in human conduct. We may have some sympathy for him, but he is
both misguided and wrong. He is misguided because, if human beings frequently behave in a predictable manner, their liberty to do otherwise is not
threatened by the discovery of the fact. And he is simply wrong as to fact.
Try to imagine a world in which human conduct was genuinely quite unpredictable: existence would be impossible. Neither law, nor justice, nor
train time-tables would be more reliable than a roulette wheel; a kind remark could as easily provoke fury as sympathy – as easily as a harsh one;
one's landlady might put one out tomorrow, or forgive one the rent. There
is not, and could not be, anything in science fiction to match it. One cannot
really imagine a society of human beings that could possibly work like this.
Indeed a major part of 'brainwashing' techniques is to mix up rewards and
punishments until the victim genuinely does not know 'where he is': unpredictable pressures drive human beings mad. The fact is that we live in a
world which is some sort of mixture of the predictable, or average, or 'most
of the people most of the time', and of the haphazard, contrary, or random.
When we try to analyse this world, and apply our orderly models, we need
help from specialists in probability – statisticians – but we have not yet
found that we need the advice of the expert in the behaviour of systems in
states of total chaos.

There is one last popular objection to mathematical economics which
has only to be stated to be seen to be absurd, namely that mathematical
economics need not be correct. Mistakes can occur in any chain of reason-

ing, whether ostensibly mathematical or not: human beings are fallible, and mathematical economists are human beings. Perhaps people feel that a mathematical error is more sinful than some other sort of error because it is harder for the non-mathematician to spot! An alternative criticism is that much mathematical economics is 'irrelevant'. This may be true; but mathematical economics has no monopoly of irrelevance. And it is absurd to blame the tools for being used for the wrong purpose. The solution, if the tools are powerful, is to employ them to better purpose.

1.4   The Role of Theory

There is, or used to be, a school of thought which was 'anti-theory' irrespective of whether the theory was mathematical or not. A definitive criticism of the intuitionist and historical schools appeared in Lionel Robbins' *Nature and Significance of Economic Science*[1] as long ago as 1932, and, since this is a book that every economist should read for himself, we will not repeat Robbins' arguments. We will, however, say something about the role of economic theory and the relation between theory and observation.

'Which comes first, theory or observation?' is a perpetual chicken-and-egg question. We need not try to 'solve' it. We can say that without some sort of notion of what one is looking for, observation is pretty hopeless: there is an infinite number of facts that one might observe! And we can say that, without some observations, theorising is pretty hopeless: there is an infinite number of theories that one might construct! We want theory and observation to proceed closely together, but their original precedence or protocol is of no interest. Observation suggests what phenomena need explaining; theory offers explanation; observation is again required to test the theory, and throw up the next round of problems.

When we say 'theory' we mean:

a set of assumptions about behaviour

a logical analysis

a set of conclusions or 'predictions'.

The role of mathematical analysis is to help with the second step: 'if we assume so and so, what follows?' We are used to doing this by ordinary or verbal reasoning, or, in first-year economics, with the help of some Euclidean geometry. But ordinary reasoning is verbal logic, and Euclidean geometry is two-dimensional logic. 'Mathematics' is a catch-all title for any sort of logical argument conducted with the help of symbols. We can regard ordinary verbal reasoning as a branch of mathematics, if we like, or we can regard mathematics as a development of ordinary reasoning for cases in which verbal methods are cumbersome and inefficient. None of this matters very

[1] Macmillan, London, 2nd ed.

much. What matters is that we have to take the second step, to discover the logical implications of our assumptions, and we want the logical tools for the job. The selection of the tools in each case is a matter of convenience and our own technical skill. The greater is our command of the tools, the more intricate and potentially fruitful are the theories that we can handle.

Suppose, for example, that the observed phenomena we wish to explain are the behaviour of prices, wages, and profits in certain specified circumstances. We must start with some behavioural assumptions, such as profit maximisation by firms. We also need to know something about the technological limitations on the firm, and thus might assume constant returns to scale as well as diminishing returns to each factor separately. We now have to work out all the implications of these assumptions to discover the testable predictions of the theory. If we have done our job efficiently the theory will explain (i.e., predict) the behaviour we set out to explain, but it is almost certain that it will also predict other behaviour that we have not yet observed. The theory is tested by seeing if these additional predictions conform to the facts, and for this task we need to know some quite difficult statistical theory. Before we do our testing, however, we wish to discover *all* the implications of our basic assumptions. This purely logical process is one of the tasks undertaken by the economic theorist, and to be efficient in making his logical deductions he will need to use tools appropriate to the complexity of the basic assumptions. If the theory is simple, verbal analysis may be sufficient, whereas if the theory is complex mathematical analysis will be almost always necessary, and the attempt to rely on verbal reasoning alone will only leave us in a state of uncertainty as to whether a particular prediction is or is not logically implied by the theory at hand.[1] Only

---

[1] This point was illustrated dramatically to both authors when they were attending a conference some years ago. The first paper was given by a mathematical economist who presented a four-equation model of the behaviour of firms, deduced all its testable implications, and showed how he had gone about testing some of them. Because of the mathematical nature of the tools used to make deductions, the paper was regarded by many of the audience as being 'impossibly difficult'. The second paper was given by a literary economist. Here the discussion centred (in purely verbal terms) on an important applied problem concerning the workings of the British economy. The model involved would have been very complicated. It had not, in fact, been formally specified, but must, at a guess, have involved about a dozen unknowns, and their relations over time, as governed by a set of unspecified simultaneous equations. Proper specification and solution would have been very difficult. As things stood, we did not even know if the model *had* a solution, but, because the argument was all conducted verbally, no one seemed to think they were doing difficult economics. When an essentially complex theory is loosely and informally sketched, the intellectual effort subsequently devoted to its verbal analysis can only be a waste of time. No one could possibly have answered any of the questions posed in that discussion about the implications of the model being discussed without a formal specification and the application to it of some quite complex mathematical analysis. To pretend otherwise was self-delusion.

an obscurantist could regard this as a desirable situation. Thus we see that the mathematical and the verbal economist are not separated by their subject matter or their philosophy of social science, but only by the tools used to accomplish a step common to both: the discovery of all the implications of a stated set of hypotheses.

1.5   How to use this Book

We first make some general observations on the use of this book addressed to all readers, and then some specific ones addressed to the two groups of readers we have already singled out.

(i) The mathematics in this book is definitely non-rigorous. That it would cause the hair on the heads of our mathematical and statistical colleagues to stand on end is probably an understatement. Indeed many of them might regard it as a scandal that the book were ever published! You may well ask why we should have proceeded in the face of this view. There are many reasons. Two important ones may be singled out.

First, we believe that many students of economics have been frightened off mathematics by being exposed to a tedious, mechanical, and totally unmotivated approach. In the interests of the victim of this treatment who wishes to learn economics, we try to compensate by adopting the rule of introducing no technique until it is evidently needed, and then no more of it than is to be immediately employed.

More fundamentally, however, we believe that mathematics is a subject, like economics, in which the correct teaching technique is to cover the same subject several times with increasing rigour. Historically, the fully rigorous development of a subject does not spring from some genius's mind in a single act of spontaneous creation. Rather, problems occur, and techniques – at first rather crude ones – are invented to handle them. Exploration of further problems sooner or later reveals some inadequacy in the techniques, which are then subjected to close scrutiny, and in due course improved. This process[1] may go on for a long time until the 'fundamental underpinnings' of the technique are fully developed to the satisfaction of the mathematical theorists. The 'finished article', or final state of the theory or theorem, emerges from the process with the property that it is carefully designed to take care of the problems and criticisms that have contributed to its development. In our opinion it is impossible for a student totally unacquainted with the development to understand and appreciate

[1] For a fascinating study of the process of the historical development of mathematics together with an implied criticism of current pedagogical techniques see Imre Lakatos, 'Proofs and refutations', *British Journal for the Philosophy of Science*, 4 part article, 1963–4, vol. 14, pp. 1–25, 120–39, 221–45, and 296–342.

the final product. He needs to re-live some of the historical development – which after all was necessary for his elders and betters. He needs to get an approximate idea of what the calculus is all about, to master the technique of differentiation, and attack his problems in economics with these tools. Soon he will find that his rudimentary understanding is not sufficient. When he has encountered problems for which his existing knowledge is inadequate, he can return for a further investment in theory motivated by his *need* to know more; and his new theoretical knowledge can then be applied to the problem that led him to seek it. *We view this book as the first step in a continuing process.* The student who goes on to further work in 'mathematical economics' will need to work through the calculus a second, and possibly a third, time, getting a thorough grounding in its basic theory: otherwise he will be a blind rule-follower rather than a master of his tools. But the theory will mean more to him when he knows why he needs it and when he encounters problems that cannot be solved with the tools learned here.[1]

(ii) We have tried very hard to make this book self-contained. If you are learning mathematical techniques from it you may find, however, that our treatment leaves you confused or otherwise unsatisfied at some points. When this happens you should never hesitate to read the treatment of the same problem in another book. Indeed to read two different treatments of the same problems is very often desirable. There are many books which can be used for such reference: three that we recommend are by J. Parry Lewis, Sylvanus P. Thompson, and R. D. G. Allen.[2] Lewis's book is the least rigorous of the three; Thompson's is a classic by a mathematician, designed to take all the fear out of the calculus (in our opinion the attempt is completely successful, and the only limitation of the book for economists is that all of the applications are to physics); Allen's book is another classic, this time by an economist, which is more rigorous than Lewis's book, has more contact with economics than either of the other two, and for the student who finds himself at home with moderately rigorous analysis it is to be strongly recommended.

---

[1] This is a pedagogical approach adopted, with or without conscious understanding, by most economists. We go over the same subject matter with more and more rigour and depth several times in elementary, intermediate, and advanced courses. We implicitly recognise that the student cannot appreciate why a formal development of some model is needed until he has used a cruder version of the same model and has begun to encounter problems which his cruder model cannot handle.

[2] J. P. Lewis, *An introduction to mathematics for students of economics*, Macmillan, London, 1959.

Sylvanus P. Thompson, *Calculus made easy*, 3rd edition, St Martins, 1946.

R. G. D. Allen, *Mathematical analysis for economists*, Macmillan, London, 1963. (First issued 1938.)

(iii) Answers to exercises will be found at the back. We have offered hints for the more difficult questions, and the answer generally includes a further hint. It pays to have a serious shot at an exercise before looking up the answer!

Some sections are starred, thus *. This means both that they are difficult and that their comprehension is not assumed in what follows. They may therefore be skipped entirely on a first reading without subsequent penalty. Some exercises are starred too. This means simply that they are difficult. We have *not* adopted the policy common in mathematical texts, of leaving to you to prove *in the exercises* results that will be *required* in the next chapter. If you cannot do a starred exercise, simply go on, and do not be discouraged. At some later stage you will probably come back to it and find it quite easy.

There may be no course available to you which covers material close to that of this book. We have tried very hard to make the book manageable to the reader who has to work entirely on his own. (If you can persuade a couple of friends to work through the book in parallel with you, discussion of problems can be very helpful: we speak from personal experience.)

Readers with only O-level mathematics: This book is designed to overcome any fears of mathematics you now have, and to teach you a substantial amount of mathematics beyond what you now know. We assume, however, that you have completed a course in elementary economics so that we may use economic concepts that are familiar to you to introduce mathematical ones that are not.

At the beginning we have gone very slowly. Chapter 3 reviews some basic concepts in analytical geometry and algebra that are included in every O-level syllabus, and which are necessary for the economic analysis that follows. We try to introduce these ideas very gently at first, and from the outset we place the accent on understanding what is going on rather than on blindly memorising a set of rules. If you are prepared to work hard on the basic mathematical chapters and will persevere, taking much time at the beginning, we are certain that you will overcome your worries about mathematics and master all the techniques in this book: after all, every student of economics at the University of Essex has done so in his second year, and we believe that other students can do what ours can.

One of the most important psychological obstacles to the non-mathematically oriented reader is the off-putting appearance of page upon page of symbols. We know this is so, and both the authors have been struck, while writing this book, by the advantages of the lecture (in which each line of development need be written up only after the class is satisfied with the previous line) over the printed page (in which the whole argument is committed to print before the reader begins on step one). There are one or two hints we can give on how to proceed.

(i) Experiment to find your own best method of tackling mathematical arguments. When reading a new article on economics in which mathematics is used, one of us habitually stumbles through the argument hastily, without understanding how each step follows from the previous one, all the time cursing his mathematical ineptitude, and saying that he should never have pretended to be an economist. By the time he has got to the end he has begun to develop some idea of what the author is aiming at, and whether the alleged conclusions are interesting enough to justify the effort of finding out if they really do follow. If the answer is 'yes' he reads the article again, this time a little more slowly to get a feel for the structure of the argument, but still without following each detailed step, and still suffering from an inferiority complex about his mathematical ineptitude. On the third reading he perseveres, and moves on only when he can reconstruct for himself every step of the argument.

You may find that your optimal technique for reading mathematical economics is either similar to or very different from this. The object of describing it is to suggest that you are not unique in finding mathematical arguments difficult to follow, and that you will have to develop your own personal way – possibly an eccentric one – of approaching such arguments.

(ii) You should always remember one very important dictum: *other people's mathematics are very much harder to follow than your own*. If you want to test the validity of this, take some mathematics that you can now handle (possibly two simultaneous equations such as $Y = 10 + 2X$ and $Y = 40X$) and write down the steps whereby you arrive at a solution. Now show your page or two of mathematics to a friend with a roughly similar mathematical background: the odds are that he will take a long time to follow you, and will complain of steps omitted. It really is very much easier to work out a mathematical problem step by step for yourself on a blank piece of paper than to follow through three or four pages of manipulations already completed by someone else. There are two practical suggestions that follow from these general observations that may be of value to at least some readers. First, it often helps to cover up the page of the book you are reading and move the cover down line by line as each step follows from the previous one. Second, and much more important, it almost always pays to write down the steps of a mathematical argument on a separate piece of paper of one's own. This way you develop your own mathematical agility as you work through the book.

(iii) Do not expect to understand everything the first time you read a chapter. In mathematics, as in economics, the significance of doing something in a particular way is often not apparent until you have become familiar with it in use. For this reason it often pays, once the greater part of a chapter has been grasped, to start the next chapter immediately although parts of the previous one are still not understood. When you run into trouble in the new chapter because you did not fully understand something earlier, you can then return to the point in question and study it again with your mind clearly focused on that point and with a new motivation to master it since you now see why you need it.

To Students with substantially more Mathematics than O-level: You will find the first mathematical chapters, especially Chapters 3 and 5, tedious and unnecessary. You should either skip such chapters completely or read them very rapidly. In some topics, however, we do go well beyond the standard A-level syllabus, and if you wonder if we have any new mathematics to teach you at all, you should sample Chapter 11 immediately.

Without doubt you will wish to concentrate on the economics, and our general advice to you is to skip or read very cursorily those mathematical chapters that deal with techniques you have already studied, and to concentrate on the economics chapters (the only one of which you might consider skipping being Chapter 2). If you think this book has nothing to teach you in either mathematics or economics you should read Chapters 11 and 12 immediately. If you still think this after reading them, then you were very probably correct in your original conjecture. If you found economics you did not know, or had not seen presented in this form in Chapter 12, then you should return to Chapter 2 (or possibly 4) and read on through all the development of the economic models.

1.6 The Selection of Contents

In this book we concentrate on calculus methods because of their wide applicability and crucial importance in the development of economics. Other techniques are, however, increasingly used, so it is important to know what is left out and where it may be found.

The main mathematical topic left out is linear, or matrix, algebra. This is used extensively in econometrics, and in the modern techniques of programming, and even a slight acquaintance with it is indeed very useful. It is, however, a big subject, and we did not wish to write too big a book. A little linear algebra, and a fascinating application, will be found in a basically non-mathematical text-book, *Interindustry Economics*, by H. B. Chenery and P. G. Clarke. A serious course in linear algebra can be found in wonderfully self-contained form in Chapter 3 of J. Johnston's *Econometric Methods*. The relevant chapters of Allen's two volumes between them cover a great deal of linear algebra, together with economic applications.

In the chapters on dynamics, we felt that we had to choose between introducing differential equations or difference equations, not wishing to take the space required to discuss both. We have chosen differential equations, partly because they follow naturally from the earlier work in this book, and partly because there exist already superb introductions to difference equations for non-mathematicians. One is in W.J.Baumol's *Economic Dynamics*, which is accessible to any second or third year economist, and another is S.Goldberg's *Difference Equations*, written specially for social scientists. The topic is thoroughly covered in R.G.D.Allen's *Mathematical Economics*, with applications.[1]

Our aim in this book is to introduce no mathematics that we do not use in economic applications, and to use none that we have not explained. This means, of course, that we have been very selective in our choice of mathematical topics, and much is omitted that 'every school boy ought to know'. We do not see why he should, unless it can be shown to be useful, and useful in the solution of problems more interesting than that of finding the length of time required to fill the bath when some fool has left the plug out. In fact, most of what we have omitted that comes in the usual A-level and first-year university syllabus *is* useful, if one happens to have the right problem, and a much more inclusive survey of the mathematics will be found in J.Parry Lewis's *An Introduction to Mathematics for Students of Economics* (Macmillan, Papermac). Parry Lewis's volume is very useful, but it should be noted that its object is very different from that of the present volume: it covers a great deal more mathematics, but no economics. It may therefore be regarded as a preparation for a course in mathematical economics, or as a reference book.

We discussed in 1.2 above the courses that a student might take and the texts that he might read after finishing this book. We have not yet considered the possibility that he will have become interested in mathematical ideas themselves. If this should happen, two obvious books in which mathematical ideas are developed in a fashion intelligible to readers without a strong technical background are Allen's *Basic Mathematics* (Macmillan) and *What is Mathematics?* by R.Courant and H.Robbins (Oxford University Press).

[1] W.J.Baumol, with a contribution by R.Turvey, *Economic dynamics: an introduction*. Macmillan, N.Y., 1959.

R.G.D.Allen, *Mathematical analysis for economists*, 2nd edition, Macmillan, London, 1963.

Samuel Goldberg, *Introduction to Difference Equations*, John Wiley and Sons, N.Y., Science Editions (paperback), 1961.

CHAPTER 2

SOME FAMILIAR RESULTS
FORMALLY DERIVED

2.1 Some Definitions

In this chapter you will first begin to follow formal proofs of some of the propositions to which you were introduced verbally in your first-year economics. No mathematics other than elementary algebra is required. The point of this chapter is not so much substance as style: we must learn how to set up a proposition, even a simple and familiar one, in such a fashion that we may proceed in formal, step-by-step fashion to obtain a proof. Thus we are concerned here with the idea of making formal deductions. At the end of the chapter you will be invited to construct further formal proofs for yourself and, when you have done this, you will be well on your way to overcoming any fears and prejudices you may have had about the use of mathematics in economic theory.

What is done in this chapter can in fact be done more elegantly and, in some ways more satisfactorily, when we have the powerful tools of the calculus at our command. Thus, this chapter may be dispensable, but for those who do not already have calculus we regard it as a necessary transition, and good practice in its own right.

As a first step in our analysis we must introduce some notation:

C = total costs,
R = total revenue,
Π = total profits

We use a subscript notation to indicate the level of output with which the costs, revenue and profits are associated. Thus C_1 means the level of costs when one unit is produced, C_2 means the level of costs when two units are produced, and similarly for C_3, C_4, and all other levels of output. In the same way, R_1, R_2, Π_1, Π_2, etc., denote the levels of revenue and profit at the corresponding rates of output.

In economic theory we do not wish to be confined to arithmetic examples. Thus we do not wish only to be able to consider the behaviour of costs, revenues, or profits, when output is at some specific rate, say 50 or 100 units per day: we are interested in how costs, revenues, and profits *change* as the rate of output changes from one rate to another *whatever* that rate may be. We use the letter n to specify some particular rate of output without committing ourselves to what that rate is. Thus, just as C_2 meant the level of costs when two units were produced each period, C_n means the level of costs when n units are produced each period. Similarly R_n and Π_n refer to the level of total revenue and total profits when n units are produced and sold each period.

To discuss changes we also need to be able to refer to related rates of output without saying numerically what any of the outputs are. We might refer, for example, to output at the rates of 3, 4, and 5 units per period, at the rates of 31, 32, and 33 units per period, or at any three other adjacent rates. To do this we refer to the rates $n-1$, n, and $n+1$. This indicates that we have three output rates that differ from each other by one unit. Each of these rates of output will have an associated level of costs, revenues, and profits and we now write

$$C_{n-1}, C_n, C_{n+1},$$
$$R_{n-1}, R_n, R_{n+1},$$
$$\Pi_{n-1}, \Pi_n, \Pi_{n+1},$$

to refer to them.

In more general terms we could refer to the levels $n-a$, n, and $n+b$, where a and b were any numbers. In the problems considered in this chapter we are always interested in successive units of output so that, in our particular case, we have $a=b=1$.

Employing this notation[1] we can now define average and marginal concepts:

$$AC_n = \frac{C_n}{N}, \tag{1}$$

$$AR_n = \frac{R_n}{N}, \tag{2}$$

$$A\Pi_n = \frac{\Pi_n}{N} = \frac{R_n - C_n}{N}. \tag{3}$$

The first expression says, for example, that average cost, when N units are produced, is equal to the total cost when N units are produced (C_n), divided by the number of units (N). Similarly, for average revenue and average profit. Throughout the chapter n, $n-1$, and $n+1$ are used in two ways, and this can be confusing unless one is clear about what is being done. First, they are used as subscripts to indicate the rate of output at which the variable quantity is being measured. Thus C_n means the level of *costs* when n units are produced per period. Second, they are used as symbols for the actual number being produced each period. Thus if we had actual numbers

---

[1] In what follows AC stands for the single variable average cost, *not* A *times* C, and similarly for AR etc.

for expression (1) we would replace C_n by a number of shillings which represented the cost of producing n units of output, while we would replace the N in the numerator by the number of units of output being produced each period. To avoid confusion on this point we have used a lowercase n whenever it is a subscript and an uppercase N whenever it stands for the number of units produced. Thus, for example, C_n stands for the level of *costs* when N units are produced while N stands for the actual *number of units* being produced.

Marginal concepts are defined as follows:

$$MC_n = C_n - C_{n-1} = \Delta C_n, \tag{4}$$

$$MR_n = R_n - R_{n-1} = \Delta R_n, \tag{5}$$

$$M\Pi_n = \Pi_n - \Pi_{n-1} = \Delta\Pi_n. \tag{6}$$

The first expression defines the marginal cost of the nth unit as the difference in total cost between producing at the rates of n units per period and $n-1$ units per period. We use the symbol Δ (the Greek capital delta) to indicate a change in something. Thus, MC_n is the same thing as ΔC_n and MR_n is the same thing as ΔR_n.

2.2 Some Formal Proofs

We may now proceed to prove four important propositions that occur in the elementary theory of the firm. To do this we need nothing more than the concepts already introduced and the rules of elementary algebra.

I *In perfect competition the price of the product, the firm's marginal revenue, and its average revenue always coincide, while, whenever the firm's demand curve slopes downward, the firm's marginal revenue is necessarily less than its average revenue.*

This is a well known proposition needed for the elementary theory of the firm and we now wish to prove it formally. We first note that average revenue and price always coincide since they are the same thing. This is a matter of definition, but just to check that we have been consistent in our definitions of terms we can write down the definition of average revenue when N units are produced and sold, and check that it is the same as the definition of price. We know that

$$AR_n = \frac{R_n}{N} \tag{2}$$

and $$R_n = Np_n \tag{7}$$

where p_n is the price ruling when N units are sold. We divide both sides of (7) by N, obtaining AR_n on the left-hand side and p_n on the right.

Now consider marginal revenue when sales go up from N to $N+1$ units.

$$MR_{n+1} = R_{n+1} - R_n \tag{5}$$

Since the revenue from the sale of a particular number of units is that number of units *times* the price associated with that number we may write

$$MR_{n+1} = (N+1)p_{n+1} - Np_n$$

$$= Np_{n+1} + p_{n+1} - Np_n$$

Collecting the terms containing N and factoring we now have

$$MR_{n+1} = N(p_{n+1} - p_n) + p_{n+1} \tag{8}$$

or $\qquad MR_{n+1} = N \, \Delta p_{n+1} + p_{n+1}.$

Expression (8) shows the marginal revenue from the $(N+1)$th unit to be composed of two terms: the revenue gained from selling the $(N+1)$th unit plus a term for the change in price multiplied by the number of units already being sold (N) before the change in price.

The basic assumption of perfect competition is that the price facing a firm does not change as that firm's output and sales change. This may be written

$$p_{n-1} = p_n = p_{n+1} = \bar{p} \tag{9}$$

for all n, which says that the price associated with each level of output is the same. Notice that we call the price $\bar{p}$. It is a common and convenient notation to put a bar over a variable to note that it is to be held constant. A bar therefore indicates that a quantity which might have been thought to be subject to variation is in fact going to be held constant. Substituting (9) into (8) we get

$$MR_{n+1} = N(\bar{p} - \bar{p}) + \bar{p}$$

$$= \bar{p}. \tag{10}$$

Thus for perfect competition we have proved that

$$MR = \bar{p} \tag{11}$$

for any level of output N.

Now consider any firm facing a downward-sloping demand curve. In this case the higher the output the lower the price, which is expressed by

$$p_{n-1} > p_n > p_{n+1} \tag{12}$$

and which is read 'P-N minus one exceeds P-N which in turn exceeds P-N plus one'.

If we now consider (8) in the light of (12) we see that $p_{n+1} - p_n$ is negative

so that
$$N(p_{n+1} - p_n) < 0. \tag{13}$$

The 'inequality sign' $<$ is read 'is less than'. Comparing (13) and (8) we see that

$$MR_{n+1} < p_{n+1} \tag{14}$$

$$< AR_{n+1}. \tag{15}$$

If you inspect expression (8) you will see that MR falls short of AR by the term we have singled out in (13). This term expresses the loss on the N units *already being sold* when the rate of sale rises from N to $N+1$. The term gives the fall in price caused by raising the rate of sales and applies it to all the N units already being sold.

We have now proved what we set out to prove. We have now completed a formal proof and we can move on to try a second one.

II *Profits are maximised at the point at which marginal cost equals marginal revenue.*

To prove this proposition we first write down the expression for the change in profits when production is increased by one unit:

$$\Delta\Pi_n = \Pi_n - \Pi_{n-1} = (R_n - C_n) - (R_{n-1} - C_{n-1}). \tag{16}$$

We now remove the brackets to obtain[1]

$$\Delta\Pi_n = R_n - C_n - R_{n-1} + C_{n-1}. \tag{17}$$

At this stage our expression in (17) looks superficially ridiculous: adding the costs and subtracting the revenues associated with $n-1$ units of production in order to obtain profits certainly seems odd. Let us, however, merely write the terms in a different order:

$$\Delta\Pi_n = R_n - R_{n-1} - (C_n - C_{n-1}). \tag{18}$$

The first two terms give the change in revenue and the second two terms the change in costs when production goes from $N-1$ to N units. Using expressions (4) and (5) we can write this as

$$\Delta\Pi_n = MR_n - MC_n. \tag{19}$$

Now take the current level of output as $N-1$ units and ask if it is worth while raising or lowering output: if $\Delta\Pi_n > 0$ then we are not at the profit-maximising point, and profits can be increased by raising output; if $\Delta\Pi_n < 0$ then profits are lowered by raising output, and can be increased by lowering output; finally if $\Delta\Pi = 0$ then profits can neither be raised nor lowered by changing output, i.e., profits are as high as they can possibly be at the present level of output. Thus if $\Delta\Pi_n > 0$ we should raise output, and if

[1] In case you have forgotten, $-(a-b) = -a+b$.

$\Delta\Pi_n < 0$ we should lower output, and only if $\Delta\Pi_n = 0$ can we be at the profit-maximising output. Using (19) we can now write:

when $\Delta\Pi_n > 0$, $MR_n - MC_n > 0$ or $MR_n > MC_n$;   (20)

when $\Delta\Pi_n < 0$, $MR_n - MC_n < 0$ or $MR_n < MC_n$;   (21)

when $\Delta\Pi_n = 0$, $MR_n - MC_n = 0$ or $MR_n = MC_n$.   (22)

Thus when $MR_n > MC_n$ output is below the profit-maximising level, when $MR_n < MC_n$ output is above the profit-maximising level and only when $MR_n = MC_n$ can output be at the profit-maximising level. This proof is almost ridiculously simple. The expression for a change in profits is written down in terms of costs and revenues and the terms are merely re-grouped to show that the expression can be written in terms of marginal cost and marginal revenue. If the reader will reflect on the amount of time spent by himself and his class mates on grasping this principle when it was presented verbally or through numerical examples he should be impressed both with the economy and the conclusiveness of mathematical reasoning. The proof given above is nonetheless clumsy compared to the one we can give when we have calculus tools at our command.

III   *Fixed costs do not affect the profit maximising level of output.*

We have seen from II above that profits are maximised when $MC_n = MR_n$. We now merely need to show that fixed costs do not affect marginal costs. This is easily done if we divide costs into a fixed component that does not change with output and a variable component that does:

$$C_n = VC_n + \overline{FC}.   (23)$$

Variable costs are a function of (i.e., they vary with) output, while fixed costs are the same for all levels of output. (We remind ourselves of this latter assumption by writing a bar over the symbol for fixed costs.) We now re-call the definition of marginal costs from expression (4):

$$MC_n = C_n - C_{n-1}.   (4)$$

Substituting (23) into (4) gives

$$MC_n = VC_n + \overline{FC} - (VC_{n-1} + \overline{FC})   (24)$$
$$= VC_n - VC_{n-1}.$$

Thus marginal cost is a function solely of variable cost. A change in FC does not affect MC and hence does not affect the profit-maximising position.[1] When one thinks of the generations of businessmen and accountants

---

[1] Over the period of time over which the costs are fixed. If there is a longer time period over which these costs are variable then, over that time period, they do enter into marginal costs.

who have reasoned, and still do, that because their rent (or any other fixed cost) has risen it is necessary in the interests of profit maximising to raise prices (and hence lower output) one realises that even the most simple mathematical propositions are not always understood and, when they are understood, they can be of great practical value.

IV   *The marginal cost curve cuts the average cost curve at the lowest point on the average cost curve.*

We divide this proof into three parts. We first prove that when the marginal cost of the Nth unit is less than the average cost of $N-1$ units, the average cost of the N units is less than the average cost of the $N-1$ units. In symbols we wish to show that if (and only if)

then
$$MC_n < AC_{n-1} \qquad (25)$$

$$AC_n < AC_{n-1}. \qquad (26)$$

In fact it is more convenient to start by reversing the argument, and prove that if (26) holds then (25) must also hold. We begin by assuming that (26) holds and we undertake a series of manipulations of this inequality. Each step seems arbitrary but the purpose is to produce an expression which proves what we require to prove. Thus as we manipulate (26) we are trying to get it into a form that looks like (25). Substituting in the definitions of AC_n and AC_{n-1} from (1) gives

$$\frac{C_n}{N} < \frac{C_{n-1}}{N-1} \qquad (27)$$

Now notice that total cost when N units are produced equals total costs when $N-1$ are produced plus the extra cost of producing the Nth unit:

$$C_n = C_{n-1} + (C_n - C_{n-1}). \qquad (28)$$

We were led to write down (28) by a verbal argument but it checks formally since the right-hand side of (28) is merely the left-hand side with C_{n-1} added and taken away again. If we now substitute (28) into (27) we get:

$$\frac{C_{n-1} + C_n - C_{n-1}}{N} < \frac{C_{n-1}}{N-1}. \qquad (29)$$

Multiply both sides of expression (29) by $N(N-1)$ to give

$$(C_{n-1} + C_n - C_{n-1})(N-1) < NC_{n-1}. \qquad (30)$$

Multiplying out the left-hand side:

$$NC_{n-1} + NC_n - NC_{n-1} - C_{n-1} - C_n + C_{n-1} < NC_{n-1}. \qquad (31)$$

Next subtract NC_{n-1} from both sides of the expression to get

$$NC_n - NC_{n-1} - C_{n-1} - C_n + C_{n-1} < 0. \tag{32}$$

Next we add C_{n-1} to both sides to get

$$NC_n - NC_{n-1} - C_n + C_{n-1} < C_{n-1}. \tag{33}$$

Next we factor the left-hand side of the expression to obtain

$$(N-1)(C_n - C_{n-1}) < C_{n-1}. \tag{34}$$

(If you are in any doubt about this you can multiply (34) out yourself and check that it yields (33).)

Next we divide through by $(N-1)$ to obtain

$$C_n - C_{n-1} < \frac{C_{n-1}}{N-1} \tag{35}$$

From the definitions in expressions (1) and (4) we can rewrite (35) as:

$$MC_n < AC_{n-1}. \tag{36}$$

We have now proved what we set out to prove, that if $AC_n < AC_{n-1}$ then it must also be true that $MC_n < AC_{n-1}$. The next step is to show that if (25) is true then (26) is also true. We do not bother to go through this because it is done merely by reversing the steps we have just taken. The result is that if either (25) or (26) holds, so must the other.

The steps by which we got from (26) to (36) are each very simple algebraic manipulations: the trick, or art, in this sort of thing lies in knowing which manipulations to make. If one starts with a relation such as (26) and merely wonders more or less blindly what else is implied by it, then the manipulations must also be more or less blind. If, on the other hand, one starts with a pretty shrewd idea of what one is after, the manipulations can at least be carried on in a purposeful manner. At first sight manipulations of this sort often look arbitrary; but with practice you will find that you can attack such problems in an increasingly systematic fashion.

We next prove that if

$$MC_n > AC_{n-1} \tag{37}$$

then

$$AC_n > AC_{n-1} \tag{38}$$

which is to say that if the marginal cost of the Nth unit exceeds the average cost of $N-1$ units then average cost will be rising. This is done merely by duplicating all the steps by which (25) was shown to follow from (26) but with the inequality sign reversed. If you re-do the proof for yourself reversing all inequalities and working out each step for yourself you will discover what we pointed out in the introduction: other people's mathematics are always much harder to follow than your own. We strongly advise you to try it for yourself, using our steps as a guide, before reading on.

Finally we show that if

$$MC_n = AC_{n-1} \tag{39}$$

then

$$AC_n = AC_{n-1}. \tag{40}$$

This is again done by duplicating the above steps, this time replacing the inequality sign with an equality sign. There is really no need for you to work all through this again unless you are still worried by it. Knowing when it is not necessary to reduplicate a series of repetitive calculations is a sign of mathematical sophistication.

When all these steps are done they provide us with the proof we require, that $AC_n \gtreqless AC_{n-1}$ according as $MC_n \gtreqless AC_{n-1}$. This is merely a summary way of stating proposition IV: average cost of N units falls short of, exceeds or equals the average cost of $N-1$ units according as the marginal cost of the Nth unit falls short of, exceeds, or is equal to, the average cost of $N-1$ units.

All of the four proofs given here are relatively inefficient. In particular the proof of IV is very cumbersome. Until we have the calculus they are, however, the best we can do and they do show that we can prove our verbal propositions symbolically whenever we wish. When we have mastered the tools of differential calculus we shall use them to prove many more propositions of this sort, much more economically. Many more elementary propositions could, however, be proved in this fashion, and you should try one or two for yourself as suggested in the questions at the end of this chapter.

Enough should have been said here to show that we can substitute mathematical reasoning for the verbal reasoning usually used in basic text books, that the mathematical reasoning is sometimes more compact, and that there is nothing basically terrifying about the whole thing. Anyone with a reasonable ability to handle elementary economic theory does have, *whatever he himself may think*, the ability to master the mathematics that underlies this theory. If you think you have not, or if you are frightened to try, then your only problem is a psychological one. You have the ability but you must persuade yourself that you have. You should realise that your block against mathematics, if you have one, may be the result of uninspired or even downright bad teaching when you were very young or, as is equally probable, the result of neglect of mathematics on your own part as a result of a total lack of interest because you could see no great use for it. If you have already, or are now, studying basic economics, the use is staring you in the face: mathematics is a practical tool of great power in making deductions from a set of assumptions. All you now need to do is to prove to *yourself* that you can master mathematics – you have already proven it to us if you have survived a course in basic economic theory.

2.3   A Digression on Necessary and Sufficient Conditions

In any logical discourse, it is extremely important to distinguish between conditions that are necessary and those that are sufficient for some result to hold. We might wish to prove, for example, that if a is true then b must also be true, and we might conjecture that it would be convenient to reverse the argument, and prove this by showing that if b is true then a must also be true. This alone is not valid. (Can you see now the difference between an invalid procedure and the argument we used on page 23?) The following example shows why the suggested procedure is not valid. The fact that if someone is a man he is necessarily a member of the human race does not prove that if someone is a member of the human race he must be a man (for a woman is also a member of the human race). Clearly, being a member of the human race is necessary if one is to be a man, but it is not sufficient. Also, being a man is sufficient to ensure that one is a human, but it is not necessary – since being a woman will do just as well.

In general we can state these relations as follows. A necessary condition for a result a is one that must be present if a is to occur, but by itself is not enough to guarantee that a will occur. A sufficient condition for a is one whose presence is enough to guarantee that a will occur; but from the fact that it is sufficient we cannot tell if it is required for a to occur. A condition (or set of conditions) is necessary *and* sufficient for a to occur if it *must* be present for a to occur, and if its presence alone is also enough to guarantee that a will occur.

The relations work in both directions, but not symmetrically. If z is a necessary condition for a, then a is a sufficient condition for z. In words: if z must occur if a is to occur, then the occurrence of a is sufficient to tell us that z must have occurred. If z is a sufficient condition for a, then a is a necessary condition for z. In words: if the occurrence of z is sufficient for a to occur, then a must necessarily have occurred if z is to have occurred. Finally, if z is both necessary and sufficient for a, then a is also necessary and sufficient for z.

We often distinguish these relations by use of 'if' and 'only if'. Thus the statement 'a occurs *if* z occurs' means z is a sufficient condition for a and that a is a necessary condition for z. The statement 'a occurs *if and only if* z occurs' means that z is a necessary and sufficient condition for a.

These distinctions are extremely important, and they are probably best clarified by considering examples. A number of examples are included in the questions at the end of this chapter, and you should try them all before reading on to the next chapter.

Exercises

1 Manipulate the definition of average variable cost to get an expression in terms of the wage rate (which is a parameter to one firm) and the average product so that it will be clear by inspection that *AVC and AP always vary inversely with each other and thus AVC is at a minimum when AP is at a maximum.* (*Hint:* You start with $AVC = TVC$ divided by the quantity of the variable factor and end with $AVC = w/AP$, where w is the price of the variable factor.)

2 Prove that a specific tax of t per unit raises the marginal cost curve by t. (*Hint:* Ask how the tax enters into the expression for total cost, then write down the definition for marginal cost with and without the tax.)

3 Prove that a lump sum tax leaves marginal cost unaffected.

4 Assume that consumption is related to income by a linear consumption function $C = aY + b$. (i) Prove that the marginal propensity to consume ($\Delta C/\Delta Y$) is equal to a. (ii) Derive the expression for the average propensity to consume. (iii) Prove that the average propensity always exceeds the marginal propensity if $a > 0$.

5 If a is necessary and sufficient for z and at the same time b is necessary and sufficient for z what can you say about the relation between a and b?

6 You are told that (1) *provided they are not currently running a budget deficit* the government will raise its expenditure either (2) *if unemployment rises above* 3% or (3) *if there is a balance of payments surplus.* Under no other circumstances would expenditure be raised. Consider the three conditions singly, and state whether each is necessary, sufficient, neither or both to produce the result of a rise in government expenditure. Next take the conditions in pairs and ask if each pair holding simultaneously is necessary, sufficient, neither, or both. Finally take all three conditions as a single set and ask the same question of this set.

7 You are told that in order to get into a London club you must (1) be a male, (2) be an old boy of a public school, and (3) have a reference from an existing member. In the manner of question (6) take these conditions one at a time, then in pairs, then all together, and ask if each single or composite condition is necessary, sufficient, neither, or both, to gain entrance to the club.

CHAPTER 3

SOME FUNDAMENTAL TECHNIQUES

A: FUNCTIONS AND GRAPHS

Economics is concerned with the behaviour of measurable quantities such as wages, prices, national income, and employment, and with the relations between two or more of these quantities. In Part A of this chapter we present some of the basic mathematical ideas that are useful in analysing relations between quantities. Most of the concepts in Part A are used, whether ostensibly or not, in a principles course, so that you will find many ideas that are familiar in at least some contexts. Part B of this chapter contains no new ideas, but some useful tricks. Most of it is in any school algebra book; but there is a lot in a school algebra book that is not in Part B simply because we do not require it. Hence Part B can be used for revision at any time: it is not important to read it in sequence, and you may, if you wish, go straight on, coming back to B only when you find some gap in your knowledge that requires it.

3A.1 Quantities and Distances

If we observe that during 1966 one household bought 50 lbs of meat while another household bought 90 lbs, we have observed two quantities. It is always possible, and very often convenient, to relate these quantities to

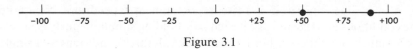

Figure 3.1

distances on a one-dimensional scale. In Figure 3.1 we mark a zero as our *point of origin*, i.e., the point from which all measurement begins; we agree to measure positive quantities to the right of the origin and negative quantities to the left. This is an arbitrary convention, and we could just as well have reversed our directions of measurement. We also select arbitrarily a specific distance to correspond to a specific quantity. In the scale in Figure 3.1 we have used the following relation:

$$1 \text{ lb of meat purchased corresponds to } \tfrac{1}{55} \text{ of one inch} \qquad (1)$$

or, what is the same thing,

1 inch corresponds to 55 lbs of meat purchased.   (2)

We can now show our two households on the scale. In Figure 3.1 the two household's expenditures on meat are shown by the two dots.

In the above example we could not have negative quantities because it is impossible for a household to spend less than nothing on meat. Now, however, consider a firm that is both buying and selling meat. This firm holds a stock of meat in deep freeze. Sometimes it adds to its stock by buying meat, and sometimes it reduces its stock by selling meat. If we let purchases be positive numbers (they add to stocks) and sales be negative numbers (they subtract from stocks), the transactions in which we are interested can range over negative as well as positive quantities. The lower limit is no longer zero but that set by the total stocks of meat held, since the firm cannot sell more than it has (unless we are dealing in a futures market). Now

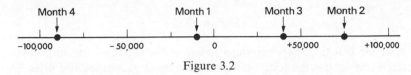

Figure 3.2

the firm's purchases and sales can be illustrated in Figure 3.2, where it is supposed that in four successive months the firm sells 10,000 lbs of meat, buys 75,000 lbs, buys 40,000 lbs and sells 90,000 lbs (and the scale is obviously different from that of Figure 3.1).

We have now taken one of the initial steps in geometrical development: *we have related measurable quantities to physical distances.* Before proceeding, you should ponder on the power of abstractions that we normally accept without a moment's thought. What could be less obviously related than one dozen eggs and the distance from London to Nassau, and what could be less obviously related than two dozen eggs and the distance from London to Darwin? And yet by observing that

1 dozen eggs = $\frac{1}{2}$ of 2 dozen eggs   (3)

and

the distance from London to Nassau

= $\frac{1}{2}$ of the distance from London to Darwin   (4)

we are on our way to establishing a formal similarity. Rearranging both expressions we have

$$\frac{1 \text{ dozen eggs}}{2 \text{ dozen eggs}} = \frac{1}{2} \qquad (5)$$

and

$$\frac{\text{distance London to Nassau}}{\text{distance London to Darwin}} = \frac{1}{2}. \qquad (6)$$

Since the left-hand sides of (5) and (6) are both equal to $\frac{1}{2}$ we can equate them to each other, writing

$$\frac{1 \text{ dozen eggs}}{2 \text{ dozen eggs}} = \frac{\text{distance London to Nassau}}{\text{distance London to Darwin}} \qquad (7)$$

which is read: *quantitatively one dozen eggs stands in the same relation to two dozen eggs as does the distance from London to Nassau to the distance from London to Darwin*. It is this relation of proportionality that allows us to represent physical quantities such as a number of eggs by distances.

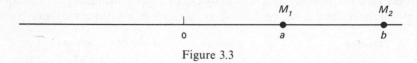

Figure 3.3

Next we can take two big steps towards abstracting from unnecessary detail. First we use the letter M to indicate meat purchases and sales. In a particular example M will take a numerical value such as 20,000 lbs. In the example of household purchases given above we had $M = 50$ and $M = 90$; and in the second example of the firm's purchases and sales M took the values of $-10,000$, $+75,000$, $+40,000$, and $-90,000$ in four successive months. M is called a *variable* and it stands for a particular magnitude, meat sales and purchases in this case, but the actual quantity it takes on will, as we have already seen, vary from example to example. As a matter of convention, letters at the end of the alphabet, w, x, y, and z, are commonly used to indicate variable quantities, but we are free to choose other letters and it is often convenient, as in the above example, to choose a letter as a memory aid (M reminds us that we are talking about meat).

The second step is to suppress the actual numbers on our scale and deal only in *relative* distances and *relative* quantities. If M takes on two successive values, the second being twice as large as the first, we can show this by points M_1 and M_2 on Figure 3.3. Notice that the values of M_1 and M_2 correspond to distances measured from the origin. If we let a stand for the point on the scale at which M_1 is located, and b stand for the point at which M_2 is located, then the quantity M_1 corresponds to the distance from O to a, which we write Oa, while the quantity M_2 corresponds to the distance from O to b, which we write Ob. Since we are told that

$$M_1 = \tfrac{1}{2}M_2 \qquad (8)$$

we must measure our distances so that

$$Oa = \tfrac{1}{2}Ob \qquad (9)$$

3A.2 Relations between Variables: Co-ordinate Geometry

In economics we are not only concerned with variable quantities such as a firm's purchases of meat, but also with the *relation between* two or more measurable quantities, such as meat purchases and the price of meat. Suppose we are told the wholesale prices of meat on the four months for which

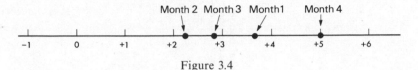

Figure 3.4

the firm purchased and sold the quantities of meat recorded in Figure 3.2. We use the variable p to stand for price. Assume that the values are as follows: month 1, $p=3{\cdot}7$, month 2, $p=2{\cdot}25$, month 3, $p=2{\cdot}8$, month 4, $p=5{\cdot}00$. These four prices can be plotted on a price scale as shown in Figure 3.4. You will note that we have allowed for negative as well as for positive prices. These will not occur in the present example but they can be given an economic meaning: a negative price is a subsidy paid to the consumers of a commodity. Thus if the price of a commodity is £1 the purchaser must give up £1 to obtain a unit, if the price is zero the commodity is a free good, and if the price is $-£1$ the purchaser receives a gift or subsidy of £1 on every unit of the commodity that he obtains.

In the present example we are concerned with the *relation* between the two variables, sales and purchases of meat and the price of meat. How can we study this relation? First, we can write the data down in a table.

TABLE 3.1

Month	Quantity	Price
1	$-10{,}000$	$3{\cdot}7$
2	$+75{,}000$	$2{\cdot}25$
3	$+40{,}000$	$2{\cdot}8$
4	$-90{,}000$	$5{\cdot}00$

But if we wish to *see* the relationship diagrammatically, what shall we do? This problem was solved some 300 years ago by René Descartes. His solution is one of the great landmarks in the history of mathematics: it produced co-ordinate geometry, and a union between algebra and geometry which we exploit whenever, for example, a lecturer in economics says 'We can show this relation in an algebraic equation or in a graph'. The solution, as we all know today, is to set the two scales in Figures 3.2 and 3.4 at right angles to each other with their origins at the same point, thus making it possible for a single point in the diagram to refer to the two separate scales simultaneously. Now we can show the price ruling in a particular month and the amount bought or sold in that month by a single dot. In Figure 3.5 we combine Figures 3.2 and 3.4 in the manner we have just described.

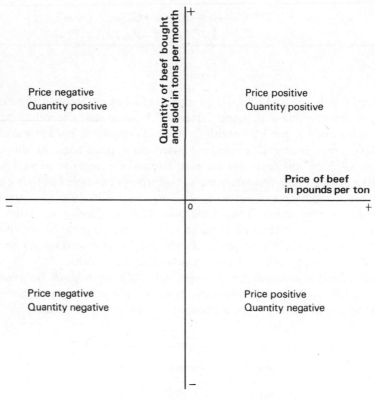

Figure 3.5

As a matter of convention the horizontal axis is often called the X-axis or the abscissa, while the vertical axis is often called the Y-axis or the ordinate. But this is only terminology, and we shall never again have occasion to use the terms abscissa and ordinate in this book. Some of you, like the present authors, will have been frightened by bad mathematics teachers who thought it was more important to memorise names, and to learn by rote how to carry out complex operations, than to understand the essential ideas behind what you were doing. If so, you may still feel, as we do, a vague feeling of distaste whenever new terminology is encountered. Of course, naming things is not mathematics, and the purpose of names is only to make discourse easier by providing a commonly understood set of labels.

Setting the two lines perpendicular to each other as in Figure 3.5 divides

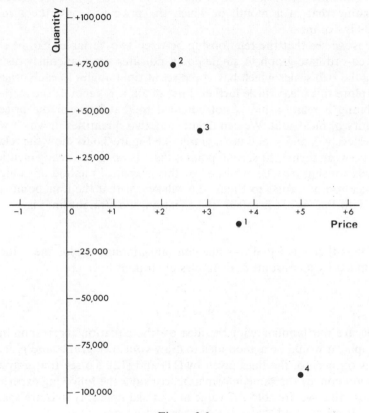

Figure 3.6

our total space into four parts, referred to as quadrants or orthonts. The upper right-hand quadrant is the one in which both variables are positive (or zero *on* one or other of the axes), and is often referred to as the *positive quadrant*. Everywhere in the lower right-hand quadrant, y is negative (or zero) and x positive (or zero); everywhere in the upper left-hand quadrant y is positive and x negative; everywhere in the lower left-hand quadrant both variables are negative. In many economic problems we can rule out negative values of all the variables as being impossible, and when we draw graphs to show the relation between such variables we usually give only the positive quadrant (as, say, with the usual text-book demand curve).

We are now ready to take the data from Table 3.1 and plot them on a graph. Each dot in Figure 3.6 shows the quantity of meat bought or sold in a given month, and the price ruling at the time. Reading upwards, the dots refer to months 4, 1, 3, and 2. Thus, dot 4 is 90,000 lbs below the origin on the quantity scale and 5·00 to the right of the origin on the price scale, indicating that in a month in which the price was 5·00 the firm sold 90,000 lbs of meat.

Thus we see that the relationship between two variables can be shown on a co-ordinate graph. A single point indicates simultaneously distances along the two scales which have been set at right angles to each other. Let us explore this idea a little further. First of all, it is general: the method of exhibiting a relationship is not confined to that between the price and quantity of meat sold. We can denote any two quantities in which we are interested by x and y, and use a graph like Figure 3.6 to show the relationship between them. The second point is that, as we have already mentioned, the relationship may be exhibited by this graphical method *or* in algebra. Application of a ruler to Figure 3.6 will reveal that the four points lie on a straight line. What is called 'the equation of a straight line' is

$$y = ax + b. \tag{10}$$

This says that y is equal to some constant amount b, plus the value of x multiplied by a constant a. Examples of straight lines are

$$y = 2x + 3 \tag{11}$$

$$y = 5x - 1. \tag{12}$$

If you are not familiar with the idea of 'the equation' corresponding to 'a graph', it would be a good idea to draw your own graph, and plot a few points on each of the lines given by (11) and (12). To see that graph and equation convey the same information, consider the following experiment. Suppose that we are told the value of x in example (11), and are asked to find y. If we are told that x is three, we find y from

$$y = (2).(3) + 3 = 9.$$

If we had the graph instead of the equation, we should find y by starting at the point corresponding to 3 on the x-axis, moving vertically to the graph of the relationship, and then horizontally to the y-axis.

The use of co-ordinate geometry is not confined to straight lines. In Figure 3.7, we have plotted several curves. Each one of them illustrates a possible relationship between x and y, and, in each case, if we were given the x-value, we could read-off the corresponding y-value. The equations of some of these curves are quite complex, and we shall not write them down, but if we had them instead of the graphs we could use them to calculate y for given x. Since we have not got them, and are not bothering with numerical examples, we have suppressed the scale in Figure 3.7. The variables y

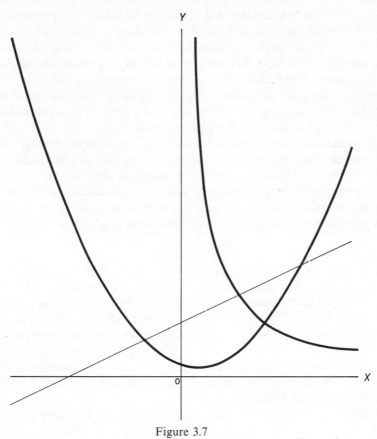

Figure 3.7

and x increase in the usual directions along the two axes, but as it is immaterial to our illustration whether one inch corresponds to one unit of x or to 20 we have left out the scale entirely. This is a simplification – or suppression of irrelevant detail – which we shall often employ.

3A.3 Functional Relations

The idea that there is a relationship between x and y can be expressed quite generally. We may draw illustrative graphs, as in Figures 3.6 and 3.7; but

2*

we may also write

$$y = f(x)$$

which is read 'y is a function of x' or 'y equals $f - $ of $- x$'. This simple way of writing 'there is a relationship between x and y' is a purely notational device, but it is remarkably convenient and important, and is worth some study. We already know that a graph is the geometrical representation of the relationship between two variables, or, as we shall now say, of a function. If we have the graph, we may use it to read-off the value of y, given x; and similarly, if we have the function written out algebraically, we can calculate y, given x (in fact, we shall have to do this to draw the graph!). Thus a graph or function provides us with a *rule* for getting the value of one variable given the other. When we say that $y = f(x)$, we assert that a rule exists, although without saying what it is. Our rough intuitive idea of there being 'a relationship' between x and y has now become formal: we say that the function f is a *mapping rule from x to y*. The reason for calling it a *mapping* rule will be clear from our geometrical illustrations.

There are now many things to be said about functions and their use and interpretation. Let us start by getting the notation quite clear. In elementary algebra we learn that brackets mean 'multiply'. Thus

$$a(x + b) = ax + ab.$$

The brackets in $f(x)$ mean nothing of the sort. $f(x)$ is to be read 'function of x', and f is not a quantity with which one may multiply, add, divide, etc.: it stands for the *mapping rule* for getting from x to y, and a rule that cannot be operated on as if it were a number. Think of the graph of the function: x and y can be added to, multiplied etc., but the graph cannot.

Since, however, we can multiply or divide, add to or subtract from y in the ordinary way, $ay = af(x)$: multiplying y by a is the same thing as multiplying $f(x)$ by a, since the value of $f(x)$ is y. It is the letter f itself which cannot be treated in this way.

Functions are frequently denoted by Greek letters such as ϕ and ψ, and other letters from the Roman alphabet such as g. Another notation is to repeat the letter on the left-hand side. Thus $y = y(x)$ means the same thing as $y = f(x)$: there is a functional relationship between x and y. Economists frequently use this notation because it serves to remind us of the variables we are discussing. Thus 'investment depends on the rate of interest' can be written $I = I(r)$, and 'consumption depends on the level of income' as $C = C(Y)$.

It is probably not at all clear why it helps to have a way of writing down 'there is a functional relationship' when we do not know what it is. The answer is that we may know enough *about* the relationship, or mapping rule, to advance our discussion even though we do not know the precise form of the function. The converse of this argument is that for some purposes the precise relationship may not matter, but only certain of its characteristics. In this case, we do not want to be encumbered with particular functional forms, and it is a great convenience to have a notation that allows us to dispense with any particular piece of information that is not presently important.

An illustration may clarify some of these ideas. It is widely believed that drinking contributes to road accidents. If we write A for the number of accidents per year, and C for consumption of alcohol per year, we may write

$$A = A(C):$$

there is a functional relationship between drinking and accidents. We do not know the form of A, which is to say that we have not got the mapping rule, but we do know something about it: if drinking increases, we believe that accidents do. This tells us that A is an *increasing function* of C: if C rises, so does A. This is sufficient information to allow us to answer the question 'Will a reduction in drinking lead to a reduction in accidents?' This is obvious; but in many cases we do not know if a particular function everywhere increases or decreases, or increases over some values of x and not at others. In such a case it may well be that the mere discovery of this basic property of the function will be sufficient to solve our problem, and the subject of enquiry will therefore be into the direction of change of the function. Again, if this is sufficient to solve the problem, we may not know, and shall not care, what the particular functional form may be, and shall give thanks for a notation that allows us to proceed in general terms.

3A.4 Some Simple Functions

We have seen that a function is a mapping rule which gets us from x to y. As it is a rule it tells us what we have to do, when we have the value of x, in order to find the corresponding value of y. Thus the rule might be 'add ten', or 'divide by two', 'take the square root' – or do all three of these things in sequence. It is a good deal quicker to write down the rules symbolically. Thus the rule to add ten, divide by two, and take the square root can be written

$$\sqrt{\frac{x+10}{2}}. \tag{13}$$

This is an expression that contains only x, without y, as are

$$10+2x \tag{14}$$

and
$$5-2x+x^2. \tag{15}$$

This suggests that, when we are interested in the rule itself, we do not have to write '$y=$' all the time. We can speak of 'functions of x' of which (13), (14), and (15) are examples, without having to introduce y. y is indeed only another name for the value of the function, which is the value we obtain when we perform the operations directed by the rule. If our interest is for the moment in the rule, and the operations we have to perform, we may talk simply of x and $f(x)$ without y.

Now let us consider the rules in examples (14) and (15). We give x any value we wish, insert that value into the expression in place of x, and calculate the value of the whole expression. Table 2.2 shows the results for selected values of x in (14).

TABLE 3.2

x	$f(x)=10+2x$
0	10
1	12
10	30
50	110

We can do the same thing for the other function and obtain Table 3.3.

TABLE 3.3

x	$f(x)=5-2x+x^2$
0	5
1	4
10	85
50	2405

You should calculate one or two values for each function to satisfy yourself that you can do it if necessary. This shows that you really do understand what the rules require. Once you are sure that you do know what is going on, further calculation is a purely mechanical exercise. You should never confuse dexterity at extended calculation with mathematical understanding. Unfortunately, they are often confused in the classroom, and all too many students come to believe that they have no taste for mathematics because they are, quite rightly, bored by the repeated performance of routine calculations that could be done faster and more accurately by machine.

A little experimentation will soon show us that there are families of functions, each family displaying certain common characteristics. The simplest family is that of the linear functions, of which (11), (12), and (14) are members. Here are three other members of the family:

$$-4x + 5 \qquad (16)$$

$$0.5x \qquad (17)$$

$$2x - 10. \qquad (18)$$

We have already encountered the general *linear function*

$$ax + b. \qquad (10)$$

In this expression a and b are called parameters while x is a variable. Assigning a value to the two parameters singles out a particular member of the family. For any one member of the family, e.g., $2x - 10$, the parameters are constant. Given the values of the parameters, we may read off the values of the function as the value of x is allowed to vary.

Another very common function is the quadratic

$$ax^2 + bx + c. \qquad (19)$$

(15), on page 38, is a member of this family. Any other member is obtained by giving particular numerical values to the parameters a, b, and c.

All members of the quadratic family have certain characteristics in common, and are distinctively different from all members of the linear family. These general characteristics are worthy of study since in many practical problems particular linear or quadratic functions will occur.[1] Then our general knowledge of the characteristics of these functions allows us to handle the particular case being studied without having laboriously to rediscover these characteristics in each specific case. We could, of course, always select a large number of values of x, calculate the corresponding values of $f(x)$, plot these on a graph and join them up, but if we had to do this each time we encountered a quadratic we would be involved in a lot of tedious calculations. Again, the economy of mathematical abstraction comes to our rescue. It is easy to prove that there is one and only one quadratic that passes through any three points, and thus we need only plot

[1] For example, we often use linear demand curves which give rise to quadratic total revenue curves (e.g., if $p = 100 - 2q$, $TR = pq = 100q - 2q^2$).

three points from our function to determine its complete shape. It is clearly a great economy to know about the general characteristics of families of functions. Thus a parabola may look something like this: ∪ or this: ∩. In both cases it is symmetrical about a line drawn perpendicularly through its high or low point. A linear function on the other hand looks like this: ╱ or this: ╲.

It is convenient at this point to go through some taxonomy of functions. You should read this section to become acquainted with the vocabulary, and then refer back to refresh your memory when necessary. An *increasing function* is one the value of which always increases as the value of the variable increases. A *decreasing function* is one the value of which decreases whenever the value of the variable increases. The classes of increasing and decreasing functions are together called *monotonic functions*, and we may therefore speak of monotonic increasing or monotonic decreasing functions. The straight line of (10) provides an example of a monotonic function. If the coefficient b is positive we have a monotonic increasing function as in

$$2x + 10. \tag{20}$$

If the coefficient b is negative we have a monotonic decreasing function as in

$$-2x + 10. \tag{21}$$

Many functions increase as x increases over some range of values and decrease as x increases over other values. Such functions are not monotonic. A simple example is the quadratic (19). Thus consider

$$2x^2 - 3x + 10. \tag{22}$$

You should compare for yourself the effect on the value of the function of increasing x from -4 to -3 and from $+3$ to $+4$.

If y is a *single-valued function* of x, then to every value of the variable x there corresponds one and only one value of y. Similarly, if x is a single-valued function of y, then to every value of the variable y there corresponds one and only one value of x. The relation is not symmetrical: x may be a single-valued function of y without y being a single-valued function of x. Thus in the case of a quadratic, in which y is a single-valued function of x, x is not a single-value function of y: two x-values map into each y-value. This asymmetry occurs frequently in the functions we deal with in economics. Thus consider a ∪-shaped marginal cost curve: each level of output gives a unique level of marginal cost, but to a value of marginal cost there correspond *two* levels of output. (It is a good exercise to look over the functional relations encountered in a principles course, and classify them. You should be able to find several common examples of functions that are single-valued one way round but not the other.)

3A.5 Dependence

When we discussed the relationship between road accidents and drinking, it was very clear that we had a causal relationship in mind. The existence of a function, or mapping rule, from one variable to another does *not*, however, imply anything about causation. It is very important to be clear about this. If we want to deal analytically with a causal relationship, we shall obviously write it in functional form; but the assertion that there exists a mapping rule between two variables says nothing about causes. When we write $y = f(x)$, we are only saying 'let y be the value obtained when we operate on x by the rule f'. If we also suppose that x stands for some observable quantity and that y stands for another observable quantity, then when we write $y = f(x)$ we only say 'the value of y can be found by operating on x in the manner directed'. This, of course, means that x and y are systematically associated. This systematic association may be because x influences y, because y influences x, because although x and y are not related they are both influenced by some common causal factor z, or because y and x just happen to have varied with each other by chance.

Let us consider examples of each of these possible interpretations of functional relations. When we write $q = d(p)$, where q is *one* household's demand for butter and p is the market price of butter, we understand that variations in p cause variations in q but that variations in q do not cause variations in p. When, however, we write $Q = D(p)$ where p is still the market price of butter but Q is now the *market* demand for butter, we understand that changes in Q will now cause changes in p as well as vice versa. Now consider the third possible reason for the existence of a systematic relationship. When we say that in postwar Britain there has been a strong positive relation between purchases of motor cars and purchases of gramophone records, which can be written $C = C(G)$, we do not imply that running a car causes people to buy more gramophone records, or that having more gramophone records causes people to buy more cars. We do know, however, that purchases of both cars and records are increasing functions of income, and that income has been rising throughout the postwar period. Thus the positive relation between C and G follows from no causal relation between these two variables but from a common influencing factor, income. Finally, an example of a relation arising by chance is the famous one between the number of storks in Denmark (S) and the number of births in that country (B). When we write $B = B(S)$, which expresses an empirically observed relation, we are not committing ourselves to the theory that babies are brought by storks, although we *are* saying that storks and births have been observed to vary together in some systematic fashion.

A common case of a functional relation that does not imply any causal relation is a *time series*. Most economic variables vary over time. When we graph any variable on the y-axis with time on the x-axis we obtain a time-series graph. Since, given t, we can then read off the value of the variable x, we can write

$$x = x(t) \tag{23}$$

which is read: x is a function of time. In no sense does this imply that the mere passage of time causes x to vary.

The mathematical language of functions is, appropriately, free of causal implications, as we may now see. Suppose we say that y is always four times as large as x. Two other ways of saying the same thing are to say that x is one quarter as large as y and that y minus $4x$ must be zero. We can write

$$y = 4x \tag{24}$$

$$x = 0.25y \tag{25}$$

and $$y - 4x = 0. \tag{26}$$

These are three ways of writing the same functional relation. To express the same three forms in general terms, we can write

$$y = y(x) \tag{27}$$

$$x = x(y) \tag{28}$$

and $$f(x, y) = 0. \tag{29}$$

Equations (22) and (23) are called the *explicit forms* of the function. In (22) y is written as an explicit function of x, while in (28) x is written as an explicit function of y. Equation (29) is called the *implicit form* of the function. All the terms are gathered onto the left-hand side and the whole expression is thus equal to zero. In which of the three forms we choose to write the function is clearly only a matter of convenience. Transformation of one into another is accomplished by transferring terms from one side of the equation to the other, and whether or not it can be done is a matter only of algebra, not of causal direction.

The term on the left-hand side of each of (27) and (28) is called the dependent variable, and the terms on the right-hand side are called the independent variables (or variable, if there is only one). As far as mathematics is concerned, the distinction between dependent and independent variables is arbitrary: $y = y(x)$ implies $x = x(y)$. The convention may be used, however, to express information we have about the causal relation between the variables. Assume, for example, that crop yield, C, depends solely[1] on the amount of rainfall, R. This allows us to write

$$C = C(R). \tag{30}$$

If, however, we can deduce the amount of crop if we know the rainfall, then we must be able to deduce the amount of rainfall if we know the crop. Thus we also have

$$R = R(C). \tag{31}$$

As far as mathematics is concerned, it does not matter which of these two forms we choose, (30) or (31). But, of course, the causal relation is clearly defined in this case. The amount of rainfall influences the crop yield; the crop yield does not influence the amount of rainfall.

As a matter of convention, whenever we think we know the direction of the causal link between variables we write the causes as independent variables and the effects as dependent ones. Thus, it would be consistent with our ideas about the physical facts to write equation (30) instead of equation (31). Again, if we wanted to say that crop yield C depended on fertilizer, F, sunshine, S, and rainfall R, we would write

$$C = C(F, S, R). \tag{32}$$

In equation (32), C is the dependent variable and F, S, and R are the independent variables. This is the first time that we have encountered a function of more than one variable, and we need merely to note here the convention of placing all the variables inside the brackets and separating them by commas. Thus $y = y(x, z)$ says that y is a function of two variables x and z. An example of a function of more than one variable in economics is $P = MV/T$, where P is the price level, M is the quantity of money, V is the velocity of circulation of money, and T is the total volume of transactions. If we wished to say merely that the price level was a function of these three variables without committing ourselves to the exact form of the relation in the way that we did above, we would merely write

$$P = P(M, V, T). \tag{33}$$

This is a convenient moment to introduce yet another piece of terminology, knowledge of which will facilitate later discussion. The variables that appear in brackets after the functional symbol are often referred to as the *arguments* of the function. Arguments and independent variables are nearly, but not quite, the same thing, and the distinction can be important. Suppose that we have $y = f(x/z)$, and compare this with $y = g(x, z)$. In both functions, x and z appear as the independent variables. In the first case, however, their ratio appears explicitly, whereas in the second case they appear sepa-

---

[1] This is a simplification for purposes of illustration, but crop yield certainly depends partly on the amount of rainfall.

rated by a comma. What this means is that f is an unspecified mapping rule from the *ratio* x/z, whereas g is some unspecified mapping rule from pairs of values of x and z entered separately. In the case of $f(x/z)$ the value of neither variable matters for itself, but only as it affects x/z. Hence in this case we say that x/z is the *argument* of the function, while in the case of $g(x, z)$ we say that both x and z are arguments. Obviously, if we are dealing with causal relationships, it is a matter of some importance to be clear about what the arguments of the functions are: functions are mapping rules from their arguments to the dependent variable.

Examination of the implicit form $f(x, y) = 0$ suggests the question: what is mapped into what in this case? The answer is that the rule provides the operations on x and y simultaneously such that the result is zero for any pair of x and y. It therefore gives implicitly a rule for mapping from x to y or vice-versa.

In drawing graphs of functions, it is the usual convention to plot the independent variable on the x-axis and the dependent variable on the y-axis. The popularisor of graphical analysis in economics, Alfred Marshall, decided to reverse this practice in the case of demand and supply curves. He put the independent variable, price, on the y-axis and the dependent variable, quantity, on the x-axis. This practice persists to this day, to the everlasting confusion of students, although in the case of every other diagram the normal practice is adopted with the dependent variable on the y-axis and the independent one on the x-axis. We have decided, in the interests of consistency and convenience, to defy the Marshallian tradition: all the demand and supply diagrams in this book are drawn with quantity, the dependent variable, on the y-axis. Thus they are the 'wrong way up' from the point of view of economics textbooks, but the 'right way up' according to general practice. You must realise that it is only a matter of convenience, and you should be prepared to redraw any familiar economic diagram with the axes reversed.

3A.6 Functions and Equations: Roots

At school we learn to solve 'equations' like the quadratic

$$x^2 - 3x - 10 = 0. \tag{34}$$

A 'solution' is the value (or values) of x that makes this true. Now suppose that we write

$$f(x) = x^2 - 3x - 10. \tag{35}$$

Is this an 'equation'? The answer is no. The equality sign merely assures us that the two sides are equal: on the left-hand side we say that there is a rule for operating on x, and on the right-hand side we spell out the rule. *A function is not an equation.* The 'equals' sign is used in two ways in mathematics. In (35) above it is used to mean 'is the same as'. Thus $(a+x)^2 = a^2 + 2ax + x^2$ is true for any x, and the equality sign merely asserts that we have two ways of saying the same thing: we have what is called an identity. Suppose, however, that we 'equate $f(x)$ to zero'. If $f(x)$ is given by (35), the equation of $f(x)$ to zero gives us (34) which is *not* true for any x. We now want to find the value(s) of x for which it *is* true, so we shall review the methods of solving the equation.

The function $x^2 - 3x - 10$ is graphed in Figure 3.8. It is apparent from inspection of the Figure that there are two values of x for which the value of the function is zero, -2 and $+5$. They are called the *roots of the function*.

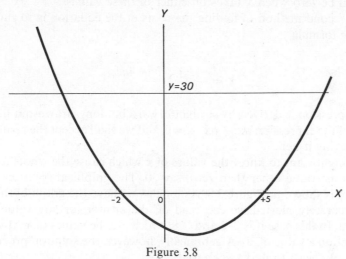

Figure 3.8

There are two standard methods for finding the roots of a quadratic equation (both are taught in school algebra, so we shall not justify them here). The first method is that of factoring the quadratic

$$ax^2 + bx + c \qquad (36)$$

into an expression of the form

$$(lx + d)(mx + e) \qquad (37)$$

such that[1]

$$ax^2 + bx + c = (lx + d)(mx + e). \qquad (38)$$

Since we wish to find values of x for which the function has a value of zero we merely set (37) equal to zero. Now if we have the product of two terms, say PQ, equal to zero, either P must be zero or Q must be zero. Hence to 'satisfy' our equation, we must have either

$$lx + d = 0$$

[1] For footnote see page 46.

or $$mx + l = 0.$$

The first is true if $x = -d/l$, and the second if $x = -l/m$. The result is that $f(x) = 0$ if x has either of these values. In the case of the example in (34) above the factoring is easy:

$$x^2 - 3x - 10 = (x-5)(x+2). \tag{39}$$

You can satisfy yourself that (39) is correct by multiplying out $(x-5)(x+2)$. We now know that the roots of the function are $+5$ and -2: the value of $f(x)$ will be zero when x takes on either of these values.

The second method of finding the roots of the equation is to substitute into the formula

$$x = \frac{-b \pm \sqrt{b^2 - 4ac}}{2a}. \tag{40}$$

This expression is derived by straightforward but long-drawn-out manipulation of the expression $ax^2 + bx + c = 0$, and we shall accept the result without deriving it here.

We might want to know the values of x which cause the whole function to be some value other than zero, say 30. The graphical solution to this problem is shown in Figure 3.8. As long as we have the graph of the function accurately plotted we can read off the answer for any value of the function. In this case it is -5 and $+8$, which are the values of x which give the function a value of 30. Algebraically, however, the solution proceeds as follows. We wish to find x such that

$$x^2 - 3x - 10 = 30, \tag{41}$$

---

[1] In case you have forgotten how to multiply $(lx+d)(mx+e)$, we offer a reminder. Write

$$lx+d$$
$$mx+e$$

multiplying the top line by mx gives $lmx^2 + mdx$

multiplying by e gives $elx + de$

and adding gives $lmx^2 + (md+el)x + de.$

Comparison of this with $ax^2 + bx + c$ shows that factoring consists of finding, if we can, values for l, m, d, and e such that

$$lm = a$$
$$md + el = b$$

and $$de = c.$$

and by subtracting 30 from both sides of the equality sign we have

$$x^2 - 3x - 40 = 0 \tag{42}$$

which factors as follows:

$$x^2 - 3x - 40 = (x-8)(x+5). \tag{43}$$

We now set this function equal to zero and discover the roots to be $+8$ and -5.

Thus any problem of finding the value of x such that the function takes on a stated value, V, can be turned into a problem of finding the roots of a new function which is found by subtracting V from the original function. Thus the problem: find x such that

$$ax^2 + bx + c = V \tag{44}$$

is the same as the problem: find x such that

$$ax^2 + bx + (c - V) = 0. \tag{45}$$

This is the form in which it is convenient to solve the problem, which is why finding x such that the function has the particular value of zero is a problem of such general significance. There is nothing magical in setting the function equal to zero. It is just that putting the function equal to any value V can always be transformed into a problem of putting another function equal to zero.

So far we have considered quadratics which have real roots in the sense that there are two real values of x for which the function has a value of zero. Now consider taking a quadratic, such as the one labelled 1 in Figure 3.9, and slowly increasing the value of the parameter c. This shifts the curve upwards, and it is visually obvious from the Figure that the roots move closer and closer together. Finally when we have shifted the curve up as far as curve 4, the two roots coincide in a single point. This means that there is only one value of x for which the whole expression is zero. An example of such a quadratic is

$$f(x) = x^2 - 6x + 9 \tag{46}$$

which factors into

$$f(x) = (x-3)(x-3) \tag{47}$$

which is zero if, and only if, $x = +3$.

If we increase the value of the constant yet further the curve rises above the x-axis throughout its whole range. *There is no value of x for which the value of the function is zero.* In this case we say that the function has no 'real roots'. If we substitute the values of the parameters into (40), we shall find in these cases that b^2 is less than $4ac$, so that the expression inside the square root sign is negative. Since in our ordinary number system it is not possible to have a number whose square is negative, it follows that the

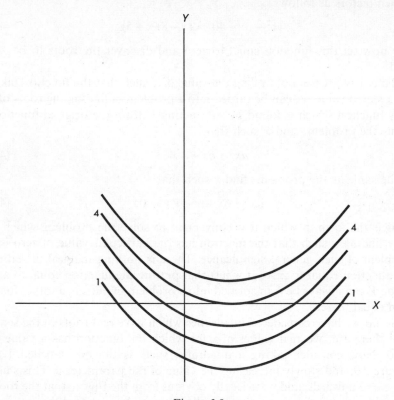

Figure 3.9

square root of a negative number does not exist in our ordinary number system.

To illustrate these ideas, let us consider a demand function. If the quantity of a good demanded depends on its price, we write

$$q = f(p).$$

In Figure 3.6, we plotted four points on a linear demand function for meat, of which the equation is

$$q = 1,000,000 - 50,000p. \tag{48}$$

Now let us derive the total revenue function. Total expenditure by consumers, which is the same thing as suppliers' total revenue, equals price per unit times number of units bought, so we may write

$$TR = pq. \tag{49}$$

From (48) we already have an expression for q, and substituting that into (49) we get a quadratic in p:

$$TR = p(1{,}000{,}000 - 50{,}000p)$$

$$= 1{,}000{,}000p - 50{,}000p^2 \tag{50}$$

which is plotted in Figure 3.10.

Since (50) is a quadratic we expect it to have two roots, and inspection of Figure 3.10 suggests that this particular function will have real roots.

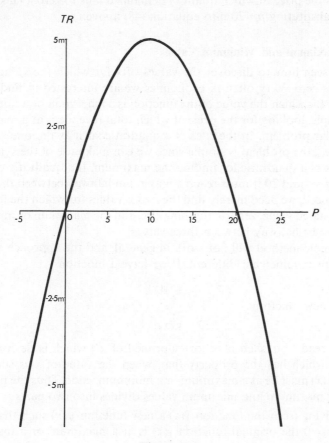

Figure 3.10

To find these roots we set the function equal to zero,

$$1,000,000p - 50,000p^2 = 0$$

and, dividing through by 50,000, we get

$$20p - p^2 = 0$$

or

$$p^2 - 20p = 0.$$

Factoring,

$$p(p - 20) = 0 \tag{51}$$

so that the roots are seen to be zero and $+20$. This indicates that total revenue is zero both at price zero and at price £20. The first case is obvious: if the product is given away no revenue is earned. The second point of zero revenue is the price at which quantity demanded falls to zero. (This can be seen by substituting $p = 20$ into equation (48) above.)

3A.7 Maximum and Minimum Values

We have seen how to discover the values of x for which the value of the function is zero. Very often in economics we are interested in finding the value of x for which the value of the function is a maximum or a minimum. For example, looking for the price at which total revenue is at a maximum is a familiar problem. In the case of a quadratic such as the one we have just studied, the problem is simple since we can make use of the symmetry properties of a quadratic for finding the maximum. If a quadratic cuts the x-axis at zero and 20 it must reach a maximum halfway between these two points. Indeed, we need merely find the two x-values for which the function has some stated value, zero or anything else, and the maximum or minimum point must be halfway between these values.

This simple method will not work in general, and the approach that we must adopt is somewhat different. If we have a function

$$y = y(x), \tag{52}$$

we find a new function

$$y'(x) \tag{53}$$

(which is read 'y-dashed of x' or 'y-primed of x') which is derived from $y(x)$, and which has the property that, when the value of x is such that $y'(x) = 0$, $y(x)$ must be at a maximum or a minimum value. Thus the problem of finding maximum and minimum values divides into two parts:

(1) deriving from the function $y(x)$ a new function $y'(x)$ such that when $y'(x) = 0$ the original function $y(x)$ is at a maximum or a minimum value;

(2) solving the equation $y'(x)=0$ which means finding the value(s) of x
   for which the function $y'(x)$ is zero.

We already know how to do step (2) in simple cases, and later in this book
we shall study the technique of differentiation which is the method of deriving the desired function $y'(x)$ from any given function $y(x)$.

3A.8   Slopes, Chords, and Tangents

Consider the linear function

$$y = ax + b. \tag{54}$$

Both the parameters a and b can be given specific graphic interpretations.
Let us see if we can discover what these interpretations are. To discover the

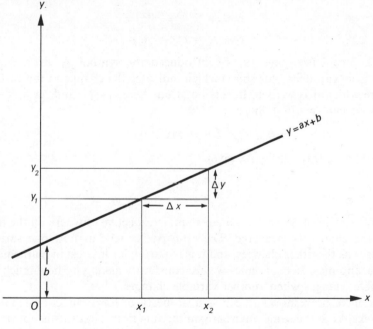

Figure 3.11

significance of the parameter b we let x take on the value of zero. (54) then
reduces to $y=b$. Thus we see that b tells us the value that y takes on when
x is zero. Graphically, b determines the point at which the line representing
the function cuts the y-axis ($x=0$) as is shown in Figure 3.11.

   The significance of a is a little less obvious, but basically what a does is
to determine the direction and the magnitude of changes in y associated

with changes in x. Clearly if a is positive then the larger is x the larger is y, so that x and y vary directly with each other, while if a is negative y varies inversely with x. Inspection also shows that the larger is the magnitude of a the bigger are the changes in y for given changes in x. Geometrically, b corresponds to the slope of the line plotted from the function in question. Let us make certain that this is so.

Give x any particular value designated by x_1 and calculate the corresponding value of y, which we designate by y_1. Then let x take on another value x_2, and calculate y_2, the corresponding value of y. This gives us:

$$y_1 = ax_1 + b \tag{55}$$

and
$$y_2 = ax_2 + b. \tag{56}$$

Subtracting one equation from the other gives us

$$y_2 - y_1 = ax_2 - ax_1 \tag{57}$$

or
$$y_2 - y_1 = a(x_2 - x_1). \tag{58}$$

In Chapter 2 (see page 19) we introduced the symbol, Δ (read 'capital delta', or 'cap delta' for short) which indicates the change in the variable before which it is written. In this notation, $\Delta y = y_2 - y_1$, and $\Delta x = x_2 - x_1$. Thus we can rewrite (58) as

$$\Delta y = a\,\Delta x, \tag{59}$$

and dividing through by Δx gives

$$\frac{\Delta y}{\Delta x} = a. \tag{60}$$

Thus the ratio of Δy to Δx is a constant, irrespective of where on the function the change is measured. The ratio $\Delta y/\Delta x$ tells us how one variable changes as the other changes, and it is of particular interest in mathematics and economics. In economics we are constantly asking by how much one variable changes when another variable changes.

We have now shown that it is a property of linear functions that the ratio $\Delta y/\Delta x$ is the same anywhere on the function. That this is not true of non-linear functions can easily be seen graphically. If in Figure 3.12 we start at point α, where x is Oa and y is Ob, and make a change to the point β, the value of x increases by ac and of y by bd. The ratio $\Delta y/\Delta x$ is bd/ac which is the slope of the line joining the two points α and β. Now move β to another point β' on the curve, and the slope of the line joining α and β will change. Thus the ratio $\Delta y/\Delta x$ depends on the point from which one begins, the size of the change in x, and the direction of the change.

The line joining α and β is called a *chord*. In general, a chord is a straight line joining any two points on a curve. The slope of a chord between two points always indicates the ratio $\Delta y/\Delta x$, where Δy and Δx are the changes in y and x between the two points in question. This is illustrated in Figure 3.12. The ratio $\Delta y/\Delta x$ is often called the *incremental ratio*.

In Figure 3.12 the line TT is drawn tangential to the curve at α. The slope of the tangent is denoted by dy/dx. Now consider the relation between the slope of the tangent TT and the slope of the chord between α and β as β

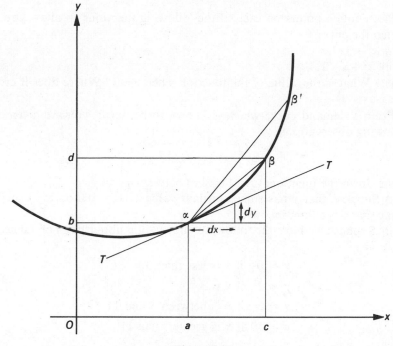

Figure 3.12

is brought closer and closer to α. It is visually clear from an inspection of Figure 3.12 that the slope of the chord gets closer and closer to the slope of the tangent as the chord is made smaller and smaller. We write this $\Delta y/\Delta x \to dy/dx$ as $\Delta x \to 0$ where the $\to$ sign is read 'approaches'. Thus we are saying that the slope of the incremental ratio, which geometrically is the slope of the chord, approaches the slope of the tangent as the increment Δx in x approaches zero (geometrically as the chord through α gets smaller and smaller).

This completes our introduction to those basic ideas of analysis that we require to take the next step in our mathematical treatment of economics. Some of the ideas will have been more familiar than others; but we are

prepared to bet that there is not one in this chapter which was not encountered, however disguised or verbalised, in your principles course.

In the remaining part of this chapter, we shall review some useful algebra.
Then we shall get on with some economics, and only come back to mathematical technique (in Chapter 5) when we find that more equipment is
imperative.

Exercises

1 Plot enough points on each of the following functions to allow you to
sketch the curve.
  (i) $x^2 + 3x$
  (ii) $x^2 + x - 2$
(*Hint:* What is the value of the function when $x = 0$? Where does it cross
the x-axis?)

2 From a demand curve which is known to be linear, you are given the
following observations:
$$at\ p = 10,\quad q = 60$$
$$at\ p = 12,\quad q = 50.$$

Write down the functional relationship between q and p.

3 (i) Suppose that y has some constant value, c (say, 100 or 15). Can we
say that y is a function of x?
  (ii) Suppose we have the following information about pairs of values of
x and y:

$$y = 0\quad \text{if } x \text{ is less than 3}$$

$$y = 2\quad \text{if } x \text{ is 3}$$

$$y = 5\quad \text{if } x \text{ is between 3 and 11}$$

$$y = 50\ \text{if } x \text{ is greater than 11.}$$

Can we say that y is a function of x?

4 In which of the following does the letter f symbolise a function? Identify
the argument(s) of the function in each case.
  (i) $y = f(x, z)$
  (ii) $y = f(w/v)$
  (iii) $y = ax^6 + bx^5 + cx^4 + dx^3 + ex^2 + fx + g$
  (iv) $y = f(x + z)$

5 Explain in words the meaning of the following:
  (i) $C = cY$
  (ii) $C = C(Y)$
where C and Y have their usual meaning in macro-economics.

6 (i) Write down the following argument in functional form, and say which
are increasing and which decreasing functions. 'It is lack of religious

belief that undermines marriage and leads to divorce. We have seen in this century declining attendance at church and a shocking increase in divorce, which establishes the point beyond doubt.'

(ii) Which of the functions corresponds to a statement about observed facts, and which to a hypothesis or belief?

(iii) Given the same observations, can you find another explanation?

(iv) Do you think the argument is well supported? How might it be further tested?

B: INEQUALITIES, INDICES, LOGARITHMS

3B.1 Inequalities

In Chapter 2 we encountered the symbols used for the relationships 'greater than' and 'less than':

$y > c$ meaning 'y is greater than c' or 'y exceeds c'

$y < c$ meaning 'y is less than c.'

If we wish to say that some variable is positive, we merely replace c by zero and write $y > 0$.

There are rules for manipulating inequalities, just as there are for manipulating equalities. We have developed some and shall develop others when we want them, so we shall only give an illustration here. Suppose we are told that

$$2x - 4 > 0$$

(two-x minus four is positive). If we add the same quantity to both sides, we obviously do not disturb the inequality. So we may add 4 to both sides to get

$$2x > 4.$$

Again, if we multiply both sides by the same positive number, we do not disturb the inequality. So we may multiply both sides by $\frac{1}{2}$ to obtain

$$x > 2.$$

Thus our chain of reasoning allows us to say 'if $2x - 4$ is positive, x must exceed 2'. Since in economics we are frequently interested in the signs of variables, i.e., whether they are greater or less than zero, manipulations of this sort are very useful.

Suppose now that we do not know that x exceeds some value c, but only that it is not less. 'Not less' equals 'greater than or equal to'; 'not more' equals 'less than or equal to'; and the symbols are

$x \geqslant c$ meaning 'x is greater than or equal to c'

and $x \leqslant c$ meaning 'x is less than or equal to c'.

We can use these symbols to say in a compact way that a variable cannot be negative. Thus $x \geqslant 0$ reads 'x is greater than or equal to zero', or 'x is non-negative'.

The cases $>$ and $<$ are known as 'strong inequalities', while $\geqslant$ and $\leqslant$ are known as 'weak inequalities'.

3B.2   Indices

There are two simple forms of specific functions that turn up very frequently. One is the 'polynomial' which takes the form

$$a + bx + cx^2 + dx^3 + \cdots + mx^n. \tag{1}$$

Here x appears in a series of additive terms in each of which it is raised to a higher power. The general polynomial reduces to a linear relation if $c, d, \ldots, m = 0$, and to a quadratic if $d, \ldots, m = 0$, and so on. The other function very commonly encountered is the exponential function

$$a^x. \tag{2}$$

In this function the variable x appears as the exponent of the parameter a, hence the name exponential function. An example is $y = 2^x$, which gives $y = 2$ for $x = 1$, $y = 4$ for $x = 2$, $y = 8$ for $x = 3$, and so on. We can postpone a serious consideration of exponential functions for another 11 chapters, but we shall encounter simple examples of polynomials very soon, and it is necessary to recall some elementary results on indices so that we can handle these functions when they occur.

We know that x^2 is merely a short-hand way of writing $(x)(x)$, while x^3 stands for $(x)(x)(x)$, and so on. Thus where x is a positive integer (whole number), x^n is merely a direction which tells us to multiply n x's together. This is very simple for positive integers, but we must wonder if we can give any meaning to x^n either when x is a fraction or when it is negative.

Before we consider this question let us recall the rule for multiplying indices. $(x^2)(x^3)$ is short-hand for $(xx)(xxx)$ which is five x's multiplied together and written x^5 in our notation. Thus $(x^2)(x^3) = x^5$. In general we can simplify $(x^n)(x^m)$ for any n and m without writing all the x's out as we did above, by using the rule

$$(n^x)(x^m) = x^{n+m}, \tag{3}$$

or, *when multiplying merely add indices*. The common sense of this is that if you first take n x's and multiply them together, and then do the same with m x's, and then multiply the two results, you will have multiplied $(n + m)$ x's together. (If you are not convinced, try it for a few specific values, for example $(x^3)(x^4) = (xxx)(xxxx) = (xxxxxxx) = x^7$.)

Now let us return to our question about negative and fractional indices.

Take negative ones first. Without yet knowing how to interpret x^{-2} let us apply our multiplication rule to $(x^5)(x^{-2})$. According to the rule of adding indices this gives us $x^{5-2}=x^3$. We also know that, if we start with x^5 and wish to obtain x^3, we must divide by x^2. Writing it out in full,

$$\frac{xxxxx}{xx} = xxx = x^3. \tag{4}$$

Thus if we interpret x^{-2} as $1/x^2$, the application of our original multiplication rule gives us the correct answer. Hence we interpret negative integer indices by

$$x^{-n} = \frac{1}{x^n}, \tag{5}$$

and this gives us

$$(x^m)(x^{-n}) = \frac{x^m}{x^n} = x^{m-n}. \tag{6}$$

Now let us consider fractional indices. We again start by blindly applying our multiplication rule to a particular example. Take $(x^{1/2})(x^{1/2})$: according to our rule we have

$$(x^{1/2})(x^{1/2}) = x^{1/2+1/2} = x^1 = x. \tag{7}$$

Now we know that the number whose square is x is $\sqrt{x}$. Thus if we interpret $x^{1/2}$ as $\sqrt{x}$ the application of the multiplication rule above produces the correct answer. We also know that $(\sqrt[3]{x})^3=x$, so if we interpret $x^{1/3}$ as $\sqrt[3]{x}$ we shall again get correct answers when we apply our multiplication rule to $x^{1/3}$. In general, then, we have $x^{1/n}=\sqrt[n]{x}$.

An extension of the same line of argument will suggest that $x^{2/3}=\sqrt[3]{x^2}$, and in general $x^{n/m}=\sqrt[m]{x^n}$. (If you are not sure of this one, try $(x^{3/2})(x^{-1/2})$ and $(x^{3/4})(x^{1/4})$.)

We now know how to interpret fractional indices as well as positive and negative integers. We must just check briefly on two particular integers, zero and unity. Consider first x^1. According to the basic rule of the meaning of positive-integer indices, this says 'take x once' and the answer to this is clearly x. Let us try applying our rule to $(x^3)(x^{-2})$, which gives

$$(x^3)(x^{-2}) = x^{3-2} = x^1 = x. \tag{8}$$

Proceeding according to first principles we have

$$\frac{xxx}{xx} = x \tag{9}$$

which checks. Thus we have $x^1=x$.

Finally, to see what meaning we can give to x^0, let us consider a problem that gives x^0 as an answer. For example,

$$(x^2)(x^{-2}) = x^0 \tag{10}$$

according to our rule. Now, writing it all out, we have

$$\frac{xx}{xx} = 1. \tag{11}$$

It is clear that this result holds generally so that

$$(x^n)(x^{-n}) = x^{n-n} = x^0 \tag{12}$$

and

$$\frac{nx\text{'s}}{nx\text{'s}} = 1. \tag{13}$$

Thus if our rules are to give us correct answers for multiplying together x's raised to various powers we must understand x^0 to be unity.

So far we have seen that we multiply two terms with x raised to powers by adding the powers together. Now let us quickly investigate subtraction, multiplication, and division of indices. Consider x^3 and x^2. If we subtract indices we get x^1 which is the result we would get from x^3/x^2. This result generalises and we see that

$$\frac{x^m}{x^n} = x^{m-n} \tag{14}$$

which says that to divide x^m by x^n merely subtract the indices.

Now what would happen if we took x^3 and multiplied the index by two to get x^6? Since $x^3 = (xxx)$ and $x^6 = (xxxxxx)$, this suggests that we have squared the original number by multiplying its index by 2. Indeed

$$(x^n)^m = x^{nm} \tag{15}$$

means that x^n has been raised to the mth power. Finally, this gives by analogy a result we have already obtained: that if we divide the index by some number m we are taking the mth root of the original number. Thus

$$(x^n)^{1/m} = x^{n/m} = \sqrt[m]{x^n} \tag{16}$$

which is a result we have seen before.

All of this may be summarised in the following rules (which should make sense by now and not just be rules blindly committed to memory):

(1) $x^n = n$ x's multiplied together
(2) $x^1 = x$ (which is obvious from (1))
(3) $x^0 = 1$ (which is not obvious from (1))
(4) $x^{-n} = 1/x^n$
(5) $x^{1/n} = \sqrt[n]{x}$
(6) $x^{n/m} = \sqrt[m]{x^n}$
(7) $x^{-1/n} = 1/\sqrt[n]{}$
(8) $x^{-n/m} = 1/\sqrt[m]{x^n}$
(9) $(x^n)(x^m) = x^{m+n}$
(10) $(x^n)(x^{-m}) = x^n/x^m$
(11) $x^{nm} = (x^n)^m$

3B.3 Logarithms

Indices are the basis of logarithms and this is therefore a convenient moment to revise logarithms. We are not interested in doing sums, but we are interested in principles. If you learned to use log tables without ever understanding why, or have now forgotten, you should read this section (for which you will *not* need log tables!). If you are confident of your understanding, you should go straight on to 3.4 below.

Consider the so-called 'exponential function',

$$y = a^x. \qquad (17)$$

We can also write

$$x = \log_a y. \qquad (18)$$

This says that, if y is equal to a constant a raised to a variable power x, then we *define* the variable x to be *the logarithm to base a of y*. In less cumbersome language the phrase 'the logarithm to the base a of y' means the power to which a must be raised to give it a value equal to y.

The great value of logarithms is that they reduce the processes of multiplication and division to those of addition and subtraction, and the processes of finding powers and roots to those of multiplication and division. Let us recall how this is done. Assume that we have

$$y = (a^{x_1})(a^{x_2}) \qquad (19)$$

which, simplified by adding exponents, gives

$$y = a^{x_1 + x_2}. \qquad (20)$$

We can exploit this in multiplying any two numbers, which we denote by

3

y_1 and y_2. If we already know the values of x_1 and x_2 that solve the equations

$$y_1 = a^{x_1} \qquad (21)$$

$$y_2 = a^{x_2} \qquad (22)$$

we merely add these exponents to obtain

$$y_3 = (y_1)(y_2) = a^{x_1 + x_2}. \qquad (23)$$

If we know the value of $a^{x_1 + x_2}$ we have the solution to our problem.

Let us try an example of this technique by performing the multiplications:

$$y = 301 \times 562 \times 46. \qquad (24)$$

Now, if some benevolent person has solved for x the equation

$$y = 10^x$$

for all possible values of y, and entered the results in a table of 'logarithms', we only have to look up the values of x that solve the three equations

$$301 = 10^{x_1} \qquad (25)$$

$$562 = 10^{x_2} \qquad (26)$$

$$46 = 10^{x_3}. \qquad (27)$$

The table, in fact, gives us the following results:

$$x_1 = 2 \cdot 4786$$

$$x_2 = 2 \cdot 7497$$

$$x_3 = 1 \cdot 6628$$

which says that 10 raised to the power 2·4786 is equal to 301 and so on. We calculate the product as follows:

$$y = 301 \times 562 \times 46$$

$$= 10^{2 \cdot 4786} \times 10^{2 \cdot 7497} \times 10^{1 \cdot 6628}$$

$$= 10^{6 \cdot 8911} \qquad (28)$$

Now we know that the number we require is 10 raised to the power 6·8911, and we merely consult our table once again to find the 'anti-logarithm' of 6·8911, which is 7,781,500, and we have our answer. (An anti-logarithm merely means the value of y which has that specific number – 6·8911 in this case – as its logarithm.)

If we wish to divide two numbers, we merely subtract their logarithm. Say we have

$$y_3 = \frac{y_1}{y_2} = \frac{10^{x_1}}{10^{x_2}} = 10^{x_1 - x_2}. \qquad (29)$$

Thus we merely find the logarithm of y_1 and y_2, subtract, and look up an anti-logarithm. We present an example:

$$y_3 = \frac{187}{17} = \frac{10^{2 \cdot 2718}}{10^{1 \cdot 2304}}$$

$$= 10^{2 \cdot 2718 - 1 \cdot 2304}$$

$$= 10^{1 \cdot 0414}. \qquad (30)$$

Now we consult our table of anti-logarithms to find that 10 raised to the power 1·0414 is 11 (i.e., 11 is *the* number whose logarithm is 1·0414).

We raise a number to a power by using the relation

$$(y^x)^n = y^{xn}. \qquad (31)$$

Assume we wish to raise 86 to the sixth power. We first look up the logarithm of 86, which is 1·9345, so that $86 = 10^{1 \cdot 9345}$. Now we can solve our problem as follows:

$$86^6 = (10^{1 \cdot 9345})^6 = 10^{1 \cdot 9345 \times 6}$$

$$= 10^{11 \cdot 6070} \qquad (32)$$

and the table shows that the anti-logarithm of 11·6070 is 404,550,000,000 which is our answer.

Finally, if we wish to take the nth root of a number, we use the relation

$$(y^x)^{1/n} = (y)^{x/n}. \qquad (33)$$

Thus we merely divide the logarithm of a number by n in order to take the nth root of the number – a most convenient result! As an example, assume we wish to find the fifth root of 261. We look up a table of logarithms to discover that

$$261 = 10^{2 \cdot 4166}$$

so that

$$(261)^{1/5} = (10^{2 \cdot 4166})^{1/5} = 10^{2 \cdot 4166/5} = 10^{0 \cdot 4833} \qquad (34)$$

The table now shows us that $10^{0 \cdot 4833}$ is 3·043, and we have found the fifth root of 261, which would have been a very difficult task without logarithms. If, instead of the fifth root, we had wanted the 4·72th root, this would have been really very difficult without logarithms, but, using logarithms, it requires only that we can divide 2·4166 by 4·72, and have the necessary tables.

Changes of Base: Up to this point we have been dealing with logarithms to the base 10. These are called common logarithms. Clearly, however, the logarithm 'trick' can be worked for *any* base *a*. Instead of solving the equation $y = 10^x$ for all y's we could just as well have solved the equation $y = 5^x$ for all y's. If we gathered these results in a table we would have a set of logarithms to the base 5. For practical purposes we use bases for which the values have been worked out in advance. The equation $y = a^x$ has been solved for $a = 10$ for all eight-digit values of x and the values recorded in tables of logarithms.

We can, however, change over to any other base very easily. We change from base *a* to base *b* merely by multiplying logarithms to the base *a* by a constant equal to logarithm to the base *b* of *a*:

$$\log_b y = \log_a y \log_b a \qquad (35)$$

The proof of the conversion formula is not something one needs to carry around in one's head, but it is worth working through it once or twice just to be satisfied that it really works. Start by letting

$$p = b^q$$

so that

$$q = \log_b p.$$

Then

$$\log_a p = \log_a (b^q)$$
$$= q(\log_a b)$$
$$= (\log_b p)(\log_a b). \qquad (36)$$

Thus we can move from one logarithm base to another with complete ease. In a practical case we need to calculate a single constant, $\log_b a$, and multiply our logarithms to the base *a* by this constant to get the logarithms of the same numbers to the base *b*. In theoretical work a base other than 10 is commonly used. We shall need this later, but so very much later that there is no point in considering it now.

3B.4   The Log-linear Function

Arithmetic examples of logarithmic manipulations are undeniably tedious. Let us now show that the principle of logarithms is useful for more than doing sums by looking at a particularly interesting and important function.

Experience in Part A of this chapter, and a little reflection, will suggest that linear relationships are much easier to handle than non-linear ones. On the other hand, if we refused to work with any non-linear functions, the models of the world that we might build would be rather restricted. Now consider the function

$$y = ax^b \qquad (37)$$

which says that y is equal to x raised to some given power b, all multiplied by a constant a. (37) does not look very tractable as it stands, but a very simple trick will do wonders. We simply take logarithms of both sides to get

$$\log y = \log a + b \log x. \qquad (38)$$

(38) is *linear in the logarithms of the variables x and y*. If we draw our usual co-ordinate diagram, and put $\log y$ on the vertical axis, $\log x$ on the horizontal, the graph of (38) will be a straight line with intercept equal to $\log a$ and slope equal to b. Thus the incremental ratio is simply given by

$$\frac{\Delta \log y}{\Delta \log x} = b. \qquad (39)$$

(You should refer back, if necessary, to 3A.8.) (37) is, of course, non-linear in the 'natural numbers'. (38) is called the *logarithmic transformation* of (37), and is linear in the logs. Comparison of (37) and (38) suggests that we may start with an awkward non-linear relation, and, by making the transformation, get a function which is very easily handled indeed. This circumstance is very widely exploited: functions of the form of (37) are used regularly in economics, and we shall meet frequent examples in this book. When we have learned, in Chapter 5, to take derivatives, we shall discover even more convenient properties.

Exercises

1 (i) If $\log_{10} 3 = 0 \cdot 4771$, find *without using log tables* $\log_{10} 9$ and $\log_{10} 27$
   (ii) If $\log_{10} 16 = 1 \cdot 2041$, find *without using tables* $\log_{10} 4$ and $\log_{10} 2$
   (iii) Find $\log_{10} 6$.
2 If $2x + 3 > 4$, show that x is positive.
3 Can you find a 'logarithmic transformation' of
   (i) $y = 7x^{1/3}$
   (ii) $y = 10 + 3x^b$
   (iii) $y = 2(-x)^2$?
4 Given that $\Delta \log y / \Delta \log x = 3$ and $\log y = 1$ when $\log x = 0$, find the function relating x to y in natural numbers.

CHAPTER 4

SIMPLE LINEAR MODELS

A. A COMPETITIVE MARKET

4A.1 The Solution of a Numerical Example

We shall now develop the simple theory of a competitive market. The only additional technique required is the method of solving simultaneous linear equations. If you have forgotten how to do this, there is no need to look it up in a mathematics text, since we shall develop the method we require quite easily as we proceed. The analysis of a simple competitive market is useful not only as an exercise in technique but also because it will serve to illustrate some fundamental ideas that will recur frequently throughout this book. We shall exploit the model itself extensively , handling more and more ambitious questions as our technique increases, until we finally have a very thorough and general treatment of it.

Our simplest case is that in which both demand and supply curves are straight lines, described by the linear functions

$$q^d = a + bp \tag{1}$$

$$q^s = c + dp \tag{2}$$

where q^d denotes the quantity demanded and q^s the quantity supplied. q^d is read 'q-superscript d' or 'q-super-d' for short. These are behavioural equations: they state assumptions about market behaviour. The assumption that the functions are linear may look rather restrictive, and unlikely to be satisfied in the real world. We shall find, however, that we can learn a good deal, of a general nature, even on this simple assumption; and, besides, a straight line may lie sufficiently close to a curved one over some range that, for small changes at least, the treatment of the curve as though it were the straight line leads to acceptable approximations to the correct answer. (The technique of 'linear approximations' to non-linear relationships is widely used in the physical sciences.) Anyhow, we need more technique before we drop this assumption, which we do in Chapter 10. To complete the theory of competitive price determination set out in (1) and (2), we add the equilibrium condition

$$q^d = q^s. \tag{3}$$

In a specific case, we might know the actual numerical values of the parameters a, b, c, d. We should then insert them, and solve for equilibrium
price and quantity. Thus let us start by solving the numerical example given
in equations (4), (5), and (6).

$$q^d = 1200 - 2p \qquad (4)$$

$$q^s = 4p \qquad (5)$$

$$q^d = q^s. \qquad (6)$$

(What value has been given to the parameter c in this example? What must
the supply curve look like?) From (6), we know that the price must be at
the level which equates supply and demand. Hence we substitute (4) and
(5) into (6), which eliminates both q^d and q^s, and we obtain

$$1200 - 2p = 4p. \qquad (7)$$

Collecting terms we have

$$6p = 1200 \qquad (8)$$

whence $\qquad\qquad\qquad\qquad p = 200$

and $\qquad\qquad\qquad\qquad q = 800. \qquad (9)$

There are two points to notice about the method of solution, which we shall
use again and again.

(1) We started with three equations in three unknowns (q^d, q^s, p). By substituting the behaviour equations, (4) and (5), into the equilibrium equation (6), we obtained a single equation (7), in one unknown, p.

(2) Having solved for p, we obtain equilibrium q by substituting the
equilibrium value of p into *either one* of the behavioural equations. (You
may check arithmetically that, with $p = 200$, $q = 800$ is obtained from (4) *or*
(5); but this is no accident. Why not?)

4A.2 The General Solution of the Linear Model

We are now equipped to start the study of an important and fascinating
topic frequently referred to as 'qualitative economics'. In practice, we
frequently do not know parameter values, but only restrictions such as 'the
demand curve slopes down', Hence we are interested in the question of
what, if anything, we can discover about the solution of the model, and its
properties, on the basis of qualitative restrictions on the parameters. By
'qualitative restrictions' we mean (for the moment) such simple and general
notions as 'the demand curve slopes down and the supply curve up'. Evidently if restrictions like this prove to be *sufficient* to establish some
property or result, without need for numbers, we have *general* results. The

search for general qualitative results is ambitious and exciting. It unfortunately turns out that in more complicated models qualitative results are rather rare, and it is imperative to have numerical estimates of parameters before definite results can be obtained, but even then it is essential to our own understanding of the model that we know if it yields qualitative results, and if not, why not.

In the present case, we can do quite a lot qualitatively. We must start by specifying the model more carefully, and we make the following qualitative assumptions:

(i) $b < 0$, i.e., the demand curve slopes down;

(ii) $d > 0$, i.e., the supply curve slopes up;

(iii) $c < a$, because if this were not true, supply would exceed demand at zero price, and the good in question would not be an economic good: its price would be zero (you should draw a diagram to illustrate this).

We may now solve the general model of equations (1), (2), (3), where we only have the parameters in the form a, b, c, d, without numbers. We use exactly the method of our numerical example, and start by substituting (1) and (2) into (3) to obtain

$$a + bp = c + dp \qquad (10)$$

Collecting terms,

$$a - c = dp - bp.$$

Factoring the right-hand side,

$$a - c = p(d - b).$$

Dividing both sides by $(d - b)$,

$$p = \frac{a - c}{d - b}. \qquad (11)$$

Substituting (11) into (1) we obtain

$$q = a + b\left(\frac{a - c}{d - b}\right).$$

To simplify the right-hand side, we multiply and divide a by $(d - b)$, which gives $(d - b)$ as a common denominator, whence

$$q = \frac{a(d - b) + b(a - c)}{d - b}$$

$$= \frac{ad - bc}{d - b}. \qquad (12)$$

(This is a good moment to stop and do Exercise 1.)

Equations (11) and (12) are said to 'constitute the solution to the system of equations (1), (2), and (3)'. This sounds very imposing; but are we any better off contemplating (11) and (12) than we were when we had merely (1), (2), and (3)? To answer this, we must consider what we mean by a 'solution', and what use it is. First of all, we need a little terminology, for convenience of discussion. By an *endogenous variable*, we mean one that is determined within the system we are analysing: it is *dependent*, and, when we start, it is an unknown. Thus our dependent variables in this case are price and quantity. By an *exogenous variable* we mean one not determined within the particular system we are analysing: from the point of view of the analysis of a single micro-market, GNP, for example, may be taken as exogenous. (The terms 'autonomous' and 'predetermined' are also used. They are nearly, but not quite, interchangeable with 'exogenous'. The distinctions need not concern us here.) By a *parameter* we mean a fixed coefficient, such as a, b, c, or d in this model. Now, in equations (1) and (2), one dependent variable depends on another: to know one of the unknowns, you must already know the other! This is why we are not content to leave matters here. By a *solution* we mean an equation (or set of equations if there is more than one dependent variable) that expresses an endogenous variable as a function of the parameters and exogenous variables *only*. Hence equations (11) and (12) are solutions in the sense that neither p nor q appears on the right-hand side of either of them. Thus to know q, say, from equation (12) it is not necessary to know p; it is only necessary to know the parameter values, and to know that the market is in equilibrium. In this particular example, of course, we have not explicitly introduced any exogenous variables. We may imagine, however, that GNP, prices of substitutes, etc., will have their effects through the values of the parameters. If the commodity in question is not an inferior good, the demand for it increases when income increases. Thus an increase in GNP might be reflected in this model by an increase in the parameter a, the intercept of the demand equation, and perhaps a change in b as well. Similarly, a change in external circumstances that altered the conditions of supply would be reflected by changes in the parameters c and d. Thus for the moment we do not have to introduce exogenous variables explicitly: it is enough to express the endogenous variables as functions of parameters that themselves depend on exogenous variables.

What use, then, is a solution such as that provided by (11) and (12)? First of all, it is the 'general solution' to this linear system. This means, simply, that once it has been done, it need never be done again for any pair of linear supply and demand curves for any market whatsoever. Given numerical values for the parameters, we need never again solve numerically as we did in equations (7), (8), and (9): we substitute any set of parameter

3*

values directly into (11) and (12). (You should satisfy yourself that this works.) It is evident that general solutions are potentially labour-saving devices on a grand scale. Secondly, however, they may be used directly to investigate the qualitative properties of the model. Equations (1), (2), and (3) cannot be used for this, because we have not yet disentangled the endogenous variables from each other, and related them directly to the parameters. A numerical example will not do either because we cannot tell if some property which obtains if, say, $q^s = 4p$, will also hold if $q^s = 4 \cdot 5p$, and we shall get bored long before we have exhausted the (infinite!) number of possible arithmetic examples: this is precisely why we seek 'general' methods, and why mathematical analysis is so labour-saving and powerful when it provides them.

We often take it for granted in economic theory that prices and quantities are positive (the interpretation of zero and negative prices was discussed in Chapter 3 above). It is prudent, however, to check that our model does give a positive price, and this check will also serve as our first example of qualitative analysis. The solution for p was given in equation (11), so what we have to do is investigate the sign of the right-hand side of (11). It follows from assumption (iii) above, $c < a$, that the numerator of (11) is positive. Furthermore, $d > 0$ and $b < 0$ is sufficient (but not necessary: see 4A.4 below) for the denominator to be positive. Hence our qualitative assumptions are sufficient (but, again, not necessary) to ensure that this model always gives a positive price.

4A.3   An Excise Tax in a Competitive Market

We can now use our competitive model to make a qualitative investigation of a problem in public finance: what are the effects on price and quantity sold of the imposition of a specific excise tax? A specific excise tax is one of a given amount per unit sold (so much per bottle on 70-proof whisky), as opposed to an *ad valorem* tax, which is a given percentage of the price. One famous result is that a specific excise tax will raise price, but by less than the amount of the tax per unit – at least, on certain assumptions. We can now use our technique to derive this prediction for the linear case, and to try to find out on what assumptions it depends. This is an example of qualitative analysis, and we shall see how far we can get.

For demand, we shall still assume that

$$q^d = a + bp \tag{1}$$

but, in place of (2), we now have

$$q^s = c + dp^* \tag{13}$$

where p^* is the price received by suppliers after paying tax, which is less than market price p by the amount of the tax. p^* and p are therefore related by

$$p^* = p - t \tag{14}$$

where t is tax per unit. We also have, of course,

$$q^d = q^s \tag{3}$$

Thus we have a system of four equations, (1), (13), (14), and (3), in the unknowns q^d, q^s, p^*, and p, with parameters a, b, c, d, and t (we may, if we wish, call t an exogenous variable instead of a parameter: it makes no difference). As before, we proceed by substitution to obtain a single equation in one unknown. Substituting (14) into (13) we have

$$q^s = c + dp - dt \tag{15}$$

which eliminates p^*. Now substitute (1) and (15) into (3) to eliminate q^d and q^s:

$$a + bp = c + dp - dt. \tag{16}$$

Rearranging as before,

$$a - c = p(d - b) - dt$$

whence

$$p = \frac{a-c}{d-b} + \frac{d}{d-b} t. \tag{17}$$

(17) is another general solution, and we want to discover what properties of the solution, if any, can be established. We want to know, that is, if our qualitative restrictions, assumptions (i), (ii), and (iii) of 4A.2 above, are enough to tell us anything about (17), and, if they are, what happens if we change any of these assumptions. There are four points we may make at once.

(1) We had better start by checking that this solution is consistent with that of 4A.2 (11). The only difference between the two cases is that in one we have a tax and the other we do not. This suggests that we should ask what happens in the 'with tax' case if the tax-rate is zero: we obviously should get the same solution as in the 'no tax' case. Thus we satisfy ourselves that we have not made some frightful blunder by trying $t=0$ in (17). If we do this, we get $p = (a-c)/(d-b)$, which is what we found in (11).

(2) This suggests that we look at the term in (17) that does contain t, and consider the way in which p depends on t. This term is

$$\frac{d}{d-b} t$$

which contains only the slope coefficients b and d: it does not contain the intercept coefficients a and c. Thus we may say that the effect of the tax on price is independent of the intercepts. This rather striking result can be quite easily illustrated geometrically. Draw linear supply and demand curves, add a tax, and find the new price. The easiest way of shifting the intercepts but not the slopes is just to move the axes. Draw the quantity axis an inch to the left, the price axis an inch lower down, and it is obvious that the price-effect of the tax is unaltered. You will be asked to investigate in Exercise 2 the effect of the tax on quantity.

(3) Since both d and $d-b$ are positive by assumption, the effect of the tax on price is always positive.

(4) Now we know that $d/d-b$ is positive. If we can also show that it is less than unity, we shall have shown that the tax increases price, but by less than the amount of the tax. Since b, the slope coefficient of the demand curve, is negative, subtracting it from d has the effect of *adding* a positive number (this is an application of the rule 'minus a minus makes a plus'). Hence $d-b>d$, whence $d/(d-b)<1$, which is what we wanted to show.

Thus by (4) we have proved the 'tax theorem' for a competitive market, and done so quite generally in the sense that we have not had to depend on numerical examples. We have, however, only considered the straightforward case of a downward-sloping demand curve and upward-sloping supply curve. We are still left with some problems:

(i) What happens if the demand curve is upward sloping as well as the supply curve?

(ii) What happens if the supply curve is downward sloping as well as the demand curve?

(iii) For what values of the parameters does the solution break down?

We will deal with these problems in the next section; but it would pay to try them for yourself before reading on, and to consider both their graphical illustrations and economic interpretations.

4A.4   Qualitative Results with an Excise Tax

Discovering the answers to these problems turns out to be fairly laborious: we shall find several possible answers to each, depending on the assumptions we make about the relative magnitudes of the parameters in each case. Our discussion is exhaustive, and has to be: if we did not examine every possibility, we might well overlook such circumstances as that, for example, if the demand curve slopes up, but more steeply than the supply curve, and we retain our assumption that $c<a$, which we made originally to be sure of having a positive price, we shall get a negative one! A systematic treatment can clarify many points that may not be immediately obvious to the intuition.

It is helpful to remember that our solution in the tax case is

$$p = \frac{a-c}{d-b} + \frac{d}{d-b}\,t. \tag{17}$$

Problem (i): If the demand curve is upward sloping, $b > 0$. This gives rise to three possible cases:

In the first case, the positive slope of the demand curve may be less than that of the supply curve (with q on the vertical axis of the graph, the slope of the demand curve is less steep than that of the supply curve). This means that $b < d$, in which case $d - b$ and $d/(d-b)$ are both positive, p is positive, and the effect of the tax on price is still positive. Since, however, b is positive, we now have $d > d - b$, so that the tax raises price by more than the amount of the tax.

In the second case the demand curve is steeper than the supply curve, so we have $b > d$, which, at first glance, gives the result $d/(d-b) < 0$: the tax lowers the price. If $d - b < 0$, however, we also have

$$\frac{a-c}{d-b} < 0$$

if $a > c$ as we assumed, which means that the curves intersect at a negative price. Thus we do not get a positive price – intersection in the positive quadrant – in this case unless we alter our assumption about the intercepts and put $c > a$, whereupon the tax does lower the price.

Between these two cases (supply curve steeper than demand curve; demand curve steeper than supply curve) there must lie a third, that in which the two slopes are the same. This produces some rather odd and interesting results. It gives $b = d$, in which case the tax term of (17) is $d/0$. Division by zero is 'undefined' – we do not know how to do it in our arithmetic. We may call the result 'infinity' if we like, but shall be no better off. If $d - b = 0$, however, the first term in (17), which is $(a-c)/(d-b)$, is undefined too: there is no finite price that will clear the market. The reason is, of course, that if $b = d$, the two curves are parallel if $c \neq a$ as we assumed, and there is no 'equilibrium point'. (If a and c happened to be equal, the two curves would coincide, and *any* price would equate supply and demand, in which case there would not be a unique equilibrium price.)

These three cases are illustrated in Figures 4A.1, 4A.2, and 4A.3. In Figure 4A.1 the result of a tax of AB is to raise price by AC – and to raise quantity too.[1] In Figure 4A.2 it has been assumed that $c > a$, and a tax of

---

[1] Since in this model quantity is the *dependent* variable, we have put it on the vertical axis in this figure. Thus the case $0 < b < d$, for example, means that demand and supply curves both slope up, but the demand curve less steeply than the supply curve. To convert to the Marshallian

[*Footnote continues on p. 72*

EF can be seen to lower the price by *DF*. In Figure 4A.3 the curves are parallel, and there is no solution at all (see Exercise 4).

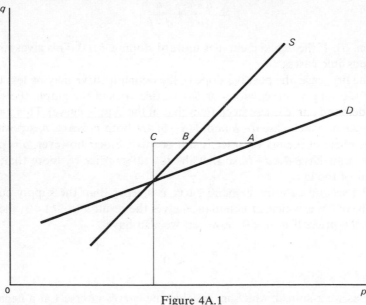

Figure 4A.1

Problem (ii): What happens if the supply curve is downward sloping as well as the demand curve? This means that $d<0$ and again there are three possible cases[1]:

$|b|>|d|$ in which case $d-b>0$ and $d/(d-b)<0$: the tax lowers the price. Notice that, since $d-b>0$, the assumption $a>c$ is in this case required for a positive solution.

$|b|<|d|$ gives $d/(d-b)>0$: the tax increases price, but we need $c<a$ to get a solution at all.

$b=d$: parallelism again.

This is a good moment to do exercise 5.

———

diagram usually drawn by economists, with p on the vertical axis, it is only necessary to remember that if $q=a+bp$ then

$$p = \frac{-a}{b}+\frac{1}{b}\cdot q$$

so that the slope of the demand curve as conventionally drawn is $1/b$.

[1] $|X|$ is read 'the absolute value of X', or 'the modulus of X'. It is defined as

$$|X| = X \quad \text{if } X > 0$$
$$|X| = -X \quad \text{if } X < 0.$$

If b and d are negative, but $|b|>|d|$, then $d-b>0$ because $(-b)$ is positive and absolutely larger than the negative d.

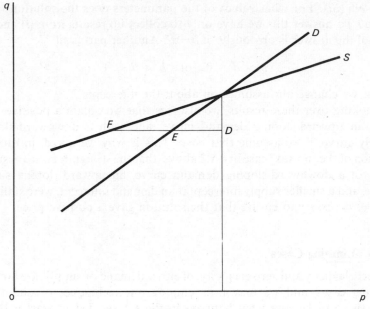

Figure 4A.2

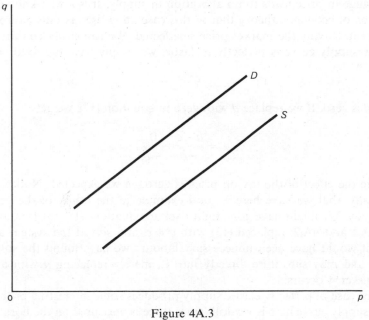

Figure 4A.3

Problem (iii): For what values of the parameters does the solution break down? To answer this we have only to collect up results from (*i*) and (*ii*). Part of the answer is obviously 'if $b=d$'. Another part is 'if

$$b > d > 0 \quad \text{or} \quad b < d < 0$$

unless we change our assumption about the intercepts'.

Looking over these results, we also see that we obtain a positive price with an upward-sloping demand curve, and with a downward-sloping supply curve, if we assume that $c>a$. This is why we noted, in our discussion of the 'no-tax' case in 4A.2 above, that the straightforward assumptions of a downward-sloping demand curve, an upward-sloping supply curve, and a smaller supply intercept than demand intercept, were sufficient *but not necessary* to ensure that the solution gave a positive price.

4A.5   Limiting Cases

Perfect elasticity and zero elasticity, of either demand or supply, are familiar limiting cases, and we may now employ our techniques of qualitative analysis to make sure what happens in these cases. Let us start with the case of a perfectly inelastic supply curve. In this case the supply curve is horizontal, and we say that the receipts of suppliers are entirely rents: a change in price leads to no alteration in supply. It is a well-known prediction of economic theory that in this case an excise tax falls entirely on the rent, leaving the market price unaffected. We can easily confirm this. If the supply curve is perfectly inelastic, we simply have the fixed supply

$$q^s = c$$

i.e., d is zero. If we replace d with zero in equation (17), we get

$$p = \frac{a-c}{-b} + \frac{0}{-b} t$$

where the effect of the tax on price is zero, as we expected. Notice, incidentally, that we have here a good example of the utility of the general solution. We might have gone right back to equations (1), (13), (14), and (3) of 4A.1 and 4A.2, replaced (13) with $q^s=c$, and solved the system again, but it would have been unnecessary labour: we have found the solution (17), and may substitute directly into it, merely replacing d with a zero whenever it occurs.

The case of perfectly elastic supply produces some interesting problems. The supply curve here is vertical (since price is measured on the horizontal axis), and it is often said that its slope is infinite. If, however, we put $d = \infty$, and substitute into (17), we get

$$p = \frac{a-c}{\infty-b} + \frac{\infty}{\infty-b} t$$

which is obviously nonsense. Something has gone wrong! It is important to consider very carefully what the cause of the trouble may be: if it is a comprehensible blunder, it can be understood and corrected, and need not recur.

In fact, direct substitution of $d = \infty$ into (17) is a perfectly straightforward blunder in mathematics, and in economics as well. The mathematical blunder is easily understood. A vertical line has no slope – it is simply undefined – and if we insist on writing the symbol ∞ whenever we meet something undefined, we may expect to obtain a silly answer: the situation would not be different if we wrote 'dog' or 'dumb blonde' for the nonexistent slope coefficient. To understand what has happened in economics, we must think out how the model works. If supply is perfectly elastic, there is one and only one price at which any output is produced at all, so equations like (11) in the no-tax case or (17) in the tax case cannot be solutions *at all*: they provide solutions *when price is an endogenous variable, but here it is fixed*. We must therefore go back to the beginning and get the supply equation right. We still have equation (1),

$$q^d = a + bp \tag{1}$$

but instead of $q^s = c + dp$, we have $p = \bar{p}$ and no equation for the quantity supplied at all. This is intuitively reasonable, since perfectly elastic supply means that suppliers will provide *any* quantity they are asked for *at the given price* $\bar{p}$, so that they determine price, and consumers alone determine quantity. We now have the three-equation model

$$q^d = a + bp \tag{1}$$

$$p = \bar{p} \tag{18}$$

and $$q^d = q^s. \tag{3}$$

To solve, we merely substitute $p = \bar{p}$ into the demand equation, obtaining

$$q^d = a + b\bar{p} \tag{19}$$

and note that $q^s = q^d$.

Before we add a tax to the model of (1), (18), and (3), it will be wise to discover the conditions for anything to be sold at all at a positive price. We can no longer use $a < c$, since c has disappeared. What we require is that the intercept of the demand curve on the price axis is to the right of the intercept of the supply curve. The latter is, of course, $\bar{p}$. The former we find by rearranging the demand equation:

$$bp = q^d - a$$

or

$$p = \frac{q}{b} - \frac{a}{b}$$

whence the intercept is $-a/b$ (remember that $b < 0$), and the condition is $-a/b > \bar{p}$.

We may now analyse the effects of a tax. We recall that, whatever may happen, market price must be equal to suppliers' price plus tax, i.e.,

$$p = p^* + t, \tag{14}$$

where p is market price and p^* suppliers' net price, as before. But there is a unique supply price, $\bar{p}$, so substitution at once gives

$$p = \bar{p} + t \tag{20}$$

and it immediately follows that price must rise by the full amount of the tax, the standard result we were trying to get! We also have

$$q = a + b(\bar{p} + t)$$

i.e., quantity falls by bt.

The analysis of this case suggests two morals that are worth some attention.

(1) A great nineteenth-century problem was 'Which determines prices, cost of production or value (marginal utility)?' Marshall answered this with the analogy of the scissors: 'Which blade cuts the string?' We are so accustomed to the simultaneous determination of price *and* quantity by demand and supply that it is easy to forget that, if one is already fixed, there is only one scissor-blade to move.

(2) Suppose that we start with a model containing a given set of endogenous variables, and the equations relating them, and work out the solution and its properties. Now someone says 'What if one of the variables is actually fixed?' (Many illustrations come to mind. 'What if the price is controlled? Wages are sticky? Interest rates are fixed?' and so on.) It is *not* correct to try substituting a fixed value into the solution, because the model itself must have been changed: if what was a variable no longer is, one or more of the behavioural equations must be altered in the appropriate way. Thus it is necessary to go back to the original formulation of the model, and see how it is to work. (In the language of 4A.*7 below, we should say that, if the number of variables in a satisfactory system was arbitrarily reduced, the number of equations remaining unaltered, the system had become 'overdetermined'.) This is a good moment to stop and do Exercise 6.

4A.6 Qualitative Comparative Statics

In 4A.2 above, we introduced the notion of 'qualitative restrictions', and suggested that they might be sufficient to establish some properties of the solution of the model. In the last few sections, we have been working out the properties and the relevant restrictions, and have discovered, among other things, that the conditions $b<0$, $d>0$, and $c<a$ are sufficient, though not necessary, to establish the proposition that the tax will increase price but by less than itself. Consider again equation (17)

$$p = \frac{a-c}{d-b} + \frac{d}{d-b} t$$

the graph of which is presented in Figure 4A.4. (17) gives price as a linear function of tax: the intercept is $(a-c)/(d-b)$, which is equilibrium price in

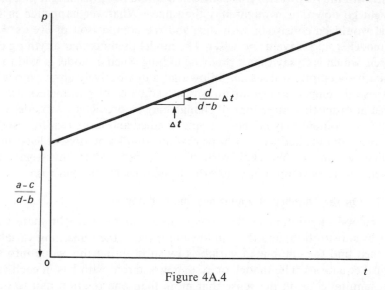

Figure 4A.4

the absence of a tax, and the slope is $d/(d-b)$, which measures the increase in price per unit increase in tax.

We may describe our result formally by saying that the slope in (17) is the rate of change of the endogenous variable, p, with respect to the exogenous variable (or 'shift parameter') t. What we have done is to differentiate the equilibrium value of the variable p with respect to the parameter t, and establish the qualitative result, $0 < d/(d-b) < 1$. 'Differentiating the equilibrium value . . .' sounds formidable, but we have really done it. [In a linear model it happens to be peculiarly easy: it can be done by inspection, almost unconsciously. If p were a non-linear function of t, then the slope (rate of change) would not, of course, be a constant. Later on we shall devote a good deal of attention to techniques which will allow us to find the relevant slope in more difficult cases.] What we are doing is often called 'qualitative comparative statics', or even 'the qualitative calculus'. It is comparative statics because we are comparing one equilibrium situation with another, asking what changes in the variables are required when exogenous changes take place, qualitative because we are trying to determine the directions of change without knowing numbers but only the signs of our parameters. In this case, of course, we have succeeded pretty well.

Imagine the situation had we failed. Suppose that the structure of the model were such that, with information like $b < 0$, $c > 0$, etc., we could not predict the direction of change in price when a tax was imposed or altered. Without numerical estimates of the parameters, we could not compare the model with the real world. Our conclusion would be 'price might go up, or it might go down, or it might stay the same'. Whatever happened in the world would be consistent with this, and the comparison of events with our model would leave us no wiser. The model predicts that anything can happen, which is to say that it predicts nothing. Such a model is said to be qualitatively empty. It does *not* follow that a qualitatively empty model is irretrievably empty, only that numerical estimates of parameters are required in order that directions of change may be predicted. A model with qualitative content may be more simply handled and more readily testable than one without; and we may hope that our simpler models, at least, have qualitative content. We shall certainly be concerned to investigate the matter, and to develop more powerful techniques for the purpose.

4A.*7   On the Number of Equations and Unknowns

The method of solution used in this chapter has been to eliminate variables by substitution, find the equilibrium value of the remaining variable, and then find the eliminated variables by substituting this value into the original equations. The model, or system, we started with has in each case been simultaneous, in the sense that more than one relation had to hold simultaneously. The question arises: how many equations do we need to determine some given number of variables? In the text, we have taken it for granted that we need the same number. (Thus if we wish to determine quantity demanded, quantity supplied, and price, we need a demand equation, a supply equation, and the equilibrium condition $q^d = q^s$.)

It is unfortunately the case, however, that in general equality between the number of unknowns and the number of equations in a system is neither necessary *nor* sufficient for a solution to exist. A complete discussion of the problem would be a large-scale undertaking, but there is no reason why it should be left an utter mystery, and we can quickly get some idea of what is involved.

Suppose, first of all, that we retain the assumption that all relations are linear. Now suppose that we are given two unknowns, y and x, and the single equation, say,

$$y = 10 + 5x.$$

We obviously cannot 'solve' for y, but only say 'the equation establishes pairs of values: given x, we can read off y'. If we were given another equation, say

$$x = 2$$

we could produce the solution, $y = 20$. We could also find the solution if we were given a second equation such as

$$y = x$$

or

$$y = 20 - x.$$

You should draw a rough graph in each case (and you will have to use the negative quadrants). You will find that each equation gives a straight line, and the solution corresponds to the point where the two lines intersect. $y = x$ defines, of course, the 45° line, and $x = 2$ can be represented by a vertical line through the point $x = 2$: the solution is the value of y where that line cuts $y = 10 + 5x$.

This is straightforward. Suppose, now, that we have $y = 10 + 5x$, and $y = x$, and are told that a third relation also holds, say $y = 2 + 2x$. If you graph these three equations, you will find that they do not all intersect in the same place: it is impossible to satisfy all three relations simultaneously, and the system has no solution, but is said to be 'over-determined'. If this should occur, it is evidence that there is something wrong with the model in the first place. It might appear now that the rule we need is simply 'do not have more equations than unknowns', but unfortunately matters are not quite so simple. There is, first, the possibility of accident: given three straight lines, they *may* all intersect in the same place. This case, however, is not very interesting since, even if one starts with an accidental solution, if one of the lines is moved by some change in data, there will then be no solution. There is, second, a possibility that we may illustrate. Suppose that we still have

$$y = 10 + 5x$$

and are given as a second equation

$$10y = 100 + 50x.$$

Consider what happens if we divide through by 10: we simply get $y = 10 + 5x$. Thus the second equation tells us nothing that the first did not tell us: it gives the same line on the graph, and gets us no nearer to a solution. It is not 'independent' of the first equation, whereas $y = x$ is independent of

$y = 10 + 5x$ (there is no factor such that multiplication or division of one equation by that factor will produce the other). This suggests that we modify our rule to read 'have exactly the number of independent equations as there is unknowns', and this is nearly correct. There remains, however, the sort of case we encountered in 4A.4 above. What if we have

$$y = 10 + 5x$$

and

$$y = 20 + 5x \quad ?$$

These two lines are parallel, and we get no solution. We cannot easily produce a general rule to deal with this case, so we shall leave the question here.

If we allow non-linear functions, matters get a good deal more complicated, as may easily be seen from a little geometrical experiment. A straight line, for example, may intersect a U-shaped curve (say, a quadratic) twice, or nowhere if it passes underneath it, or it may be tangent to it (once). The case of 'passing underneath' is the one that gives 'unreal roots' when we try to solve a quadratic that lies everywhere above the x-axis. If it cuts it once, it cuts it twice (*unless* it is vertical). But it is not easy to lay down general rules, and all we can say is 'if there appear to be more independent equations than unknowns, there is likely to be trouble; and if there are non-linear functions there may be no solution or multiple solutions, all depending on the particular case'.

Exercises

1 Show that the solution obtained for q in (12) would also have been obtained by substituting (11) into (2) instead of (1). Consider carefully why this will always work.

2 It is shown in 4A.3 that the effect of a specific excise tax on price is independent of the intercept coefficients. What does the geometrical illustration suggest about the effect of the tax on equilibrium quantity? Investigate algebraically. (*Hint*: Substitute (17) into (1) and examine the term that contains t.)

3 What are the effects of a tax of 75 per unit in the numerical example of 4A.1, equations (4), (5), and (6)?

4 In Figure 4A.3 the supply curve has been drawn below the demand curve. (i) Is this consistent with our assumption about c and a? (ii) Does it make any difference to the conclusion whether the supply curve is above the demand curve or vice versa for the case $d = b$? (iii) What happens if $d = b$ and $c = a$?

5 Provide geometrical illustrations of the answers to Problem (ii) of 4A.4.

6 Apply the techniques of 4A.5 to the cases of perfectly inelastic and perfectly elastic demand.

B. INCOME DETERMINATION

4B.1 The Multiplier

We shall now subject a simple Keynesian model to the same sort of analysis that we have just applied to a competitive market. Once again, this is not only a technical exercise: we can illustrate some important ideas, and obtain some very interesting results which illuminate the relationship between positive economics and economic policy. We shall also return to the model repeatedly in future chapters, tackling more and more ambitious questions as the technique at our command increases. We assume a simple Keynesian model, of the sort that will be familiar from any standard 'principles' text such as Samuelson or Lipsey, in which it is assumed that all investment is autonomous. This effectively allows us to ignore the monetary sector, since if we assume that investment is autonomous we do not have to concern ourselves with the determination of the interest rate and its effect on investment. We also assume that prices are constant in spite of income changes, which means that we must assume unemployed resources, and confine ourselves to income changes that do not come too close to the full-employment 'ceiling'.

The simplest case to start with is that of a closed economy with no government, and the first behaviour-equation we want is a consumption function. Let us consider the choice of possible consumption functions. We obviously make consumption a function of income, but it may perfectly well depend on other variables as well. Obvious candidates for inclusion in the consumption function are the rate of interest, the level of wealth, and past consumption, the last because the standard of living to which people are accustomed is particularly likely to influence their short-run behaviour when income changes. In the interests of analytical convenience, however, we shall leave out all variables except income, and restrict ourselves to linear functions. Hence we assume

$$C = a + cY. \qquad (1)$$

In this case, however, the average and marginal propensities to consume are unequal. The marginal propensity is given by

$$\frac{\Delta C}{\Delta Y} = c$$

and the average propensity by

$$\frac{C}{Y} = \frac{a + cY}{Y} = \frac{a}{Y} + c$$

which is plainly larger than the marginal propensity. (You should satisfy yourself that, the larger is Y, the more nearly equal are the average and marginal propensities. Illustrate geometrically.) The empirical evidence is not easy to interpret, but there is a good case for thinking that the average and marginal propensities are equal; indeed, a large intercept term can easily be shown to lead to some preposterous results.[1] We shall accordingly assume that they are equal, which means putting $a=0$. The consumption function then goes through the origin when C is plotted against Y.

On these assumptions, our behaviour equation is

$$C = cY. \tag{1a}$$

Our equilibrium condition is, of course,

$$Y = C+I. \tag{2}$$

I is assumed to be autonomous, so the unknowns are Y and C. Substituting (1a) into (2),

$$Y = cY+I.$$

Collecting terms,

$$Y-cY = I.$$

Factoring out the left-hand side,

$$Y(1-c) = I$$

and, dividing through by $1-c$, we obtain

$$Y = \frac{1}{1-c}I. \tag{3}$$

From (3) we see at once that

$$\Delta Y = \frac{1}{1-c}\Delta I$$

or

$$\frac{\Delta Y}{\Delta I} = \frac{1}{1-c}.$$

$1/(1-c)$ is, of course, the multiplier, which it will be convenient to denote by k. It is worth noting that we obtain exactly the same multiplier if we assume that there is an intercept in the consumption function. Thus if we substitute (1) instead of (1a) into (2), and solve for Y by the method just adopted, we shall find

$$Y = \frac{1}{1-c}(I+a)$$

[1] See Gardner Ackley, *Macroeconomic Theory*, Chapter X, Macmillan, New York.

This shows that we may lump all autonomous expenditure together, irrespective of whether it is on consumer goods or investment goods, into a single *multiplicand*, and that altering our assumptions about autonomous expenditure does not alter the multiplier, which depends only on expenditure flows out of current income.

It is a familiar and very important qualitative prediction from the Keynesian model that the multiplier is not only positive but greater than unity. If we want a qualitative prediction, however, we should expect to have to impose at least some qualitative restrictions. You should be able to work out for yourself what they will have to be in this case. Given the necessary restrictions, the result that $1/(1-c) > 1$ is a qualitative comparative static prediction. Just as, in the tax case, we found that price was a linear function of the shift parameter, t, here we have found that income is a linear function of the autonomous variable I. When we try to discover the value of a multiplier, we are doing comparative statics in just the same way that we do when we impose taxes, shift demand curves, etc., in microanalysis. In our analysis of the competitive market, we obtained the result that, given certain qualitative restrictions on demand and supply, a tax would raise price, but by less than itself (which we could express as $0 < \Delta p/\Delta t < 1$). The result that the multiplier is greater than unity but less than infinity, or that $\infty > \Delta Y/\Delta I > 1$, given the restriction $0 < c < 1$, is a qualitative comparative static prediction of just the same sort.

4B.2 The Effects of Taxing and Spending by the Government

A simple extension of this model, to include a government, will now allow us to investigate a number of interesting problems in fiscal policy. We shall find our simple algebraic tools sufficiently powerful for an analysis of a number of questions over which there is serious political controversy, and in the process we shall learn a good deal about the relationship between positive economics and economic policy. Let us assume that the government spends (autonomously) at the rate G on current goods and services, and that it imposes a flat-rate proportional income-tax at rate[1] t. In this analysis, t is autonomous; but as it is a coefficient rather than an expenditure flow, it is called a 'shift parameter'. This means that it will appear in our equations as a parameter, but as one that may be exogenously shifted by a change in government policy. Later on, we shall investigate the consequences of shifting it. If we now also assume that households' spending decisions depend upon disposable income, we have

$$C = cY^d \tag{4}$$

[1] We might also say 'at one hundred t per cent'. Thus a 20% tax rate requires $t = 0.2$; and $100t\% = 20\%$.

where Y^d is disposable income. Our equilibrium condition is, of course,

$$Y = C + I + G. \tag{5}$$

Before substituting, however, we must express C as a function of Y instead of Y^d. Since disposable income is income after tax, we have the relation

$$Y^d = Y - T \tag{6}$$

where T is total tax paid, or 'tax yield'. Since taxation is proportional, we also have

$$T = tY. \tag{7}$$

Substituting (7) into (6),

$$Y^d = Y - tY \tag{8}$$

and, factoring the right-hand side,

$$Y^d = Y(1-t). \tag{9}$$

We now substitute (9) into (4), which gives us

$$C = cY(1-t) \tag{10}$$

and we have eliminated Y^d, disposable income: in (10) we have managed to express C as a function simply of income, Y, and the parameters c and t. (Recall how, in 4A, when we had p^* and p, we eliminated one by using the relation expressed in equation (14): $p^* = p - t$.) If we now substitute (10) into (5) we have

$$Y = cY(1-t) + I + G. \tag{11}$$

Collecting up Y terms we have $Y - cY(1-t) = I + G$. Factoring as before, we have $Y[1 - c(1-t)] = I + G$, and, dividing through by $[1 - c(1-t)]$, this yields

$$Y = \frac{1}{1 - c(1-t)} (I + G). \tag{12}$$

In (12) we have a new multiplier, $1/[1 - c(1-t)]$, of greater generality than the one we found in (3) above. First, we must check that the two are consistent. If we assume that the rate of taxation is reduced to zero in (12), we have

$$\frac{1}{1 - c(1-0)} = \frac{1}{1-c}$$

which is the multiplier of (3) as we should expect. We also expect, for a given value of c, that the multiplier will be smaller for $t>0$ than for $t=0$. Thus we wish to confirm the inequality

$$\frac{1}{1-c(1-t)} < \frac{1}{1-c}.$$

Here we have an inequality between two fractions, a relationship that we have not encountered before. We can, however, handle it quite simply. Since the numerators on both sides are the same (both equal to one), the left-hand side will be smaller than the right-hand side if the denominator of the left-hand side is *larger* than that of the right-hand side. Thus multiplying out the denominator of the left-hand side, the condition for the inequality to hold is that

$$1-c+ct > 1-c.$$

We know that we do not disturb an equality if we subtract the same term from both sides; and we can see that subtraction of the same term from both sides will not reverse an inequality. So we subtract $(1-c)$, and our condition becomes simply

$$ct > 0.$$

But this must be true if the marginal propensity to consume and the tax rate arc both positive. Hence we have confirmed our inequality: taxation does reduce the value of the multiplier.

The remaining question is, on what qualitative restrictions will the multiplier still exceed unity? For the multiplier to exceed unity, we want

$$1-c+ct < 1.$$

We now know enough about handling inequalities to proceed directly. Subtracting 1 from both sides, the condition is

$$-c+ct < 0$$

which is the same as

$$c-ct > 0$$

or $\qquad\qquad c > ct,$

which is true if t is a positive fraction, i.e., if $0<t<1$, in which case it is true that $1-c+ct<1$. Thus we have obtained formally the not surprising result that, to obtain a multiplier greater than unity, we require that taxation of income be at less than 100 %! This confirms something of considerable importance and generality, that at no tax rate less than 100 % do we lose the qualitative prediction of the no-tax case, that the multiplier is greater than unity.

We can explore a number of problems with this model, and a numerical example appears as an exercise. Let us investigate here the question: what is the effect on the budget deficit (or surplus) of an extra unit of G? We need to be careful here about the meaning of 'an extra unit of G', which we will write ΔG. We are doing static equilibrium analysis, and G is therefore the rate of expenditure on current goods and services by the government per unit of time (just as, in static price theory, 'demand' is quantity demanded per unit of time). Hence ΔG is the *increment to the rate of expenditure*, e.g., £1 per year. We do not know, in general, whether we start from a deficit or surplus, but it makes no difference to the incremental changes, so we may proceed without bothering about the 'starting point'. We define

$$\Delta D = \Delta G - \Delta T \tag{13}$$

where ΔD is the change in the deficit (note: the change in the rate of deficit per unit of time, e.g., £100 per year). Evidently, to find ΔD, given ΔG, all we have to do is find ΔT. But $\Delta T = t\,\Delta Y$ and $\Delta Y = k\,\Delta G$, where k is the multiplier, equal here to $1/[1 - c(1 - t)]$, hence

$$\Delta D = \Delta G - tk\,\Delta G$$
$$= \Delta G(1 - tk). \tag{14}$$

Once again, we have expressed an endogenous variable as a function of an exogenous one, but is the expression in brackets in (14) positive, negative, greater than one – or unknown? First of all, tk is positive, so $(1 - tk)$ must be less than one, and the deficit cannot increase as much as G does: here is one qualitative prediction. But could the deficit actually fall? We have to explore the possibility that the increased income consequent upon additional expenditure ΔG is so large that the tax yield from it, at constant tax rates, actually exceeds ΔG. This seems intuitively a little steep, but to rule it out, we must show that $\Delta D > 0$, which it is if the bracketed term in (14) is positive, that is, if

$$1 - tk > 0.$$

Demonstrating that this inequality holds is rather laborious, but each step is quite straightforward. It is clearly true if $tk < 1$, i.e., if

$$\frac{t}{1 - c(1 - t)} < 1.$$

This is the case if

$$t < 1 - c(1 - t)$$

(if the numerator is less than the denominator, we evidently have a proper fraction). Multiplying out the right-hand side, the condition is

$$t < 1-c+ct$$

or, subtracting ct from both sides,

$$t-ct < 1-c$$

or

$$t(1-c) < 1-c.$$

We do not reverse an inequality if we divide both sides by the same positive factor, so we divide both sides by $1-c$, and our condition is

$$t < \frac{1-c}{1-c} = 1. \tag{15}$$

This is true if $t<1$, as we have assumed, so that (14) must be positive: the deficit cannot fall.

These results are quite important, and may be summarised. We have assumed a closed economy with unemployed resources and constant prices. We have also assumed that all investment is autonomous, and that consumption is a constant fraction of disposable income. On these assumptions, we have shown that, for an increase ΔG in government expenditure,

$$\Delta Y = k \, \Delta G, \quad k > 1$$

and

$$0 < \Delta D = \Delta G(1-tk) < \Delta G$$

assuming $0 < c < 1$ and $0 < t < 1$. In words, an increase in government expenditure leads to an increase in income *greater* than itself, but to an increase in the budget deficit (or reduction in the surplus, as the case may be) *smaller* than itself. It is by no means clear that all legislators, even in sophisticated countries, have grasped these simple Keynesian propositions.[1] (This is a good moment to do Exercise 1.)

4B.3 The Income: Deficit Trade Off

Each additional unit of government expenditure leads to an increased deficit, as well as to increased income. Thus in this model, society can obtain increased income at the 'cost' of increased deficit at some definite rate. We may illustrate this diagrammatically. In Figure 4B.1, changes in income are measured on the vertical axis, changes in deficit on the horizontal. It is convenient to allow the origin to represent the *status quo ante*, i.e., the starting point or initial equilibrium, and to continue to work in increments. Since, if nothing happens, equilibrium is undisturbed, the line relating ΔY to ΔD clearly passes through the origin. Since both the tax rate and the

[1] Remember that we have assumed all investment to be autonomous, and have suppressed the monetary sector. A budget deficit, however, implies an increase in the money supply, and if this stimulated private expenditure some of our conclusions would require modification.

multiplier are constant, we may expect a straight line. It only remains to determine its slope. We know from equation (14) that

$$\Delta D = (1 - tk)\,\Delta G$$

and also that

$$\Delta Y = k\,\Delta G.$$

The slope is the ratio of ΔY to ΔD, hence we simply divide ΔY by ΔD to obtain

$$\frac{\Delta Y}{\Delta D} = \frac{k\,\Delta G}{(1 - tk)\,\Delta G} = \frac{k}{1 - tk} \tag{16}$$

as the 'trade-off rate' between ΔY and ΔD. We may evaluate this expression in terms of c and t, or leave it as it stands: this is purely a matter of

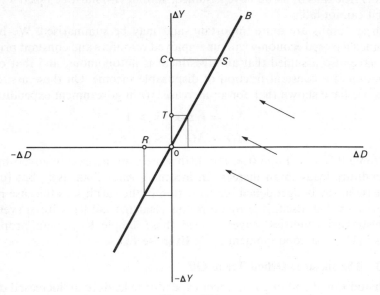

Figure 4B.1

convenience (but it is good practice to evaluate it). What we want to do is to find out what we can about its value. We have, in fact, already got enough information to determine its sign. We know that $0 < 1 - tk < 1$ from inequality (15), and that $k > 1$. Hence (16) is not only positive, not only greater than unity, but greater than the multiplier, k. This makes economic sense: a unit of ΔG leads to a larger increase in income, and a smaller increase in the deficit as we have already shown. (This is a good moment to do Exercises 2 and 3.)

Now, with the apparatus of Figure 4B.1 (or the diagram asked for in

Exercise 3), we may illuminate some problems in economic policy. Suppose that the initial equilibrium is a position of unemployment and low income. Suppose further that you have no moral or political objection to increased government spending or deficit. Then you obviously wish to move from the initial equilibrium out along the line OB, and you have no policy choice to make. (We may also suppose that there is some increment in income OC which would take the economy to full employment: then your policy would be to go to S and live happily ever after.) Consider now a man who wants increased income, is indifferent to deficits, and believes that the government should spend more. He might be of the Galbraith[1] school in the USA, believing that insufficient resources are being allocated to collective goods compared with private ones. In this country, his position might be roughly identified as that traditionally associated with the Labour Party. For this person, too, there is no problem since two things he wants, Y and G, are *positively associated in the real world*: he too goes to S, sacrificing nothing, and lives happily ever after. (But consider Exercise 3.) The moral is, of course, that if one 'good' is independent of everything else that you value, you have no choice problem because there is no opportunity cost: you take as much as is available, or as leads to satiety, whichever is the less. Similarly, if two 'goods' are positively associated, increasing the amount of one involves no sacrifice of the other, and there is no choice problem.

Now consider a person who dislikes unemployment, but also objects to increased government spending and/or deficits. Such a man might hold that citizens can spend their incomes to better advantage than the government, which should therefore refrain as far as possible from using its compulsory powers to do it for them. For simplicity, let us call such a man a Republican. We have no occasion to argue with his judgements: it is of interest merely to set out his problem. A man who wishes to increase income wishes to move north in Figure 4B.1. If he wishes to reduce deficits, he also wishes to move West. Combining the two, he wishes to move in some north-westerly direction suggested by the arrows. But the line through OB stops him: an increment of income of OT, say, simply cannot be had without an increased deficit; a reduction of OR in the deficit will cause decreased income. From his point of view, therefore, OB has become a *frontier*: he may choose a point on it, but cannot get beyond it. Since he attaches a *negative* valuation to G (or D) and a positive one to Y, while they are positively associated in the world, the Republican is in a genuine choice situation: to increase the amount of one good, he must give up some of the other (increase a dis-good). And for him, the trade-off rate, $k/(1-tk)$, represents a genuine opportunity cost ratio.

[1] See J. K. Galbraith, *The Affluent Society*, River Press, Cambridge, Mass., 1958, particularly pp. 251–3.

There are several points to notice here.

(i) It turns out that we may find perfectly genuine frontiers, other than the production frontier, and have to make choices.

(ii) The shape of the frontier, given by equation (16), depends on how society behaves. Our two basic behavioural assumptions here were proportionality in consumption and taxation. We could only give the precise location of the frontier if we knew the numerical values of c and t; but for *any* values of c and t between zero and one, which is the range of relevant values, the frontier exists, and has a positive slope.

(iii) The relationship between Y and D, being determined by the behaviour of society, exists quite independently of whether we find it convenient or inconvenient. This seems to dispose conclusively of the view that positive and normative questions can never be distinguished in social science. Where to go on the frontier depends on value judgements: knowledge of where the frontier is depends on scientific enquiry into the behaviour of society. Thus we have a clear distinction between the normative question 'where do you want to go?', and the positive one, 'where is it possible to go?' Nevertheless, some writers on the methodology of the social sciences, such as Gunnar Myrdal and Paul Streeten,[1] still maintain that it is impossible to conduct a 'value free' investigation of the behaviour of society. We shall see the distinction even more clearly in Chapters 11 and 12.

(iv) Individuals and societies can obviously make better choices (that is, adopt policies to take them closer to where they want to be, consistent with where it is possible to be) if they know where the frontiers are. Economists and econometricians try to find out for them. This disposes of the myth that an economist can give no useful advice, and make no contribution to the welfare of society, unless he actively recommends in the normative sense, and proposes solutions evolved from consideration of value as well as fact (writers of the Myrdal-Streeten school say that, as anything the economist can say has value-implications, all we can ask is honesty!). The discovery of where frontiers are – how society behaves – is no small contribution, and no one need be ashamed of devoting himself to this challenging and useful task.

(v) We may wish to move frontiers. If we are to do this successfully, we must understand the behaviour and structure of the system that determines the location of the frontiers. In the case of our illustration, it is obvious that the slope of the frontier depends upon the value of t, which is directly under the control of the government, as well as on c, which is not so easily controlled. We now see why a government that wishes to move a frontier but

[1] See particularly the Appendix by Paul Streeten to Gunnar Myrdal, *The Political Element in the Development of Economic Theory*. Routledge and Kegan Paul, London, 1953.

does not wish to change tax rates may be tempted to persuade and exhort, or even to bully and threaten, to persuade people to alter their behaviour.

(vi) Since the Government controls t, it is natural to ask 'how is the slope of the frontier altered by a change in t?' Since, however, the trade-off rate, $k/(1-tk)$, is not a simple linear function of t (remember that k is a function of t, too) we cannot answer this by simple inspection, as we have in other cases so far. This is a difficult question, as well as an important one, and to answer it we need a more powerful mathematical technique, which will be introduced in the next chapter.

4B.4 Trade-off Rates in an Open Economy

Many interesting and important policy problems arise from international trade. Governments are frequently much concerned, in particular, with the relationship between national income (and employment) and the balance of payments. A further simple extension of our linear model will allow us to examine this relationship. We consider an open economy with a government. Assume that exports, X, are autonomous, and that imports are proportional to disposable income:

$$M = mY^d. \tag{17}$$

Our equilibrium condition is now

$$Y = C+I+G+X-M. \tag{18}$$

It is important to note that (17) and (18) together mean that C stands for *total* consumption, of both domestic and imported goods together. Thus consumption of home-produced goods is $C-M$, and personal saving is $Y-T-C$, *not* $Y-T-C-M$. (Obviously we could have defined another variable C' as consumption of home goods only, and altered coefficient values accordingly: it is purely a matter of convenience, and makes no difference to the results.)

Now $Y^d = Y(1-t)$ from (9), and we combine this with (17) to obtain

$$M = mY(1-t). \tag{19}$$

We retain the other behavioural assumptions of 4B.3 above, and thus still have (10),

$$C = cY(1-t).$$

Substituting this and (19) into (18) we have

$$Y = cY(1-t)+I+G+X-mY(1-t).$$

4

We can use the same method that we used to obtain (3) and (12) above to derive

$$Y = \frac{1}{1-(1-t)(c-m)}(I+G+X) \qquad (20)$$

which you may check for yourself. This looks a bit cumbersome, but, once again, we can use some constant, k, to denote the multiplier, and evaluate subsequent expressions in terms of c, m, and t only if we have to. (It is a good exercise to check that, if m and X are zero, (20) does reduce to (12).)

We now have a more complex model, and might investigate a number of problems. Once again, we will look at one of society's choice frontiers, and find a trade-off rate. There are, in fact, several that we might look at: we could look at the pairs (Y, G), or (Y, M), or (G, M). Indeed, it is clear that 'the' frontier requires more than two dimensions: in three, with Y, G, and M, we could see the situation clearly. The trade-off between Y and M, however, is particularly interesting, since with X autonomous, a change in M is exactly matched by a change in the balance of payments surplus or deficit. The government's *policy instruments* are G and t. The analysis of changes in t presents, as we have already seen, some difficulties. We will therefore concentrate on the Y/M frontier faced by a government that can alter G at will. We already know that $\Delta Y = k\Delta G$. Working in increments, as before, we define

$$\Delta B = \Delta M - \Delta X$$

as the net change in the balance of payments deficit (note again: change in the rate at which the deficit is running per unit of time). Now,

$$\begin{aligned} \Delta M &= m\,\Delta Y^d && [\text{see (17)}] \\ &= m\,\Delta Y(1-t) && [\text{see (19)}] \\ &= m(1-t)k\,\Delta G && [\text{see (20)}] \end{aligned} \qquad (21)$$

and $\Delta B = \Delta M$ on the assumption that X is autonomous ($\Delta X = 0$ in response to any change in G, Y, or M). We now simply take the ratio of the values of ΔY and ΔB in response to ΔG from (20) and (21):

$$\frac{\Delta Y}{\Delta B} = \frac{k\,\Delta G}{m(1-t)k\,\Delta G} = \frac{1}{m(1-t)}. \qquad (22)$$

(22) gives the slope of the frontier facing the government. Suppose, as we may, that the government regards Y as 'good' and B as 'bad'. It is important to know if the frontier has a positive or negative slope. It is obviously

positive, since m and $(1-t)$ are positive by assumption: increased income, in response to increased G, leads to an increased balance of payments deficit – which is clear enough from our basic behaviour assumption in (17), or from (21).

We have now discovered the slope of a frontier which causes governments much concern, and it is worth exploring a little further. The situation is illustrated in Figure 4B.2, where ΔY appears on the vertical axis and ΔB on the horizontal. Once again, since we are working in increments, the frontier goes through the origin (if nothing happens, nothing happens), and

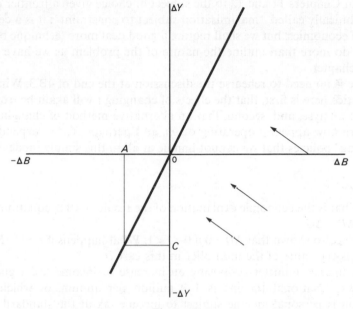

Figure 4B.2

its (positive) slope is given by (22). '$-\Delta B$' of course means either a reduction in the deficit, or an increase in surplus, depending on the starting point. The arrows indicate the desired direction of movement for a government, or anyone else, who desires higher income, but wishes to avoid balance of payments difficulties. A desired improvement in the balance of payments, such as OA, can of course be made, but only at the price of reducing G enough to reduce income by OC. The behaviour of the economy, which is summed up by the values of c, m, and t, and their inter-relations, have effectively produced a choice frontier. Let us consider a little further, however, the direction in which people or governments might wish to move.

Thus suppose that the origin in Figure 4B.2 corresponded to an initial position or 'starting point' of considerable unemployment and a substantial balance of payments surplus. A man who wished to avoid deficits might be quite indifferent to a reduction in the surplus, and thus feel that there was no choice problem so long as there was both unemployment and surplus: only when a further increase in employment threatened to run the economy into balance of payments deficit would he start to feel constrained. This suggests that the desired direction of movement, or, what comes to the same thing, whether a given frontier imposes the necessity for choice, may depend on the initial equilibrium values of variables like Y and B. We return in Chapters 11 and 12 to the subject of choice given a frontier or, as it is technically called, 'maximisation subject to constraint': it is a central topic of economics, but we shall require a good deal more technique before we can do more than outline the nature of the problem as we have done in this chapter.

There is no need to rehearse the discussion at the end of 4B.3. What we may notice here is first, that the effects of changing t will again be troublesome to analyse, and, second, that an alternative method of changing the structure now appears: operating on m, and perhaps X, by 'expenditure switching' policies that we cannot handle at all in this simple model.[1]

Exercises

1 (a) What is the economic explanation of the result of 4B.2, equation (14), that $\Delta D < \Delta G$?

(b) It is also shown that $\Delta D > 0$ if $0 < t < 1$. What happens if $t = 1$? (*Hint:* what is the value of the multiplier in this case?)

(c) A finance minister proposing an increase in income tax argues as follows: 'National Income is 140 million per annum, of which 100 million is personal income subject to income tax at the standard rate, now 15%. The increase in the rate from 15% to 20% will increase revenue by 5 million'. Comment critically on this argument. Look up a recent Budget Debate in *Hansard*, and judge for yourself if the Chancellor's forecasts of tax yield show that the error contained in the argument has been avoided, or merely leave one quite unclear as to how they were arrived at.

2 Show algebraically that $\Delta Y/\Delta D$ (equation (16)) exceeds $\Delta Y/\Delta G$ (from equation (12)). Why do you expect this result?

3 Construct a diagram, similar to Figure 4B.1, but with ΔY and ΔG on the axes, and determine the slope of the frontier.

[1] See Lipsey, *Introduction to Positive Economics*, 2nd Ed., Weidenfeld and Nicolson, London, 1966, pp. 840–4.

4 How is the situation of the Galbraithian or Labour-Party-man changed if society starts as S in Figure 4B.1 instead of O? Why are the problems of the British Labour Party – or the American Democrats – easier if they are elected at a time of unemployment (besides, that is, getting credit for curing the unemployment)?

5 Assume an economy in which

$$C = 0.8Y^d$$

$$M = 0.2Y^d$$

$$\left. \begin{array}{l} X = 80 \\ I = 120 \end{array} \right\} \text{both autonomous}$$

$$t = 0.2$$

(*Hint*: it will be found more convenient to work in fractions than in decimals.)

(a) What will be the equilibrium level of Y if $G=99$?

(b) What level of G will balance the budget?

(c) What level of G will lead to balance of payments equilibrium?

(d) If full employment income is 700, what level of G will be needed to reach full employment?

(e) What will the balance of payments surplus or deficit be at full employment?

(f) What are the trade-off rates to the Government between

　(i) Budget Deficit and Income?

　(ii) Budget Deficit and Balance of Payments Deficit?

　(iii) Income and Balance of Payments Deficit?

Illustrate diagrammatically.

(g) Check, at least in (a), that total injections *are* equal to total leakages, i.e., that $I+G+X=S+T+M$. How is home investment being financed?

(h) Describe the policy problem facing this economy. What would you do?

CHAPTER 5

INTRODUCTION TO CALCULUS: DIFFERENTIATION

5.1 Elasticity of Demand

In the previous chapter we did as much economics as we could using only linear relations and the simple tools of elementary algebra. If we are to progress further we can no longer confine ourselves to linear relations nor to what we can deduce about our relations using only those algebraic tools presently at our command. To go further we need more technique, and in this chapter we shall present enough to enable us to take our study of economics one step further. For those readers who have not gone beyond O-level mathematics this chapter is the decisive hurdle. It is a hurdle that every economist can surmount, but you must be prepared to read the chapter slowly. There is no purpose in merely memorising results: you must seek to understand them. You must not expect, however, to achieve complete mastery on first reading. Familiarity will come with practice. You should try to understand enough to be able to read on to further chapters, but you should be ready to return to this one whenever you discover you are a bit puzzled about some concept or manipulation. If, however, you were to re-read this chapter after you finished this book you would find it hard to imagine how you had ever found it difficult.

Consider what we may know about some of the functional relations in economics. At one extreme we can make only very general qualitative statements about the way in which our variables are associated. In demand theory, for example, we often do not assume more than that in the function

$$q = q(p) \tag{1}$$

quantity is a decreasing function of price. At the other extreme we sometimes know enough to specify a very precise quantitative relationship between the variables. For example, Stone has estimated that the demand for home-produced mutton in Britain during the period between the First and Second World Wars was given by the non-linear expression[1]

$$q = \frac{1}{\sqrt{p^3}}. \tag{2}$$

[1] Richard Stone, *The Measurement of Consumers' Expenditure and Behaviour in the United Kingdom, 1920–38*, Cambridge University Press, 1954, Vol. 1. The general expression is of the

[*Footnote continues on p. 97*]

In other cases we are able to specify more than just the signs of our parameters, but we are unable to specify their specific values. For example, we
may wish to say that the demand for some commodity is given by

$$q = p^{\alpha} \tag{3}$$

where $0 > \alpha > -1$. In all these cases we are putting some restriction on the
way in which demand varies as price varies; and very often our problem is
to discover, with only qualitative restrictions, the direction of change in the
dependent variable as an exogenous variable changes. In Chapter 4 we
were able to handle such problems successfully when the variables were
related by linear functions. We now seek a more general method of handling it when the variables are linked by a non-linear function as they were
in (2) and (3) above.

We shall begin by considering an example in which a concept defined in
elementary textbooks is fully satisfactory only when our variables are
linearly related. We shall find that it is necessary to redefine the concept if
we are to handle non-linear functions successfully. In elementary treatments the elasticity of demand is defined as

$$\eta = \frac{\% \text{ change in quantity demanded}}{\% \text{ change in price}}$$

$$= \frac{\dfrac{\Delta q}{q} \cdot 100}{\dfrac{\Delta p}{p} \cdot 100}$$

$$= \frac{\Delta q}{q} \cdot \frac{p}{\Delta p}$$

$$= \frac{\Delta q}{\Delta p} \cdot \frac{p}{q}. \tag{4}$$

The elasticity measured by (4) is taken to refer to the point (p, q) on the demand curve. The first term in (4) is the incremental ratio measured from
the demand function. We have seen in Chapter 3 that when the demand
curve is plotted on a graph this ratio shows the slope of the chord joining
the two price-quantity points between which the changes are being

------

form $q^* = ap^{\alpha}$ but we can remove the constant by dividing through by a and defining our new
unit of measurement of demand to be $q = q^*/a$ where q^* is demand measured in the original
units of measurement.

measured. The second term, p/q, depends solely on the point on the curve representing the original price and quantity.

Consider first the elasticity of the linear demand function

$$q = ap + b.$$

In this case we know that the incremental ratio is the same no matter where on the function we measure it. Thus $\Delta q/\Delta p = a$, and we can rewrite (4) as

$$\eta = a\,\frac{p}{q}. \tag{5}$$

This shows that the elasticity measured at any point (p, q) on the linear demand function will be independent of the size and direction of the change in price that occurs. We say that there is a *unique* elasticity associated with each point on the linear demand function, although, of course, the elasticity is different at each point.

Now consider a non-linear demand function. Take, for example, the case in which a constant sum, £1200, is spent on the commodity whatever its price. Since expenditure is constant at £1200 the equation for the demand function must be

$$pq = 1200. \tag{6}$$

This is the implicit form, but obviously yields

$$q = 1200p^{-1}. \tag{7}$$

Our elementary economics tells us that this curve should have an elasticity of unity, since total expenditure remains constant as price changes. Let us, however, try to measure elasticity by the formula given in (4). Consider the following prices and quantities, all of which satisfy equation (6).

TABLE 5.1
Values computed from the demand function
$pq = 1200$

p	q	pq
30	40	1200
32	37·5	1200
50	24	1200
25	48	1200
20	60	1200

Let us take the point $p = 30$, $q = 40$ and calculate elasticity for a change in price to each of the other price-quantity combinations shown in Table 5.1.

TABLE 5.2

Elasticities of demand measured from the point $p = 30$, $q = 40$, on the demand function $pq = 1200$

Δp	Δq	$\dfrac{\Delta q}{\Delta p}$	$\dfrac{p}{q}$	η
$+2$	$-2\cdot5$	$-1\cdot25$	$0\cdot75$	$-0\cdot9375$
$+20$	-16	$-0\cdot80$	$0\cdot75$	$-0\cdot6000$
-5	$+8$	$-1\cdot60$	$0\cdot75$	$-1\cdot2000$
-10	$+20$	$-2\cdot00$	$0\cdot75$	$-1\cdot5000$

Evidently the measure defined in (4) provides no unique number for elasticity at the point (30, 40) – and won't elsewhere. In no case does our calculated elasticity come out to be unity. Furthermore, the answer varies according to the direction and the magnitude of the changes in price that we consider. According to standard text books, elasticity should be unity everywhere on this curve. We now have a most unsatisfactory discrepancy between our results and those given in the text-books. It is a consequence of using incremental ratios on non-linear functions. In the present case, we are dealing with a curve and not a straight line, and the incremental ratio $\Delta q/\Delta p$ varies with the size and direction of the change in p that we consider. The geometrical illustration of this is given in Figure 5.1 where we illustrate what we first established in Chapter 3, that the incremental ratios in Table 5.1 are the slopes of the chords joining the pairs of points in question. Clearly with any non-linear demand function the slope of the chord joining one point m, to various other points on the curve will vary as the second point chosen varies. We want to be able to give a unique meaning to the concept of the elasticity of demand measured at a point on the demand curve. It is now evident that the measure involving the incremental ratio will not serve this purpose. What we need is a unique measure of the rate at which quantity demanded is tending to change as price changes at a particular point on the curve. To provide this measure we take the slope of the straight line that is tangent to the curve at the point in question. This is illustrated in Figure 5.1. The line TT is tangent to the demand curve at the point m, and we say that its slope measures the rate at which q is tending to change as price changes at point m. We call the slope of this tangent the *derivative of quantity with respect to price*, and we give it the symbol dq/dp.

Now consider the relation between the slope of the tangent to a curve at any point and the slopes of the incremental ratios measured from that point. Inspection of Figure 5.1 suggests that, as Δp is made smaller and

4*

smaller, the slope of the chord joining the two points on the curve comes closer and closer to the slope of the tangent. Indeed, it looks as though we could make the incremental ratio get as close as we wanted to the slope of the tangent as long as we made Δp small enough. We shall investigate this more fully in the next section, but at present we merely assert, what seems visually clear from the figure, that the ratio $\Delta q/\Delta p$ gets very close indeed to the slope of the tangent as Δp is made very small.

We may now consider what will happen to our measure of elasticity if we substitute the slope of the tangent dq/dp, at the point (p, q), for the

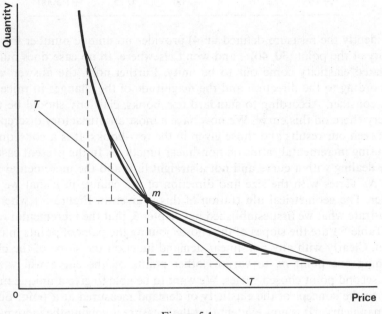

Figure 5.1

incremental ratio $\Delta q/\Delta p$. The tangent to a smooth continuous curve at a point will be unique: there is only *one* dq/dp at any point. We may now re-define elasticity as

$$\eta = \frac{dq}{dp} \cdot \frac{p}{q} \tag{8}$$

and this will give us a unique elasticity at each point on the curve.

5.2   The Concept of a Limit

In the previous section we relied on inspection of Figure 5.1 to suggest that the slope of the incremental ratio gets closer and closer to the slope of the tangent as Δp is made smaller and smaller. Indeed we suggested that we could make $\Delta q/\Delta p$ come as close as we wanted to dq/dp if we made Δp small enough. It is this latter conjecture that we need to clarify and elaborate upon. To do this we introduce the idea of a limit. We shall not attempt a formal definition of this very important concept, and will rely on a fairly intuitive treatment.

Consider the example of the function $1/x$. As x takes on larger and larger values, the value of the function becomes smaller and smaller. We can never make it actually become zero by letting x get bigger and bigger but we can make it get very close indeed to zero. If, for example, $x = 1,000,000$, then $1/x = 0 \cdot 000001$. Indeed, whatever small number you care to mention, we can make $1/x$ smaller than that by taking a large enough x. In this case we say that the value of the function $1/x$ approaches the limit of zero as x approaches infinity. We write this

$$\lim_{x \to \infty} \left(\frac{1}{x}\right) = 0 \qquad (9)$$

which is read 'the limit of the value of $1/x$ as x approaches infinity is zero'. Now let ε stand for any small number. In general we say that the value of the function $f(x)$ approaches a finite limit L as x approaches infinity if for *any* ε as small as is desired there is some large enough x such that the difference between the value of the function and L is less than ε, i.e., $L - f(x) < \varepsilon$. In other words, we are saying that we can make the value of $f(x)$ come as close to the limit as we wish even though we can never make it actually reach the limit. Next, consider the value of the function $1/x$ as x approaches zero. We cannot just let $x = 0$ because $1/0$ is not defined. But we can let x get as *close* to zero as we like. It is apparent that, as x gets very small, the value of $1/x$ gets very large. Indeed, for any finite number N you care to mention, we can make $1/x > N$ by making x small enough (all we need to do is to make x less than $1/N$). In this case we say that the value of the function $1/x$ increases *without limit* as x approaches zero.

In the previous section we were concerned with the limiting value of the incremental ratio $\Delta q/\Delta p$ as Δp approached zero. We cannot just insert $\Delta p = 0$ into the ratio because if price does not change, neither does quantity change, and the incremental ratio is $0/0 = 0$. This might lead us to think that the value of the ratio $\Delta q/\Delta p$ would approach zero as p approached zero. This would not be correct since as Δp gets smaller Δq also gets smaller. Further inspection of the diagram suggests that the slope of the chord approaches the slope of the tangent. The idea of a ratio of two increments not approaching zero as the size of the separate increments approaches zero is not an easy one to grasp. We have illustrated this geometrically in Figure 5.1 and subsequently we shall consider a numerical example.

5.3 Derivatives and Limits

We now assert what we shall be able to prove subsequently, that the slope of the tangent to the demand curve used in the previous section at the point (30, 40) is 4/3. If we say that the limit of the value of the incremental ratio measured from the point (30, 40) is 4/3, we mean that we can make the difference between $\Delta q/\Delta p$ and 4/3 less than any number ε we care to choose, no matter how small we choose ε to be. We shall see numerical examples of this later in this chapter when we consider how actually to find the limiting values of incremental ratios. In the meantime we note that we can write our assertion that the value of the incremental ratio approaches the slope of the tangent to the curve as Δp gets smaller and smaller as follows

$$\lim_{\Delta p \to 0} \left(\frac{\Delta q}{\Delta p} \right) = \frac{\mathrm{d}y}{\mathrm{d}x}. \tag{10}$$

This is read 'the limit of $\Delta q/\Delta p$ as Δp approaches zero is D-Y by D-X'.

Let us briefly consider how the slope of the tangent, $\mathrm{d}y/\mathrm{d}x$, will change as we move about the curve. Consider first a linear function. In this case it is clear that $\mathrm{d}y/\mathrm{d}x = \Delta y/\Delta x$ because the tangent to the line coincides with the line itself: the slope of the tangent ($\mathrm{d}y/\mathrm{d}x$) is the same as the slope of the line ($\Delta y/\Delta x$). The slope $\mathrm{d}y/\mathrm{d}x$ is thus the same at all points on the line. If we take any non-linear curve such as the one in Figure 5.2a, it is not the case that $\mathrm{d}y/\mathrm{d}x = \Delta y/\Delta x$. Furthermore, it is clear the $\mathrm{d}y/\mathrm{d}x$ will be different at each point on the curve. As we move to larger values of x we can see that the tangent gets steeper so that $\mathrm{d}y/\mathrm{d}x$ is itself increasing. This means that y is tending to change more and more for a given change in x. If, however, we take the curve in Figure 5.2b, then the slope of the tangent to the curve is getting smaller and smaller as y increases so that $\mathrm{d}y/\mathrm{d}x$ is diminishing as y increases. Many other cases are possible: in Figure 5.2c, $\mathrm{d}y/\mathrm{d}x$ is negative throughout and takes on a larger and larger negative value as x increases, while in Figure 5.2d, $\mathrm{d}y/\mathrm{d}x$ alternates in sign several times as x increases.

It remains now to discover how to determine the value of $\mathrm{d}y/\mathrm{d}x$. It would be possible to plot a graph of the function and then to measure the slope of the tangent at the point in question. This would be a very cumbersome procedure, and it would also have the disadvantage that we would not be able to deal with derivatives in terms more general than their precise numerical values at particular points on the function. Fortunately there are more general and more reliable methods of finding derivatives than drawing curves and measuring the slopes of tangents. It is to the study of these methods that we must now turn.

What you already know about derivatives can first be summarised:

(1) The derivative of a function $y = f(x)$ at the point x_1, y_1 is the slope of the tangent to the curve at that point. All we are going to do now is to discover an analytical method of determining this slope.

(2) The derivative is interpreted as showing how y is tending to change as x changes at the point at which the derivative is measured.

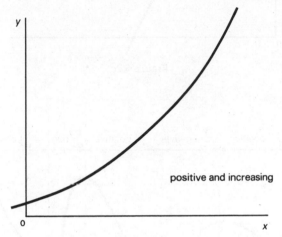

Figure 5.2a

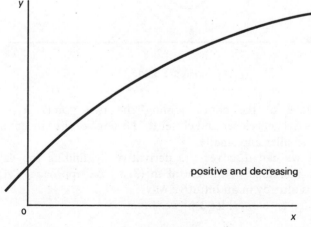

Figure 5.2b

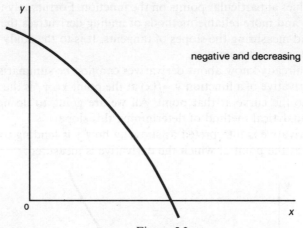

Figure 5.2c

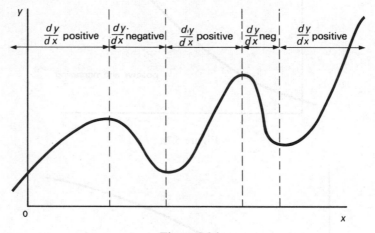

Figure 5.2d

(3) The slope of the chord joining the two points, x_1, y_1 and $(x_1 + \Delta x, y_1 + \Delta y)$ gets closer and closer to the slope of the tangent at x_1, y_1 as x is made smaller and smaller.

(4) Indeed we can discover the derivative by finding the value approached by the slope of the chord in (3) as Δx approaches zero. We have seen this already in an intuitive way.

The next step is to consider a power function

$$y = ax^n,$$

We shall show that the derivative of this function is simply

$$\frac{dy}{dx} = nax^{n-1}. \tag{11}$$

Let us see why this is so.

5.4 Evaluation of Derivatives of Power Functions

First we consider the familiar power function

$$y = x^2 \tag{12}$$

and start with some mathematical experimentation. First let us consider how y changes as we change x. If $x=6$, $y=6^2=36$. If we now let x increase to 8 then y rises to $8^2=64$. It helps to tabulate this:

first value: $36 = (6)^2$ (13)

second value: $64 = (8)^2$ (14)

or $36+28 = (6+2)^2.$ (15)

In (15) we show exactly the same calculation as in (14), but instead of just inserting the new value of x we insert the original value of 6 and the increment of 2 in x. The approach used in (15) proves to be helpful when we come to calculate derivatives in general.

Now let us consider the incremental ratio at *any* point on the function. We begin with any value of x and a corresponding value of y; we let x increase by an amount Δx; and y increases by Δy. Thus we can write

$$y+\Delta y = (x+\Delta x)^2 \tag{16}$$

which is exactly the same as (15) except that we have letters instead of the numbers of the specific example. Expanding the right-hand side of (16) gives

$$y+\Delta y = x^2+2x\,\Delta x+(\Delta x)^2. \tag{17}$$

Now since $y=x^2$ we can cancel the y from the left-hand side of (17) with the x^2 from the right-hand side. This gives

$$\Delta y = 2x\,\Delta x+(\Delta x)^2. \tag{18}$$

Dividing through by Δx gives

$$\frac{\Delta y}{\Delta x} = 2x+\Delta x. \tag{19}$$

This gives us a very neat way of calculating the incremental ratio anywhere on the function $y = x^2$. Let us try an example to check it. What is the incremental ratio when we start from the point $x = 3$, $y = 9$ and let x rise by 2? According to (19) above we have:

$$\frac{\Delta y}{\Delta x} = 2x + \Delta x$$

$$= 6 + 2 = 8.$$

(As a check on this formula you should calculate the same ratio by direct substitution into $y = x^2$.) You should try a few more examples to be sure you are satisfied that (19) gives you the correct ratios.

We have already defined dy/dx to be the limit approached by $\Delta y/\Delta x$ as Δx gets smaller and smaller, or, as we say, as Δx approaches zero. Letting Δx approach zero does not mean that $\Delta y/\Delta x$ approaches zero. Indeed what happens as Δx is made smaller and smaller is that $\Delta y/\Delta x$ approaches the value of a slope of the tangent to the curve at the point in question. This is, of course, what we wish to determine.

Let us try some examples beginning from the point (3, 9) on expression (12) above and letting Δx get smaller and smaller.

TABLE 5.4

Calculation of some incremental ratios from the point (3, 9) *on the function* $y = x^2$

x	y	Δx	Δy	$\dfrac{\Delta y}{\Delta x}$
3	9	—	—	—
5	25	2	16	8
4	16	1	7	7
3·1	9·61	0·1	0·61	6·1
3·01	9·0601	0·01	0·0601	6·01
3·0001	9·00060001	0·0001	0·00060001	6·0001

If we use expression (19) to calculate these incremental ratios we shall get the same results but what is happening will become more obvious.

Evidently as we take smaller and smaller changes in x the ratio $\Delta y/\Delta x$ approaches 6. Looking at expression (19) we see that as Δx gets smaller and smaller the value of $\Delta y/\Delta x$ gets closer and closer to $2x$ because the Δx term becomes more and more insignificant. This shows what we earlier asserted, that the ratio $\Delta y/\Delta x$ does not approach zero as Δx approaches

TABLE 5.5
Calculation of some incremental ratios from the point (3, 9) on the function $y=x^2$ from (19)

when x goes from 3 to	$2x$	Δx	$2x + \Delta x$
5	6	2	8
4	6	1	7
3·1	6	0·1	6·1
3·01	6	0·01	6·01
3·0001	6	0·0001	6·0001

zero: in this case the ratio gets closer and closer to 6 as the increments are made smaller and smaller.

We shall now repeat our experiments with the function $y=x^3$. Before reading on, however, you should try to do this for yourself. You can expand $(x+\Delta x)^3$ to get an expression analogous to (19), and can then substitute into it to see what happens to the ratio $\Delta y/\Delta x$ as Δx gets very small. If you do this you will have gone a long way to discovering how to differentiate for yourself. We now proceed: if

$$y = x^3 \tag{20}$$

then we can write

$$y + \Delta y = (x + \Delta x)^3. \tag{21}$$

Expanding the right-hand side gives

$$y + \Delta y = x^3 + 3x^2\,\Delta x + 3x(\Delta x)^2 + (\Delta x)^3. \tag{22}$$

Using (20) we can cancel out the y on the left-hand side with the x^3 on the right. If we simultaneously divide through by Δx this gives us

$$\frac{\Delta y}{\Delta x} = 3x^2 + 3x\,\Delta x + (\Delta x)^2. \tag{23}$$

Again we see that if we let Δx get smaller and smaller this expression will get closer and closer to $3x^2$ because *all* terms involving Δx approach zero as Δx approaches zero. Indeed, by letting Δx be some particular small value the value of (23) can be made to come as close to $3x^2$ as is desired. We say that the limit of $\Delta y/\Delta x$ for the function $y=x^3$ as Δx approaches zero is $3x^2$ and we write this as

$$\lim_{\Delta x \to 0} \frac{\Delta y}{\Delta x}(y = x^3) = 3x^2. \tag{24}$$

Thus the slope of the tangent to the curve $y = x^3$ is 3 when x is 1, 12 when x is 2, 27 when x is 3, and so on. This tells us what we shall see if we actually draw the curve: that the curve gets steeper as x increases. Thus y is more responsive to changes in x the larger is x.

It is really very remarkable that we have been able to discover a technique for measuring the slope of the tangent gradient to the curves $y = x^2$ and $y = x^3$ so easily. If you have grasped what has gone before you will find nothing more difficult than this in what is to come.

Having found $\Delta y / \Delta x$ for $y = x^2$ and $y = x^3$ the next obvious step is to try to find a general rule to cover all power functions. The general function of this type is written

$$y = ax^n \tag{25}$$

where a and n are parameters (in the two previous cases we had $a = 1, n = 2$, and $a = 1, n = 3$). Now if x changes by Δx, y will change by Δy and we have

$$y + \Delta y = a(x + \Delta x)^n. \tag{26}$$

We now need what is called the 'general expansion of $(x + \Delta x)^n$'. This is provided by the Binomial Theorem, which you may have learned at school (and doubtless forgotten, as the present authors keep doing). The Binomial Theorem provides a very powerful method of dealing with expressions like $(x + \Delta x)^n$: if n is a large number we can avoid the tedious business of repeated multiplication by substituting into the 'general expansion'; and since the general expansion gives the answer as a function of n, we can use it when n is unknown, as it is here. It is worth looking up the Binomial Theorem in a school algebra book; but as it is rather forbidding, and we want to avoid here the lengthy digression that would be required to set it out, we will show how our problem can be handled rather informally.

We set out below some of the steps in successive multiplication of $(x + \Delta x)$ by itself.

$$x + \Delta x$$

$$\frac{x + \Delta x}{x^2 + 2x \ \Delta x + (\Delta x)^2}$$

$$\frac{x + \Delta x}{x^3 + 3x^2 \ \Delta x + 3x(\Delta x)^2 + (\Delta x)^3}$$

$$\frac{x + \Delta x}{x^4 + 4x^3 \ \Delta x + \cdots}$$

$$\frac{x + \Delta x}{x^5 + 5x^4 \ \Delta x + \cdots}$$

We see that the exponent on the first term is exactly equal to the number of multiplications performed, while in the second term we have x to a power one lower, times Δx. The dots indicate terms left out in higher powers of Δx and lower powers of x which can easily be put in by completing the multiplication or by looking up the Binomial Theorem. Now, if we simply trust that what is true for $n = 1, 2, \ldots, 5$ is true for any n (which is proved by the Binomial Theorem), we have

$$(x + \Delta x)^n = x^n + nx^{n-1} \, \Delta x + \cdots \qquad (27)$$

Now

$$y + \Delta y = a(x + \Delta x)^n$$

$$= ax^n + nax^{n-1} \, \Delta x + \cdots \qquad (28)$$

so if we subtract (25) from (28), we have

$$\Delta y = anx^{n-1} \, \Delta x + \cdots$$

If we divide both sides by Δx, we have the incremental ratio

$$\frac{\Delta y}{\Delta x} = anx^{n-1} + \cdots$$

Now to find the limit, we let Δx approach zero. The omitted terms on the right-hand side, however, all contain Δx to some power, starting with one, and ascending. Hence as Δx approaches zero, the omitted terms all approach zero, and we can write the derivative of (25) as

$$\frac{dy}{dx} = \lim_{\Delta x \to 0} \frac{\Delta y}{\Delta x} = anx^{n-1}. \qquad (29)$$

We now know how to differentiate any power function! If, for example,

$$y = 2x^3 \qquad (30)$$

then

$$\frac{dy}{dx} = 6x^2;$$

and if

$$y = \tfrac{1}{2}x^8, \qquad (31)$$

$$\frac{dy}{dx} = 4x^7.$$

Just as a check we can try the straight line through the origin

$$y = ax$$

where the power 1 is understood on the x. Applying the rule

$$\frac{dy}{dx} = nax^{n-1}$$

gives

$$\frac{dy}{dx} = (1)(a)x^{1-1}$$

$$= ax^0$$

$$= a. \tag{32}$$

(If you have forgotten that $x^0 = 1$ you should review Chapter 3, pages 56–59.) This result checks with our earlier discussion about straight lines.

Summary

We have defined the derivative of y with respect to x as

$$\frac{dy}{dx} = \lim_{\Delta x \to 0} \frac{\Delta y}{\Delta x}. \tag{33}$$

y and x are linked together by the function $f(x)$ and it will be convenient for some work that follows to write the definition of a function in a slightly expanded form. First, as a matter purely of notation, we denote the small change in x as h instead of Δx. Next we notice that the change in y (i.e., Δy) is equal to the new value of the function after x has increased by h *minus* the original value. Thus $\Delta y = f(x+h) - f(x)$. We can now rewrite the definition of a derivative as

$$\frac{dy}{dx} = \lim_{h \to 0} \frac{f(x+h) - f(x)}{h}. \tag{34}$$

This is nothing more than a rewrite of (33) since the numerator in (34) merely defines Δy and h is merely another symbol for Δx. The definition of a derivative given in (34) is extremely important and will provide the starting point for further proofs as we need them. You should not read on until you are satisfied that (34) says the same thing as (33).

5.5   Rules for Compound Expressions

We now need to play only a few variations on the theme in the previous section to increase greatly our power to find derivatives of more complex expressions.

Addition Rule   Consider the function

$$y = 2x^3 + x^2, \tag{35}$$

which is an example of the general function

$$y = ax^n + bx^m. \tag{36}$$

To discover how to differentiate this we employ a simple stratagem. We use two new variables, w, and, v, and let $ax^n = u$ and $bx^m = v$. Now we re-write (36) accordingly as

$$y = u + v \tag{37}$$

and can proceed as before. First let u and v increase by some amount $\Delta u + \Delta v$ which will increase y by some amount Δy. This gives

$$y + \Delta y = u + \Delta u + v + \Delta v. \tag{38}$$

We now use (37) to remove y, u, and v from (38) giving us

$$\Delta y = \Delta u + \Delta v. \tag{39}$$

Since we want the ratio of Δy to Δx we divide (33) through by Δx to give

$$\frac{\Delta y}{\Delta x} = \frac{\Delta u}{\Delta x} + \frac{\Delta v}{\Delta x}. \tag{40}$$

We have defined in (33) a derivative as the limit of an incremental ratio as the denominator approaches zero. In the case of (40) this gives us

$$\lim_{\Delta x \to 0} \frac{\Delta u}{\Delta x} = \frac{du}{dx} \tag{41}$$

and

$$\lim_{\Delta x \to 0} \frac{\Delta v}{\Delta x} = \frac{dv}{dx}. \tag{42}$$

Now, substituting (41) and (42) into (40) gives

$$\lim_{\Delta x \to 0} \frac{\Delta y}{\Delta x} (y = u + v) = \frac{dy}{dx} = \frac{du}{dx} + \frac{dv}{dx}. \tag{43}$$

(43) gives the rule for differentiating a sum, and we apply it at once to (35). Since $u = 2x^3$ we know from (29) that $du/dx = 6x^2$, and since $v = x^2$ we have $dv/dx = 2x$, so that by (43)

$$\frac{dy}{dx} = 6x^2 + 2x. \tag{44}$$

The general result in (43) tells us that when y is the sum of a number of terms in x, dy/dx is the sum of the derivatives of each of the individual terms. In (44) we apply this to a particular function.

Subtraction Rule We prove this in the same way as the addition rule and we shall not work through it. It is, however, an excellent exercise to demonstrate for yourself that if

then

$$y = ax^n - bx^m$$

$$\frac{dy}{dx} = \frac{du}{dx} - \frac{dv}{dx} \qquad (45)$$

where $u = ax^n$ and $v = bx^m$.

Product Rule Consider the function

$$y = (10x^2)(2x^7). \qquad (46)$$

It is possible to complete the multiplication first, giving

$$y = 20x^9, \qquad (47)$$

and then to differentiate giving

$$\frac{dy}{dx} = 180x^8. \qquad (48)$$

For many purposes, however, it is often more convenient to differentiate before completing the multiplication. Indeed, in cases in which we are dealing with general functions rather than specific examples it will not be possible to complete the multiplication process. If, for example, $y = f(x) \cdot g(x)$, we are dealing with y as a product of two unspecified functions and we are quite unable to complete the multiplication. Thus we want a rule for handling products of the general form,

$$y = uv \qquad (49)$$

where

$$u = f(x) \qquad (50)$$

and

$$v = g(x). \qquad (51)$$

Applying our now familiar procedure of increasing u and v by Δu and Δv we write

$$y + \Delta y = (u + \Delta u)(v + \Delta v). \qquad (52)$$

Expanding the right-hand side we get

$$y + \Delta y = uv + u\,\Delta v + v\,\Delta u + \Delta u\,\Delta v. \qquad (53)$$

We now make use of (49) to remove y from the left-hand side and uv from the right-hand side of (53) to get

$$\Delta y = u\,\Delta v + v\,\Delta u + \Delta u\,\Delta v. \qquad (54)$$

Now we divide through by Δx to get

$$\frac{\Delta y}{\Delta x} = u\frac{\Delta v}{\Delta x} + v\frac{\Delta u}{\Delta x} + \Delta u\frac{\Delta v}{\Delta x}. \qquad (55)$$

But we already have (41) and (42) (see page 111) which tell us that the limit of the incremental ratio $\Delta v/\Delta x$ as Δx approaches zero is dv/dx and similarly for $\Delta u/\Delta x$. But we know from (50) that u is a function of x. Thus as the change in x approaches zero so also will the change in u approach zero. Thus, since $\Delta u \to 0$ as $\Delta x \to 0$ we see that the final term in (55) approaches zero as Δx approaches zero. Thus we can now write

$$\lim_{\Delta x \to 0} \frac{\Delta y}{\Delta x} = u\frac{dv}{dx} + v\frac{du}{dx} = \frac{dy}{dx}. \qquad (56)$$

(56) gives the rule for differentiating a product, and we can apply it immediately to (46):

$$\frac{du}{dx} = 20x, \qquad (57)$$

$$\frac{dv}{dx} = 14x^6. \qquad (58)$$

Now substituting (57) and (58) into (56) we have

$$\frac{dy}{dx} = (10x^2)(14x^6) \mid (2x^7)(20x)$$

$$= 140x^8 + 40x^8$$

$$= 180x^8. \qquad (59)$$

This rule shows how, as we have just illustrated, we can complete the multiplication and then take the derivative (expressions (47) and (48)) or take the separate derivatives first as in expression (59). Which we do in any particular example is purely a matter of convenience. Let us take one more example which should now appear very easy. If

$$y = x^7 \qquad (60)$$

then

$$\frac{dy}{dx} = 7x^6. \qquad (61)$$

We can however write (60) as

$$y = x^3 . x^4 \qquad (62)$$

and put

$$y = uv$$

where

$$u = x^3$$

and

$$v = x^4.$$

This gives

$$\frac{du}{dx} = 3x^2 \tag{63}$$

and

$$\frac{dv}{dx} = 4x^3. \tag{64}$$

Now applying (56) we get

$$y = (x^3)(4x^3) + (x^4)(3x^2)$$
$$= 4x^6 + 3x^6$$
$$= 7x^6 \tag{65}$$

which is the same result as we obtained in (61).

The Quotient Rule Finally consider the function

$$y = \frac{6x^6}{2x^2}. \tag{66}$$

We could rewrite this as

$$y = 3x^4 \tag{67}$$

and then differentiate to obtain

$$\frac{dy}{dx} = 12x^3. \tag{68}$$

The same considerations apply here as in the previous section: if we have two unspecified functions of x we cannot, and in any case we may not find it convenient to, complete the division before differentiating.

To handle such cases we apply our now familiar procedure, and we write

$$y = \frac{u}{v} \tag{69}$$

where

$$u = f(x)$$
$$v = g(x).$$

We let u and v change by Δu and Δv and let y change as a result by an amount Δy. Thus we can write

$$y + \Delta y = \frac{u + \Delta u}{v + \Delta v}. \tag{70}$$

Now all we need to derive our result is a bit of routine, although devious, manipulation. First, we multiply both sides of (70) by $(v + \Delta v)$:

$$(y + \Delta y)(v + \Delta v) = u + \Delta u. \tag{71}$$

Next we expand the left-hand side of (71):

$$yv + y\,\Delta v + v\,\Delta y + \Delta y\,\Delta v = u + \Delta u. \tag{72}$$

From (69) we have $yv = u$ and hence can eliminate yv from the left-hand side and u from the right-hand side of (72) to give

$$y\,\Delta v + v\,\Delta y + \Delta y\,\Delta v = \Delta u. \tag{73}$$

Multiplying both sides by v and transferring terms from the left- to the right-hand side of the expression gives

$$v^2\,\Delta y = v\,\Delta u - vy\,\Delta v - v\,\Delta y\,\Delta v. \tag{74}$$

At last we can divide both sides by Δx (since it is $\Delta y/\Delta x$ in which we are interested) to obtain

$$v^2\,\frac{\Delta y}{\Delta x} = v\,\frac{\Delta u}{\Delta x} - vy\,\frac{\Delta v}{\Delta x} - v\,\Delta v\,\frac{\Delta y}{\Delta x}. \tag{75}$$

It would be nice to eliminate the vy term on the right-hand side. We can again make use of (69) in the form $u = vy$ to give

$$v^2\,\frac{\Delta y}{\Delta x} = v\,\frac{\Delta u}{\Delta x} - u\,\frac{\Delta v}{\Delta x} - v\,\Delta v\,\frac{\Delta y}{\Delta x}. \tag{76}$$

The next step is obviously to clear v^2 from the left-hand side. Dividing through by v^2 we have

$$\frac{\Delta y}{\Delta x} = \frac{v\,\dfrac{\Delta u}{\Delta x} - u\,\dfrac{\Delta v}{\Delta x} - v\,\Delta v\,\dfrac{\Delta y}{\Delta x}}{v^2}. \tag{77}$$

Now we have the incremental ratio, and have only to look for the limits. Let $\Delta x \to 0$, and since u and v are both functions of x we can say $\Delta u,\ \Delta v \to 0$ as $\Delta x \to 0$. Now as Δx approaches zero we have already seen that each of the incremental ratios in (77) approaches the value of its corresponding derivative. Attention must be paid, however, to the last term in (77): we see that, although $\Delta y/\Delta x \to \mathrm{d}y/\mathrm{d}x$ as $\Delta x \to 0$, it is also true that $\Delta v \to 0$ as $\Delta x \to 0$ so that this last term gets smaller and smaller and, as $\Delta x \to 0$, the value of the whole term also approaches zero. Thus we can write

$$\lim_{\Delta x \to 0} \frac{\Delta y}{\Delta x} \left(y = \frac{u}{v} \right) = \frac{v\dfrac{\mathrm{d}u}{\mathrm{d}x} - u\dfrac{\mathrm{d}v}{\mathrm{d}x}}{v^2} = \frac{\mathrm{d}y}{\mathrm{d}x}. \tag{78}$$

Now let us check this by taking the example in (66) above. We have

$$u = 6x^6$$

and

$$v = 2x^2$$

whence

$$\frac{\mathrm{d}u}{\mathrm{d}x} = 36x^5 \tag{79}$$

and

$$\frac{\mathrm{d}v}{\mathrm{d}x} = 4x. \tag{80}$$

Substituting (79) and (80) into (78) gives

$$\begin{aligned}
\frac{\mathrm{d}y}{\mathrm{d}x} &= \frac{2x^2(36x^5) - 6x^6(4x)}{(2x^2)(2x^2)} \\
&= \frac{72x^7 - 24x^7}{4x^4} \\
&= \frac{48x^7}{4x^4} \\
&= 12x^3
\end{aligned} \tag{81}$$

which agrees with the result arrived at in (68) above.

5.6   The Function-of-a-Function Rule

One more device will allow us to handle most of the functions that we are likely to encounter in a wide range of elementary application. This device is called the function-of-a-function or the chain rule. Suppose we have the two functions

$$y = 2z^2 \tag{82}$$

and

$$z = 3x + 2x^2. \tag{83}$$

We could substitute (83) into (82) to obtain

$$\begin{aligned}
y &= 2(3x + 2x^2)^2 \\
&= 8x^4 + 24x^3 + 18x^2
\end{aligned} \tag{84}$$

and then differentiate to obtain

$$\frac{dy}{dx} = 32x^3 + 72x^2 + 36x. \tag{85}$$

In many cases it is convenient or necessary to keep the two functions in (82) and (83) separate. Thus we have

$$y = y(z) \tag{86}$$

$$z = z(x) \tag{87}$$

and we wish to find dy/dx. We can do this by the following very simple rule. Given (86) and (87) above it is true that

$$\frac{dy}{dx} = \frac{dy}{dz} \cdot \frac{dz}{dx}. \tag{88}$$

(88) says that if y depends on z and z depends on x and you want to know by how much a change in x influences y you find out by calculating how much a change in x influences z and how much a change in z influences y and the product of the two changes gives the answer. This result has a strong intuitive appeal, and we merely state it without proof.[1]

The chain rule can be extended as far as we wish: if, for example, $y = y(u)$, $u = u(v)$, $v = v(w)$, $w = w(x)$, $x = x(z)$ then

$$\frac{dy}{dz} = \frac{dy}{du} \cdot \frac{du}{dv} \cdot \frac{dv}{dw} \cdot \frac{dw}{dx} \cdot \frac{dx}{dz} \tag{89}$$

which is another important result.

Now let us consider some examples of the application of this rule. First we shall apply it to the problem in (82) and (83). Differentiating (82) we get

$$\frac{dy}{dz} = 4z. \tag{90}$$

Substituting (83) into (90) gives

$$\frac{dy}{dz} = 12x + 8x^2. \tag{91}$$

Differentiating (83) gives

$$\frac{dz}{dx} = 3 + 4x. \tag{92}$$

[1] A proof of this rule can be found in R. G. D. Allen, *Mathematical Analysis for Economists*, *op. cit.*, p. 169.

Thus we have

$$\frac{dy}{dx} = \frac{dy}{dz}\cdot\frac{dz}{dx} = (12x+8x^2)(3+4x)$$

$$= 36x+72x^2+32x^3 \qquad (93)$$

which agrees with the result obtained in (84).

We shall have occasion to use the function-of-a-function rule many times throughout this book. It is a very powerful tool, and it usually provides us with more than one way of obtaining a result that we require. As an example we shall show how the rule for finding the derivative of a quotient can be obtained by making use of this rule.

Consider the function $y=u/v$ where $u=u(x)$ and $v=v(x)$. We have already found how to find dy/dx by the quotient rule, but we can also find it by applying the product and the chain rules. This sort of transformation of a problem from a form in which one rule can be applied to a form in which quite another rule can be applied is a very common and very convenient dodge and what follows provides a simple example of it. Indeed in the calculus there is almost always more than one way of skinning any cat.

Let us in this case write $y=u/v$ as $y=uv^{-1}$ and then let $z=v^{-1}$ whence we have $y=uz$. Now we can apply the product rule to this function to obtain

$$\frac{dy}{dx} = u\frac{dz}{dx}+z\frac{du}{dx}. \qquad (94)$$

Since $z=v^{-1}$ we can rewrite (94) as

$$\frac{dy}{dx} = u\frac{d(v^{-1})}{dx}+\frac{1}{v}\frac{du}{dx}. \qquad (95)$$

Now we need to find $d(v^{-1})/dx$ and we use the chain rule to do so. Since $z=v^{-1}$ this can be written as

$$\frac{d(v^{-1})}{dx} = \frac{dz}{dv}\cdot\frac{dv}{dx} \qquad (96)$$

which is a simple application of the chain rule. Differentiating $z=v^{-1}$ and substituting into (96) gives

$$\frac{d(v^{-1})}{dx} = -v^{-2}\frac{dv}{dx}. \qquad (97)$$

Finally we substitute (97) into (95) to get

$$\frac{dy}{dx} = -\frac{u}{v^2}\frac{dv}{dx}+\frac{1}{v}\frac{du}{dx}$$

$$= \frac{v\dfrac{du}{dx}-u\dfrac{dv}{dx}}{v^2}. \qquad (98)$$

This is the rule for a derivative of a quotient which we have already derived and stated in (78) above.

Summary

The material in this chapter may seem like a big dose at first sight, but it all boils down to the following rules:

(1) if

$$y = ax^n$$

then

$$\frac{dy}{dx} = nax^{n-1};$$

(2) if u and v are two functions of x such that

$$y = u+v,$$

then

$$\frac{dy}{dx} = \frac{du}{dx} + \frac{dv}{dx};$$

(3) if

$$y = u-v$$

then

$$\frac{dy}{dx} = \frac{du}{dx} - \frac{dv}{dx};$$

(4) if

$$y = uv$$

then

$$\frac{dy}{dx} = u\frac{dv}{dx} + v\frac{du}{dx};$$

(5) if

$$y = \frac{u}{v}$$

then

$$\frac{dy}{dx} = \frac{v\dfrac{du}{dx} - u\dfrac{dv}{dx}}{v^2};$$

and, finally,

(6) if

$$y = y(z),$$

and

$$z = z(x),$$

then

$$\frac{dy}{dx} = \frac{dy}{dz} \cdot \frac{dz}{dx}.$$

5.7 Functions of x

So far in this chapter we have dealt with functional relations between two variables. We can, of course, just look at a function involving x without necessarily equating it to another variable. For example, we might consider the relation

$$y = 2x^3 \qquad (99)$$

and ask how y is tending to change as x changes. The answer to this question is provided by taking the derivative of y with respect to x from (99) to give

$$\frac{dy}{dx} = 6x^2. \qquad (100)$$

It might, however, be the case in another example that

$$z = 2x^3 \qquad (101)$$

in which case

$$\frac{dz}{dx} = 6x^2. \qquad (102)$$

Indeed we can just look at the function of x without setting it equal to y, z, or to any other variable and write

$$f(x) = 2x^3 \qquad (103)$$

in the manner considered on pages 37–38 of Chapter 3. In this case we can ask how the value of the function changes as x changes and we can write

$$\frac{d}{dx}(f(x)) = 6x^2 \qquad (104)$$

which tells us how the value of the function is changing as x changes. (104) is read 'D by D-X of F of X is six X squared', and it tells us the rate of change of the value of the function of x for any value of x.

A very convenient notation is a prime mark to indicate that the operation of differentiation has been performed on the function. Thus if

$$f(x) = 2x^3 \qquad (105)$$

then

$$\frac{d}{dx}f(x) = 6x^2 = f'(x). \qquad (106)$$

The last term in (106) is read as 'F primed of X'. One of the characteristics of mathematics is its ability to suppress unwanted detail. In some cases it is actually necessary to differentiate a function such as (99) above and, in the case of complicated functions, this can become a very tedious business. In other cases we can often just put the little prime mark on $f(x)$ to show that, whatever the function is, we consider it to be differentiated, and this is all we require to prove what we wish. This is a great labour saving device and we shall use it many times throughout this book. Some examples of its use are given in the questions at the end of this chapter.

5.8 Second and Higher Order Derivatives

Consider the linear demand relation

$$p = 10{,}000 - 15q. \tag{107}$$

To obtain the total revenue function we multiply through by q:

$$R = pq = 10{,}000q - 15q^2. \tag{108}$$

We now want to know how total revenue responds to changes in quantity. To do this we calculate marginal revenue:

$$MR = \frac{dR}{dq} = 10{,}000 - 30q. \tag{109}$$

(107) and (109) are both illustrated in Figure 5.3a. (109), of course, gives us the rate of change of total revenue as the quantity sold changes. (108) is illustrated in Figure 5.3b.

We can, however, also ask ourselves how marginal revenue is itself varying as quantity sold varies. We might wish to know, for example, if marginal revenue is increasing or decreasing as the volume of sales rises and by how much it is rising or falling.[1] In other words we want to find dMR/dq. Evidently, in the example used above, this can be established by differentiating expression (109), whence

$$\frac{dMR}{dq} = -30. \tag{110}$$

In this case marginal revenue is declining at a constant rate of -30 per unit increase in the quantity sold.

A moment's thought will show that what we have done is to differentiate the total revenue function given in equation (108) twice with respect to quantity. The first derivative tells us how the function R is behaving as we vary quantity, and the second derivative tells us how its rate of change (i.e., MR) is behaving as we vary quantity.

[1] It is often thought that as long as the demand curve is downward sloping the MR curve is also downward sloping – text-books always draw both curves in this way. You will find however, that this is not the case: a downward-sloping demand curve is *not* sufficient condition for a downward-sloping MR curve.

Now consider a general functional relation between x and y,

$$y = f(x)$$

and its derivative

$$\frac{dy}{dx} = f'(x).$$

We can now differentiate this function a second time as we did above and

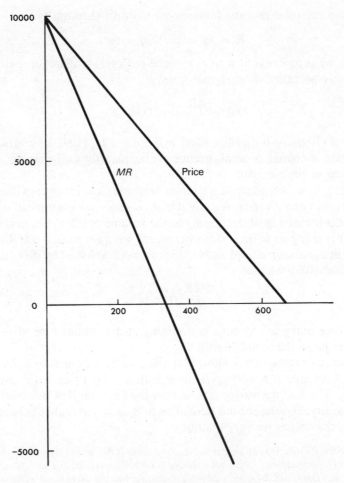

Figure 5.3a

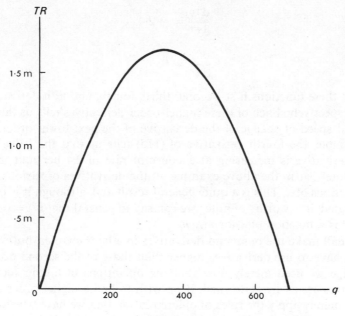

Figure 5.3b

indicate this by the following notation:

$$\frac{\mathrm{d}^2 y}{\mathrm{d} x^2} = f''(x).$$

This is read 'D-two Y by D-X squared'. The 2's on the left-hand side and the 'double prime sign' on the right-hand side both indicate that we have differentiated the function twice. If $\mathrm{d}y/\mathrm{d}x$ tells us how y is tending to change as x changes, then $\mathrm{d}^2 y/\mathrm{d}x^2$ tells us how the rate of change of y is itself changing as we change x. Evidently we can continue to ask how a function obtained by differentiation itself changes as x changes as many times as we like. Consider, for example, the following function

$$y = 10 + 2x - 3x^2 - 5x^3 + 0 \cdot 1x^4 \qquad (111)$$

$$\frac{\mathrm{d}y}{\mathrm{d}x} = +2 - 6x - 15x^2 + 0 \cdot 4x^3 \qquad (112)$$

$$\frac{\mathrm{d}^2 y}{\mathrm{d}x^2} = -6 - 30x + 1 \cdot 2x^2 \qquad (113)$$

$$\frac{\mathrm{d}^3 y}{\mathrm{d}x^3} = -30 + 2 \cdot 4x \qquad (114)$$

5

$$\frac{d^4y}{dx^4} = +2\cdot4 \qquad (115)$$

$$\frac{d^5y}{dx^5} = 0. \qquad (116)$$

We call these functions first, second, third, fourth, and fifth derivatives of (111) respectively. Each of these higher order derivatives tells us the direction and speed of change of the derivative of the next lower order. Thus, for example, the fourth derivative of (115) tells us that the value of the third derivative is increasing at a constant rate of $2\cdot4$ per unit increase in x. Note that in the above example all the derivatives of various orders are functions of x. This is a quite general result and, although it is obvious once stated, it is worthy of note: we can say in general that if $y = y(x)$ then $d^n y/dx^n$ is a function of x for any n.

We shall make use of second derivatives in a later chapter, but we shall seldom have to use derivatives higher than those of the second order. At this stage we need merely note that the operations of taking successive derivatives are easily performed. If we wish to find a higher order derivative we merely apply the rules of differentiation that we have developed to the derivative of the lower order. Full use of second derivatives in an economic application together with a chance to gain some further intuitive feel for their meaning and use must be postponed until we come to discuss the problems of maxima and minima in a later chapter.

5.9 Inverse Functions

So far we have taken a function $y = y(x)$ and calculated dy/dx. We must now consider how to find dx/dy on the same function. Consider first a simple example. If $y = x^2$ then $dy/dx = 2x$. What can we say about dx/dy on the same function? By taking the square root of both sides we can rewrite the function as $x = \sqrt{y}$ or $x = y^{1/2}$. Now we differentiate this function of y to obtain $dx/dy = \frac{1}{2}y^{-1/2} = 1/(2\sqrt{y})$. We now have

$$\frac{dy}{dx} = 2x \qquad (117)$$

and

$$\frac{dx}{dy} = \frac{1}{2\sqrt{y}}. \qquad (118)$$

Since $2x = 2y^{1/2}$ we can rewrite (117) as

$$\frac{dy}{dx} = 2\sqrt{y}. \qquad (119)$$

This shows us that on this function

$$\frac{dx}{dy} = \frac{1}{dy/dx}. \tag{120}$$

This result has a strong intuitive appeal. If at a point on a function y is tending to change by two units every time x changes by one ($dy/dx = 2$) then we should not be too surprised to learn that at the same point on the function x is tending to change by $\frac{1}{2}$ a unit every time y changes by one ($dx/dy = \frac{1}{2}$).

We are also familiar with this result in the case of a straight line. If we take the straight line $y = a + bx$ and plot it in the usual way with x on the horizontal axis and y on the vertical axis, its slope will be b. If we reverse the axes, however, plotting y on the horizontal axis and x on the vertical one, then the slope of this new straight line will be $1/b$. Analytically this is easily shown as follows:

if
$$y = a + bx,$$

then
$$\frac{dy}{dx} = b;$$

but we now write x as the dependent variable giving

$$x = \frac{y}{b} - \frac{a}{b}.$$

Taking the derivative of x with respect to y:

$$\frac{dx}{dy} = \frac{1}{b}.$$

This result is quite general and most important and we can state that for any single-valued function if $y = y(x)$ then

$$\frac{dx}{dy} = \frac{1}{dy/dx}. \tag{121}$$

5.10 Some Non-differentiable Functions

The functions that we encounter in elementary economic theory are usually all *differentiable*, which means that at every point on the function a unique derivative exists. When this is the case we are able to say quite unambiguously how fast y is changing as x changes everywhere on the function.

Graphically this means that there is a unique tangent gradient at every point on the function.

We do not need to explore in any detail the class of non-differentiable functions, but consideration of a few examples will be helpful. First, we can notice that a function that is not continuous is not differentiable. The intuitive meaning of continuous is shown in Figure 5.4. In Figure 5.4a the function consists of a series of discrete points; intermediate values do not exist. Clearly, there is no unique tangent to any of the points and we cannot define dy/dx for this function. In Figure 5.4b, the function is continuous at all values except x_1. At that point there is a sudden discrete

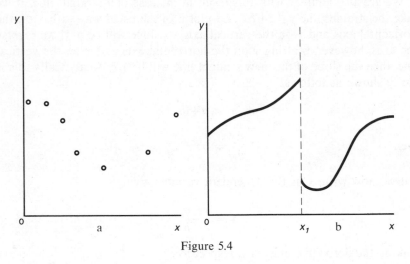

Figure 5.4

jump in the value of y. Clearly, there is no unique tangent to the curve at the point x_1.

The curve in Figure 5.5 is continuous in the sense of not taking discrete jumps but at the value x_1 it is kinked. There is no unique tangent to the curve at that point. Instead, T_1, T_2, T_3 or any one of a host of other lines are all tangent to the curve at that point. The function is not differentiable at the point x_1.

In most of the work that follows we will assume that we are dealing with smooth continuous functions that can be differentiated. It is possible to develop techniques to deal with non-differentiable functions but the pay-off at the stage of elementary economics is not great.

We have now done quite a bit of mathematics but the student who has persevered this far has gone a long way towards mastering the techniques he needs, and we must see without delaying further to what use we can put the techniques we have learned in this chapter.

5.11 Constant Elasticity Demand Curves

At the beginning of this chapter we considered the characteristics of a measure of elasticity using incremental ratios (see (4) on page 97). Later we used derivatives to redefine elasticity as $(\mathrm{d}q/\mathrm{d}p)p/q$. Let us now consider the elasticity of a demand curve of the log-linear form

$$q = Ap^\alpha \tag{122}$$

(which we encountered in Chapter 3B.4)

We calculate the elasticity as follows:

$$\eta = \frac{\mathrm{d}q}{\mathrm{d}p} \cdot \frac{p}{q}$$

$$= \alpha Ap^{\alpha-1} \cdot \frac{p}{q}$$

$$= \alpha Ap^{\alpha-1} \cdot \frac{p}{Ap^\alpha} \qquad \text{(from (122))}$$

$$= \alpha \frac{Ap^\alpha}{Ap^\alpha}$$

$$= \alpha. \tag{123}$$

The elasticity of the demand function in (122) is a constant equal to α. As we saw in Chapter 3B, we can express (122) in logarithmic form. Taking logarithms of both sides we have

$$\log q = \log A + \alpha \log p. \tag{124}$$

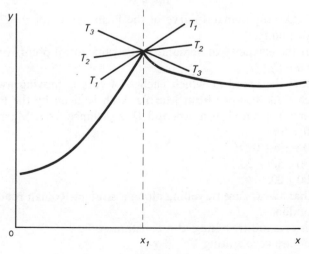

Figure 5.5

Clearly (122) and (124) are two alternative ways of writing the same functional relation. Indeed (124) is what we have called a logarithmic transformation of (122). (122) is a non-linear function, but when it is rewritten in the form of (124) we obtain an expression that is linear in the logs.

Now let us take the derivative of the log of q from (124). This is

$$\frac{d \log q}{d \log p} = \alpha. \tag{125}$$

We now see from (123) and (125) that, at least in the case of the present function, elasticity is equal to $(d \log q)/(d \log p)$. Thus, at least from the constant elasticity function, we can write

$$\frac{dq}{dp} \cdot \frac{p}{q} = \frac{d \log q}{d \log p}.$$

We shall see in a later chapter that this is a general result. In the meantime we note that we have discovered the form of the demand functions that have constant elasticities, and have discovered that, with these functions, elasticity is the derivative of the log of quantity with respect to the log of price.

Exercises

1 On pages 98–100 we considered the elasticity of the demand curve $pq = 1200$.

(a) Calculate the elasticity of this curve using the definition

$$\eta = \frac{dq}{dp} \cdot \frac{p}{q}.$$

(b) Show that any demand curve of the form $pq = C$ (or $q = Cp^{-1}$) has an elasticity of unity.

2 Show that the elasticity of demand is the same at all points on the demand curve $q = Cp^{-\alpha}$.

3 (i) Calculate the speed at which each of 4 cars is moving away from Marble Arch if its distance from Marble Arch is given by the following, where t is time measured in hours and D is distance from Marble Arch.

(1) $D = 10 + 40t$
(2) $D = 10 + 30t + 0.5t^2$
(3) $D = 100 + 50t - 20t^{-1}$
(4) $D = 300 + 20t - t^2$.

Assume that all cars are travelling along a straight Roman road leading out of London.

(ii) Which cars are travelling at a constant speed?
(iii) Which are accelerating?
(iv) Which are decelerating?

(v) As t gets larger and larger the speed of car 3 approaches a limit. What is it?

(vi) Which car returns to London? After how many hours?

4 Calculate all the non-zero derivatives of

$$y = 10 + 3x + 5x^3 + 7x^5.$$

5 Consider the derivation of a marginal revenue curve from a demand curve, first in a numerical example and then in general terms.

(a) The demand for a commodity is given by $q^d = 1000 - 3p$. Derive the total revenue and the marginal revenue functions.

(b) The demand for a commodity is given by $p = a + bq$. Prove that the slope of the marginal revenue curve associated with a linear Marshallian demand curve is always twice that of the demand curve. (This is a most convenient result to know when constructing graphs.)

(c) The demand curve for a commodity is given by $p = f(q)$. Show that marginal revenue is given by $MR = f(q) + qf'(q)$ (don't forget that $f'(q) = dq/dp$). (*Hint:* First get an expression for total revenue and then differentiate it using the product rule, to get marginal revenue.)

6 Assume that $q^d = 1000 - 5p - 0 \cdot 1p^3$ and $p = 2t^{3/2}$. This says that demand is a function of price and that price is increasing over time. Use the function-of-a-function rule to calculate the rate of change of q^d over time. Check your results by substituting $p - p(t)$ into $q^d - q(p)$ to obtain a single function $p = p(t)$ and then calculate dp/dt directly from this function.

7 Consider the following functions:

(i) $y = 10 + 2x$

(ii) $y = x^2$

(iii) $y = x^3$.

(a) Calculate dy/dx for each function.

(b) Calculate dx/dy using the inverse function rule.

(c) Express x as an explicit function of y for each function.

(d) Calculate dx/dy from each of the functions in (c) and check that you obtain the same answers as in (b).

CHAPTER 6

APPLICATIONS OF DERIVATIVES

6.1 Some familiar derivatives

Now that we have developed the concept of a derivative, it is clear that, in the comparative statics of Chapter 4, we were in fact taking derivatives. Thus a multiplier is nothing but dY/dI; and our tax theorem for a competitive market may be simply expressed as

$$0 < \frac{dp}{dt} < 1.$$

In those very simple cases, however, we were able to discover the derivatives more or less by inspection: if an endogenous variable is a linear function of an exogenous one, the derivative is pretty obviously the slope coefficient. If the intercept is zero, furthermore, 'averages' and 'marginals' are the same. Thus if we assume (closed economy, no government) that I is the only autonomous injection, and that $C = cY$, we have the simplest case of 4B.1, where

$$\frac{dY}{dI} = \frac{Y}{I} = \frac{1}{1-c}.$$

Now, however, with more equipment, we may tackle some more difficult and interesting problems.

First of all, we may notice how many familiar economic concepts prove to be derivatives. We have already remarked that the multiplier is an example. Marginal cost is another. In Chapter 2, we proved a number of standard theorems about the cost function by methods which, if rigorous, were admittedly clumsy. We may now obtain the same results more quickly and neatly, and carry the analysis a good deal further as well. Thus let the cost function be

$$C = c(q) \tag{1}$$

where C is total cost and q output. From the definition of marginal cost we know that it is

$$\frac{dC}{dq} = c'(q).$$

But we may go further. If there is any part of cost that is fixed, then it, by definition, does not vary with output, so we may rewrite (1) as

$$C = k + f(q) \tag{2}$$

where k is fixed cost, and $f(q)$ gives the relationship between total variable cost and output. Now, since k is not a function of q, the rate of change of C with respect to q is independent of k, that is,

$$\frac{dC}{dq} = f'(q), \tag{3}$$

i.e., marginal total cost equals marginal variable cost as we saw in Chapter 2.

Now, with the aid of our more powerful technique, we may consider the case of perfect competition. It is a familiar result that equilibrium for the individual firm in perfect competition is only possible where marginal cost is rising. This suggests that we may find that only some cost functions are compatible with perfectly competitive equilibrium. To investigate this question, we start by considering the cost function

$$C = aq^2 + bq + c. \tag{4}$$

Marginal cost is given by

$$\frac{dC}{dq} = 2aq + b \tag{5}$$

which is linear. Since perfectly competitive equilibrium is only possible where marginal cost is rising, it immediately follows that a must be positive if (4) is to be consistent with perfect competition. But (4) does not give us the marginal cost curve, familiar from text-book illustrations, that slopes down and then rises. To obtain this marginal cost curve, we need a total cost curve that is more complicated than a quadratic. In fact, a suitable cubic will do it. Consider

$$C = aq^3 + bq^2 + cq + d. \tag{6}$$

Marginal cost is given by

$$\frac{dC}{dq} = 3aq^2 + 2bq + c, \tag{7}$$

itself a quadratic. This will take on the conventional U-shape provided that it is 'the right way up', and not an inverted U, which involves some restrictions on the signs of the coefficients. It proves that working out the required restrictions is rather laborious (we had to do it in order to set Exercise 1,

5*

which might well be done at this point). Furthermore, after we have the technique of maxima and minima, which is the subject of the next chapter, we can discover very easily what sort of cubic will give the text-book total cost curve, so it is not worth pursuing the matter now.

We may now use our new technique to obtain in an easy and efficient manner many standard propositions of micro-theory, some of which are met in a principles course, and all of which are used so frequently that it is a good idea to have them properly established. In the next section, we shall derive the marginal revenue function, and then prove that a factor's marginal revenue product is equal to its marginal physical product multiplied by marginal revenue, after which we shall establish the relationship between marginal product and marginal cost.

6.2   Production, Cost, and Revenue Functions

We already know that marginal product and marginal revenue are derivatives, the former of the production function with respect to an input, the latter of the revenue function with respect to output, or sales. Thus suppose that, for a given capital equipment, total output is given by

$$q = g(l) \tag{8}$$

where l is labour measured in man-days. Marginal product is dq/dl or $g'(l)$. We expect positive marginal products, i.e., $g'(l) > 0$. Diminishing returns means that the marginal product curve has, at least eventually, a negative slope. When marginal product is decreasing, its derivative must be negative. Its derivative is, however, the second derivative of the output function (8), so the assumption of diminishing returns is simply expressed as $g''(l) < 0$.

We could now construct some possible production functions, as we constructed cost functions in 6.1 above, and consider what restrictions are necessary to generate a conventionally shaped marginal product curve, but we may leave this for the time being. Let us consider the marginal revenue of an individual firm. A firm in non-perfect competition has control over the price of its product: it may set price, whence demand determines sales. Thus we may write $q = q(p)$. But the two variables, price and sales, are related by the demand curve, and it is more convenient to write the function the other way round, as

$$p = f(q) \tag{9}$$

which may be interpreted as saying that the price at which any quantity is demanded is a function of that quantity. Revenue is price times sales:

$$R = pq. \tag{10}$$

If we substitute (9) into (10), we obtain

$$R = q.f(q),\tag{11}$$

i.e., we have expressed total revenue as a function of sales only, which allows us to find its derivative with respect to sales. To do this we need the product rule, which we obtained in Chapter 5,

$$\frac{duv}{dx} = u\frac{dv}{dx}+v\frac{du}{dx}$$

If we substitute q for u and $f(q)$ for v, we find the derivative of (11) to be

$$\frac{dR}{dq} = q.f'(q)+f(q).\tag{12}$$

(Perfect competition is, as we know, the special case in which price is a constant $\bar{p}$ so that $dR/dq=d(\bar{p}q)/dq=\bar{p}$.)

In the last chapter, page 121, marginal revenue was illustrated by a numerical example of a linear demand function. We may just complete the illustration in general terms, assuming that

$$p = a+bq\tag{13}$$

whence total revenue is given by

$$R = pq = q(a+bq)$$
$$= aq+bq^2.\tag{14}$$

(14), as we have already seen in Chapter 3, is a quadratic through the origin, and we easily obtain

$$\frac{dR}{dq} = a+2bq,\tag{15}$$

which shows that a linear demand function not surprisingly gives a linear marginal revenue function.

Let us now try to find an expression for marginal revenue product. This is defined as the rate of change of total revenue with respect to an input, say, labour. We clearly need to express revenue as a function of labour input, and therefore need both the production function, (8), and the revenue function (11). Substituting (8) into (11) to replace q by $g(l)$ wherever q appears, we have

$$R = g(l) \cdot f[g(l)].\tag{16}$$

The term $f[g(l)]$ may appear forbidding, but it is only a way of expressing price as a function of the variable input labour: the function f allows price to be read off when q is known, and the function g allows q to be read off when l is known, so 'f of g of l' relates prices to labour input. Now to find dR/dl we shall have to employ both the product rule and the chain rule. Since the term $p=f[g(l)]$ expresses price as a function of output which in turn is a function of labour input, the chain rule gives

$$\frac{df[g(l)]}{dl} = \frac{dp}{dl} = \frac{dp}{dq}\cdot\frac{dq}{dl} = f'(q).g'(l). \tag{17}$$

We may now apply the product rule to (16) and see that we require

$$\frac{dR}{dl} = g(l)\frac{d}{dl}f[g(l)]+g'(l).f[g(l)].$$

Substituting (17) into this, we obtain

$$\frac{dR}{dl} = g(l).f'(q).g'(l)+g'(l).f[g(l)]. \tag{18}$$

(18) looks rather cumbersome, but we may identify individual terms in such a fashion as will yield a straightforward interpretation. Remember that $g'(l)$ is marginal physical product (MPP), that $f'(q)$ is dp/dq, and that $f[g(l)]$ is price, written as a function of demand for the product and labour input. Factoring out $g'(l)$, we have

$$\text{Marginal Revenue Product of Labour} = MPP\left\{q\cdot\frac{dp}{dq}+p\right\}.$$

But from (12) we know that the expression in brackets is dR/dq, or marginal revenue, so we have proved that

$$MRP = MPP \times MR.$$

We shall need this relationship later on.

We can now establish the relationship between marginal product and marginal cost. Assuming fixed capital equipment, and that labour is the only variable input, we use (8) again:

$$q = g(l). \tag{8}$$

Let the wage per man-day be w. Define variable cost simply as

$$V = wl. \tag{19}$$

The marginal cost of another man-day, dV/dl, is obviously equal to the wage, w; but what we want is marginal cost with respect to output, dV/dq. Now, by the chain rule

$$\frac{dV}{dq} = \frac{dV}{dl}\cdot\frac{dl}{dq} \tag{20}$$

and from (8),

$$\frac{dq}{dl} = g'(l) \tag{21}$$

whence, by the rule given in 5.9, $dl/dq = 1/g'(l)$. So, substituting into (20),

$$\frac{dV}{dq} = \left(\frac{w}{g'(l)} \right) \tag{22}$$

which is to say that marginal cost of output is equal to the marginal cost of the variable input divided by its marginal product. This result illustrates the power of mathematical notation that we referred to in the last chapter. To obtain (22), we have not had to specify the actual production function $g(l)$, let alone go through the operation of taking a derivative: it is enough to write $g'(l)$ to indicate that it is the derivative, *whatever it may be*, that we are talking about, and we can obtain the general result (22) which can be applied without more ado to any particular case, or employed in any further analysis we may wish to undertake. And, indeed, we have use for it at once.

6.3* The Relation Between Marginal Product and Marginal Cost

This section is starred, to indicate that it is difficult. You may omit it on a first reading, or, if you try it and get into trouble, come back later. What we are going to prove is that, with a constant wage rate, diminishing marginal product is both necessary and sufficient for increasing marginal cost. This is generally taken for granted in the analysis of perfect competition. It is certainly required, since competitive equilibrium is only possible where marginal cost is rising, and the individual firm cannot influence the wage rate. Furthermore, it is intuitively reasonable that diminishing marginal product should give increasing marginal cost, and you may have encountered this proposition in your principles course. It turns out to be quite hard work to prove it, and there is certainly nothing else as difficult in this chapter.

In equation (22) we have expressed marginal cost in terms of the wage rate and marginal product. What we now want is the slope of the marginal cost curve, which is given by the derivative of (22), which in turn is the second derivative of (19), total variable cost. So we require

$$\frac{d^2V}{dq^2} = \frac{d}{dq} \left(\frac{w}{g'(l)} \right). \tag{23}$$

This looks a little tricky, since $g'(l)$ is itself dq/dl. w is a constant, however, so what we have to find is $\mathrm{d}(1/g'(l))/\mathrm{d}q$. To evaluate this, it will help to employ the device of a substitute variable, and then apply the chain rule. If we put

$$z = g'(l),$$

then we are seeking

$$\frac{\mathrm{d}z^{-1}}{\mathrm{d}q}.$$

Since z is a function of l, and l of q, we have to use the chain rule twice to evaluate this:

$$\frac{\mathrm{d}z^{-1}}{\mathrm{d}q} = \frac{\mathrm{d}z^{-1}}{\mathrm{d}z}\cdot\frac{\mathrm{d}z}{\mathrm{d}l}\cdot\frac{\mathrm{d}l}{\mathrm{d}q}$$

$$= -z^{-2}\cdot\frac{\mathrm{d}z}{\mathrm{d}l}\cdot\frac{\mathrm{d}l}{\mathrm{d}q}.$$

Taking this term by term,

$$-z^{-2} = \frac{-1}{(g'(l))^2},$$

$$\frac{\mathrm{d}z}{\mathrm{d}l} = g''(l), \qquad\qquad \text{(see equation (21))}$$

and

$$\frac{\mathrm{d}l}{\mathrm{d}q} = \frac{1}{g'(l)} = z^{-1},$$

so

$$\frac{\mathrm{d}z^{-1}}{\mathrm{d}q} = \left(\frac{-1}{(g'(l))^2}\right)\cdot(g''(l))\cdot\left(\frac{1}{g'(l)}\right)$$

or

$$\frac{\mathrm{d}z^{-1}}{\mathrm{d}q} = \frac{-g''(l)}{(g'(l))^3},$$

and, remembering the constant wage-rate w, we have

$$\frac{\mathrm{d}^2 V}{\mathrm{d}q^2} = \frac{\mathrm{d}}{\mathrm{d}q}\left(\frac{w}{g'(l)}\right) = \frac{-wg''(l)}{(g'(l))^3}. \tag{24}$$

Both w and the denominator are positive, so (24) is positive if and only if $g''(l)<0$, i.e., marginal product is diminishing, which is the result we wanted. It is another result that is general, in the sense that we have not had to specify a particular function; and we may take some pride in having completed a difficult proof of an important proposition which usually is only asserted.

6.4 Tax Rates and Tax Yield in a Competitive Market

So far in this chapter, we have not done any comparative statics, which we advertised in Chapter 4 as the crucial step in analysis, when one discovered what qualitative properties one's model might have. We have, however, clarified a few important ideas, and produced at least one essential result in (24). This is an example of an important use for analytical methods: discovering on just what conditions some relationship holds. In fact, we used the same methods and the same approach in deriving (24) as in our comparative static analysis, and it is clear that there is not much difference. We are not yet ready, however, for comparative static analysis of the cases just considered. To carry out comparative static analysis, we must have the relevant equilibrium conditions; and if we assume, for example, that a firm maximises profits, we cannot set out the equilibrium conditions without first developing the mathematical technique necessary to handle maxima. What we may do now is return to our competitive market.

Recall equation (17), 4A.3:

$$p = \frac{a-c}{d-b} + \frac{d}{d-b} t \tag{25}$$

where t was a specific tax. Here the endogenous variable, p, is a linear function of the exogenous variable, t, and, obviously,

$$\frac{\mathrm{d}p}{\mathrm{d}t} = \frac{d}{d-b}.$$

We have already investigated the conditions in which $0 < \mathrm{d}p/\mathrm{d}t < 1$. Suppose now that we are asked about tax yield: intuition suggests that, over some range, increases in t will lead to increased yield, whereas, over others, further increases in tax may so reduce the quantity demanded as to reduce yield. The question is obviously of some interest to policy makers. The general answer from standard supply and demand analysis is the familiar 'it depends on elasticities', but let us obtain a specific answer for our linear case. (Anyhow, since the elasticity changes as we move along a linear function, it is not a particularly useful concept in this case.) We assume that the demand curve slopes down and the supply curve up. We define tax yield as

$$T = tq \tag{26}$$

and, from the demand equation,

$$q = a + b\bar{p} \tag{27}$$

where $\bar{p}$ is the equilibrium price under taxation,[1] given by (25). Substituting (25) into (27), and (27) into (26),

$$T = t\left[a+b\left(\frac{a-c}{d-b}+\frac{d}{d-b}t\right)\right]$$

$$= at+\frac{b(a-c)t}{d-b}+\frac{bdt^2}{d-b}$$

$$= \frac{ad-bc}{d-b}t+\frac{bd}{d-b}t^2. \tag{28}$$

What we have done here is to express tax yield, T, as a function of tax rate, t, and (28) shows that it is a quadratic. This is not surprising, since $T=tq$, and we have already found that q is a linear function of t. We now differentiate (28) to obtain

$$\frac{dT}{dt} = \frac{ad-bc}{d-b}+\frac{2bdt}{d-b}. \tag{29}$$

It is not immediately obvious if this is positive or negative, or at what values. The expression $(ad-bc)/(d-b)$ is the solution for q in the absence of tax as may be seen from (25) and (27). With $d>0$ and $b<0$, the second term in (29) is obviously negative. So (29) is positive if

$$|ad-bc| > |2bdt|$$

i.e., if $$ad-bc > -2bdt. \tag{30}$$

We can see that this inequality is satisfied, and dT/dt consequently positive, for at least some values of t. Given the parameters, the left-hand side is constant, while the right-hand side varies with t. As t approaches zero, the right-hand side approaches zero, and we know that $ad-bc>0$. So we know that there must exist at least some values of t at which the inequality is satisfied, although we cannot discover by this means how close to zero they must be. Now suppose that t is large. For constant $ad-bc$, we can obviously always find a t-value so large that the inequality is not satisfied – in the limit, we can let t approach infinity. Thus we know that there is some

[1] You may have noticed that we have sometimes used $\bar{p}$ to denote the equilibrium price just discovered, and sometimes to denote some given constant price. This seems like sloppiness in notation, and we have remarked on the utility of good notation! Both uses of the bar over a variable are common in the literature, and the reason is that mathematics is a subject with a history: notation is invented as circumstance requires – or genius suggests – and there is often neither time nor occasion to standardise. Evidently every writer, in this situation, must accept the responsibility for making himself plain when he uses any symbol whose meaning is not absolutely prescribed by common usage. Equally evidently, mathematics encounters the common problems of language.

value of t at which dT/dt becomes negative, although we do not know how large it must be. If dT/dt is positive for small t and negative for large t, there is evidently some value of t which gives a maximum value of T. Finding this value must again wait until we have a little more technique, but we can at least confirm what common sense requires, that it is a maximum, not a minimum. Let us try putting $t=0$ in (28): we see that $T=0$. This shows that the quadratic function $T=f(t)$ goes through the origin. But we have already seen that T has positive values for at least some values of t close to zero, so it must rise to the right of $t=0$. As it declines at some large values of t, it must have a maximum somewhere in the positive quadrant.

6.5 The Multiplier and the Rate of Income Tax

In Chapter 4B, on the theory of income determination, we encountered some interesting problems that we could not then solve. One, which is obviously important to government policy, is to find the effect on the value of the multiplier of a change in the tax rate. Presumably every Chancellor would like to know the solution to this problem, as well as to know how a change in the tax rate affects the trade-off rate between government expenditure and the budget deficit. We can handle these problems with the technique we now have; and it is not easy to see how else they could be handled, save perhaps by the most involved geometrical devices. Let us start with the effect on the value of the multiplier of a change in the rate of income tax. From equation (12) of 4B.2, the multiplier in a closed economy with proportional income tax is

$$k = \frac{1}{1-c(1-t)}. \tag{31}$$

Our problem is solved by differentiating k with respect to t, but here the multiplier is a non-linear function of the tax rate, so simple inspection is not sufficient to discover the derivative. We require

$$\frac{dk}{dt} = \frac{d}{dt}\left(\frac{1}{1-c+ct}\right).$$

This may be evaluated by the useful substitution trick we have already used. We introduce a new variable, z, and put

$$z = 1-c+ct$$

so that

$$k = z^{-1}.$$

Now

$$\frac{dk}{dz} = -z^{-2} = \frac{-1}{(1-c+ct)^2}$$

and

$$\frac{dz}{dt} = c.$$

By the chain rule

$$\frac{dk}{dt} = \frac{dk}{dz} \cdot \frac{dz}{dt}$$

$$= \frac{-c}{(1-c+ct)^2}$$

which is what we want. It is perhaps more conveniently rewritten as

$$\frac{dk}{dt} = -ck^2. \tag{32}$$

The rate of change of the multiplier with respect to tax rate is negative, and depends on the square of the multiplier itself times the marginal propensity to consume – a result we are hardly likely to have discovered by verbal or intuitive methods! Notice, incidentally, that in (32) we actually have a second derivative, since k itself is the first derivative of income with respect to autonomous expenditure. If we let A stand for all autonomous expenditure, then

$$k = \frac{dY}{dA} \quad \text{and} \quad \frac{dk}{dt} = \frac{d}{dt}\left(\frac{dY}{dA}\right).$$

This illustrates the fact, to which we shall return in Chapter 9, that if there is more than one variable in a function, we may evaluate its derivative first with respect to one variable, holding the other constant, and then with respect to a second variable, holding the first constant. Evidently this presents no difficulty: we have just done it, and we shall do it again. (This is a good moment to do Exercise 8.)

6.6 Deficits and the Level of Income Tax

Armed with the result in (32), we can tackle the next question arising from 4B.2. We saw there that an increase in government spending led to a less-than-equal increase in the deficit because of the tax yield on the increased income. The question is: would the ratio $\Delta D/\Delta G$ be larger or smaller if the tax rate were higher? The higher the tax rate, the smaller the multiplier, as we have just seen, and the smaller the multiplier the less the increase in taxable income following upon the injection, ΔG. On the other hand, the higher the tax rate the greater the yield from whatever increase in income does take place. So the question is, can we determine, with qualitative information only, which of these two forces proves the stronger?

The relevant equation is (14) from 4B.2:

$$\Delta D = \Delta G(1 - tk). \tag{33}$$

We want to discover, if we can, the sign of

$$\frac{d}{dt}\Delta D = \frac{d}{dt}[\Delta G(1 - tk)]. \tag{34}$$

For this exercise, ΔG is to be regarded as a constant which may perfectly well be taken to be unity: we are interested in the effect on ΔD, per unit ΔG, of changing t. So all we really need is

$$\frac{d}{dt}(1 - tk).$$

To evaluate this, we require the product rule:

$$\frac{d}{dt}(1 - tk) = -\left(t\frac{dk}{dt} + k\frac{dt}{dt}\right).$$

But dt/dt is obviously unity, and we have just found dk/dt in (32), hence

$$\frac{d}{dt}\Delta D = -(-ctk^2 + k)$$
$$= k(ctk - 1). \tag{35}$$

Now, ctk is obviously positive; but is it greater than unity? In 4B.2, equation (15), we showed that $1 - tk > 0$, i.e., that $tk < 1$. Since $0 < c < 1$ by assumption, it follows that $ctk < 1$, so (35) is negative: increasing the tax rate reduces the increase in deficit per unit ΔG, i.e., the greater tax yield per unit increase in income offsets the effect of a smaller multiplier. This is another qualitative prediction which we could hardly have discovered by other means.

6.7 Income Tax and the Income-Deficit Trade-Off

It is now easy to answer a question we raised in 4B.3 and could not answer there: how is the frontier relating changes in the deficit to changes in income shifted by a change in the tax rate? Since we are working in increments, it must still go through the origin: only its slope can be affected.

The origin itself, however, now corresponds to different values of Y and D as we shift t. This sounds like a formidable complication, but actually will cause us little trouble. The reason for the shift is that a changed tax rate alters the value of the multiplier, and therefore alters the equilibrium level of income for any given autonomous expenditure. Hence if we assume constant autonomous expenditure, the origin in our incremental diagram, which corresponds to the initial equilibrium or *status quo ante*, is shifted. The $\Delta Y : \Delta D$ frontier, however, goes through the origin by definition, whatever initial equilibrium values may be, and its slope is a function of c and t only, so the effect on its slope of changing t can be considered independently of the effect on the initial equilibrium of changing t. We recall that its slope was given by equation (16) in 4B.3:

$$\frac{\Delta Y}{\Delta D} = \frac{k}{1-tk}. \tag{36}$$

Its rate of change with respect to the tax rate must be

$$\frac{\mathrm{d}\,(\Delta Y/\Delta D)}{\mathrm{d}t} = \frac{\mathrm{d}}{\mathrm{d}t}\left(\frac{k}{1-tk}\right). \tag{37}$$

Notice here that we are asking for the derivative of an incremental ratio. This need not trouble us, since we have learned that we may always look for the derivative of a function, $\mathrm{d}f(x)/\mathrm{d}x$, without having to write '$y =$' first; and it follows that we may look for the derivative without worrying about what y may or may not symbolise. In (36), we see a function which happens to measure a particular slope, and if we take the derivative of that function with respect to t, then we know how that slope is altered by changing t. This once again illustrates the power of abstract symbolic methods.

Evidently what we want is the sign of (37), and it is not clear what this is going to be. We already know from (35) that increasing the tax rate reduces the deficit-generating effect of increased government expenditure; but we also know from (32) that increasing the tax rate also reduces the income-generating effect of increased government expenditure. What it does to $\Delta Y/\Delta D$ therefore depends on which effect is stronger, and there appears to be nothing for it but to evaluate (37) and look for its sign. Applying the quotient rule to (37), we get

$$\frac{\mathrm{d}}{\mathrm{d}t}\left(\frac{k}{1-tk}\right) = \frac{(1-tk)\dfrac{\mathrm{d}k}{\mathrm{d}t} - k\dfrac{\mathrm{d}}{\mathrm{d}t}(1-tk)}{(1-tk)^2}.$$

From equations (32) and (35), we have dk/dt and $d(1-tk)/dt$, and can substitute in, whence

$$\frac{d}{dt}\left(\frac{k}{1-tk}\right) = \frac{-(1-tk)ck^2 - k^2(ctk-1)}{(1-tk)^2}.$$

This looks rather unpromising, but in fact simplifies reasonably. Multiplying out the bracketed terms in the numerator,

$$\frac{d}{dt}\left(\frac{k}{1-tk}\right) = \frac{-ck^2 + ctk^3 - ctk^3 + k^2}{(1-tk)^2}$$

and cancelling ctk^3

$$\frac{d}{dt}\left(\frac{\Delta Y}{\Delta D}\right) = \frac{k^2(1-c)}{(1-tk)^2}. \tag{38}$$

(38) requires interpretation, which is not difficult. Since the squared terms must be positive, and $0 < c < 1$, the whole expression is positive, and this is all we wanted to know: the slope of the frontier connecting ΔY and ΔD is increased by an increase in the tax rate. This means that an increase in the deficit is accompanied by a larger increase in income. Thus we see that the reduction in the income-generating effect of government spending must be less than the reduction in the deficit-generating effect, so that a bigger increase in income goes with a given increase in the deficit. A bigger increase in *expenditure* is, of course, required to produce a given increase in income *or* deficit than formerly.

This is another example of a general qualitative result: we did not require numerical values for the parameters to obtain the sign of (38), but only our familiar conditions that $0 < c < 1$ and $0 < t < 1$. We do, however, find one rather anomalous implication of this result. From the point of view of the individual who dislikes deficits, the increased tax rate is a 'good thing': desired income levels can be reached with smaller deficits. Nonetheless, since the increased tax rate reduces the value of k, increased income requires larger injections of government spending than at lower tax rates. Thus the increased tax rate appears, not surprisingly, a 'good thing' to the man who wants a higher proportion of society's output devoted to the collective supply of goods and services: it now requires more government expenditure to secure full employment, which means that, from his point of view, the frontier has moved in a favourable direction. This appears curious: we normally think of the 'deficit-hater' as a man who is opposed to government expenditure anyhow, but more so if it is not fully covered by tax yield, and the 'Galbraith Man', who is in favour of government spending, as being pretty well indifferent to how it is financed. How, then, can we have moved a frontier in such a way as to please both parties?

The explanation is that to lump together deficits and expenditure as 'much the same' from the point of view of people's attitudes is a fallacy: so long as the ratio $\Delta D/\Delta G$ is constant, it does not matter which we concern ourselves with; but as soon as we consider parameter shifts which alter that ratio, it does. Lumping them together is an admissible simplification as long as they move in fixed proportions (are, that is, strictly complementary), but it will not do when we vary their proportions. Thus by investigating the properties of the frontier, we have learned something about political attitudes: if we are to make rational choices among the possibilities open to society, we must determine separately our views about the desirable fraction of GNP that should be managed by the government, and about the desirable ways of financing it.

6.8   Income Taxes and the Income-Payments Trade-Off

Application of our new techniques to the open economy is now fairly routine, involving no new analytical problems, but it is a useful exercise, and may increase our understanding of some important policy problems. For an open economy with given marginal propensities to consume and to import, and a given marginal rate of tax, we have, from 4B.4, equation (20),

$$k = \frac{1}{1-(1-t)(c-m)}. \tag{39}$$

To find the rate of change of the multiplier with respect to tax rate, we employ the substitution trick again, and let

$$z = 1-c+ct+m-mt$$

(multiplying out the bracketed terms in the denominator of (39)). Clearly

$$k = z^{-1}$$

and

$$\frac{\mathrm{d}k}{\mathrm{d}z} = -z^{-2}$$

while

$$\frac{\mathrm{d}z}{\mathrm{d}t} = c-m.$$

Hence

$$\frac{\mathrm{d}k}{\mathrm{d}t} = \frac{\mathrm{d}k}{\mathrm{d}z}\cdot\frac{\mathrm{d}z}{\mathrm{d}t}$$

$$= -z^{-2}(c-m)$$

$$= -(c-m)k^2. \tag{40}$$

This is negative because consumption of imported goods cannot exceed total consumption, i.e., $c > m$, and it is of the same form as (32), merely adjusted to take account of the fact that induced expenditure on home produced goods and services is given by $(c - m)$ in the open economy in place of c alone in the closed economy.

The trade-off rate between increased income and balance-of-payments deficit was given by 4B.4, equation (22):

$$\frac{\Delta Y}{\Delta B} = \frac{1}{m(1-t)}. \tag{41}$$

Again, we can easily find the derivative of this with respect to tax rate by putting

$$z = m - mt,$$

whence

$$\frac{dz}{dt} = -m$$

and

$$\frac{d}{dt}\left(\frac{\Delta Y}{\Delta B}\right) = mz^{-2}$$

$$= \frac{m}{(m-mt)^2}$$

$$= \frac{1}{m(1-t)^2} \tag{42}$$

which is positive: a higher tax rate allows a larger increase in income for a given increase in balance-of-payments deficit (although, from (40), it requires more government expenditure to generate the increased income). It may not be immediately obvious why this should be: the same proportion of disposable income, m, is devoted to imports, whatever the level of income, so why should an increased tax rate improve the income-deficit trade-off? The answer is simply that, with increased taxes, less of any income *is* disposable – more goes in taxes, which are not spent on imports.

We have already seen that the slope of the frontier between increments in income and increments in the balance-of-payments deficit is positive. We might well conclude that contemporary British governments are well aware of this: when they judge an improvement in the balance of payments to be imperative, and a devaluation to be unthinkable, they depress effective demand. The question naturally arises, can we apply the result of (42) to the contemporary British policy problem? The answer depends on whether the assumptions of the model are reasonably well satisfied. We assumed unemployment, constant prices, and all investment autonomous. Thus the model may fit fairly well in times of recession, but it would be unwise to apply its conclusions in times of high employment and inflation.

We should also remember that, in the real world, capital goods may be imported, and governments may import too (if only by maintaining armies in foreign countries). We shall show briefly how the model may be extended to accommodate imports by investors and government, and leave the complete analysis to an exercise.

For simplicity, assume proportionality. Thus let imported investment goods, M_i, be a constant proportion, i, of investment, and government imports, M_g, be a constant proportion, g, of government expenditure. Letting imported consumption goods, $M_c = m(1-t)Y$, as before, we have

$$M = M_i + M_g + M_c$$
$$= I + gG + m(1-t)Y. \tag{43}$$

Substituting into

$$Y = C + I + G + X - M$$

we have

$$Y = cY(1-t) + I + G + X - mY(1-t) - iI - gG. \tag{44}$$

Collecting the Y terms and factoring, as usual,

$$Y[1 - c(1-t) + m(1-t)] = I(1-i) + G(1-g) + X$$

whence

$$Y = \frac{1}{1-(1-t)(c-m)}[I(1-i) + G(1-g) + X]. \tag{45}$$

From (45) we see that our new assumptions affect the *multiplicand*, not the multiplier. But this will affect the trade-off rates between total government spending (on home and foreign goods) and income, and between income and the balance of payments. Does it change the effect of increased taxes on the trade-off rates? You are invited to find out for yourself in Exercise 10. Notice, by the way, that we might perfectly well have assumed import-content in exports while we were about it. This would have introduced no change in form. If the proportion of imported raw materials in exports is a constant, r, then in place of X in (45) we should simply have had $X(1-r)$, which is not a serious complication: again, it merely alters the multiplicand. This prompts a concluding remark about multiplier analysis. It is based on the assumption that we can make a clear distinction between autonomous expenditure, independent of current income levels, and induced expenditure, which is a function of current income levels. Autonomous expenditure always appears in the multiplicand, adjusted if necessary, as we have just seen, to make sure that we only multiply that part which is an injection to the home economy. The multiplier itself, of course, simply depends on the rate of flow of induced expenditure, and is therefore a function, as we have seen, of the parameters of the expenditure functions. Thus we may conclude that, when faced with a problem in multiplier analysis, the first question to ask is 'does this affect the multiplier or the multiplicand?' A second question is a serious empirical one which we cannot take up here: for what time periods can what items properly be treated as autonomous? If we cannot answer that, we cannot apply multiplier analysis.

Exercises

1 Total cost is given by

$$C = 5000 + 1000q - 500q^2 + \tfrac{2}{3}q^3.$$

(a) Find marginal cost.
(b) Find the expression for the slope of the marginal cost curve.
(c) Find the average total cost function.
(d) At what value of q does marginal cost equal average *variable* cost?

2 Total cost[1] for a firm in the short run is found by an econometrician to be

$$C = 77.0 + 1.32q - 0.0002q^2.$$

(a) Is it possible that this firm is selling in a perfectly competitive market?
(b) Is this cost function consistent with the law of diminishing returns?
(Assume that factors are purchased in a perfectly competitive market.)

3 A monopolist's demand curve is given by

$$p = 100 - 2q.$$

(a) Find his marginal revenue.
(b) What is the relationship between the slopes of the average and marginal revenue curves?
(c) At what price is marginal revenue zero?

4 A demand curve is given by

$$p = aq^\beta.$$

(a) Find marginal revenue.
(b) Find the elasticity of demand.
(c) Draw a graph of average and marginal revenue, and interpret your results. What restrictions will you put on the value of β?

5 Output, with fixed equipment, is given by

$$q = al^3 + bl^2 + cl + d.$$

[1] Adapted from J.Johnston, *Statistical Cost Analysis*, McGraw-Hill, N.Y., 1960, p. 65.

(a) Find marginal product.

(b) Find average product.

6* If demand and output are given by

$$p = a + bq$$

and

$$q = cl + dl^2$$

show that marginal revenue product is given by

$$\frac{dR}{dl} = ac + 2(ad + bc^2)l + 6bcdl^2 + 4bd^2l^3.$$

(*Hint:* See equation (18).)

7 Output, with fixed equipment, is given by

$$q = 101 + 0 \cdot 1l^2 - 0 \cdot 0005l^3$$

and the wage per man-day is constant at 10.

(a) Find marginal cost at $l = 100$.

 *(b) At what level of output does marginal cost start to rise? (*Hint:* Find the slope of dq/dl.)

8 Evaluate dk/dt where $k = 1/[1 - c(1 - t)]$ for $c = \frac{3}{4}$ and $t = \frac{1}{5}$.

9 Using the numerical values of Exercise 5, Chapter 4.B, find (using fractions rather than decimals)

(a) $\dfrac{dk}{dt}$.

(b) $\dfrac{d}{dt}\left(\dfrac{\Delta Y}{\Delta D}\right)$.

(c) $\dfrac{d}{dt}\left(\dfrac{\Delta Y}{\Delta B}\right)$.

10 On the assumption that there is import-content in investment and government expenditure, find

(a) $\Delta Y/\Delta B$. (*Hint:* Start by finding $\Delta M/\Delta G$. This is the sum of the direct effect, given by g, and the indirect effect due to importing out of increased income, $m(1 - t)\,\Delta Y$. Hence

$$\frac{\Delta M}{\Delta G} = g + m(1 - t)\frac{\Delta Y}{\Delta G}$$

and $\Delta Y/\Delta G$ can be obtained from equation (45). Do not forget to adjust the multiplicand for import content.)

 *(b) the sign of

$$\frac{d}{dt}\left(\frac{\Delta Y}{\Delta B}\right).$$

CHAPTER 7

MAXIMA AND MINIMA[1]

7.1 Introduction

It is very commonly assumed that decision-taking units, whether firms, households, or governments, seek to maximise something or other, 'utility', or 'profit', or 'social welfare'. Hence an acquaintance with the mathematics of maximising is peculiarly useful to the student of economics, and enables him to tackle a large number of problems, and read a large amount of literature, that would otherwise be inaccessible.

We shall continue to confine ourselves to *functions of a single variable*, but we may nonetheless consider a number of interesting applications in Chapter 8, where we shall be able to analyse far more thoroughly than hitherto the implications of profit maximisation. Many important questions require us to deal with functions of more than one variable. We are interested, for example, in the behaviour of consumers choosing among many goods, or in the policy-makers' decision when faced with the sort of frontier we encountered in Chapter 4B. We shall accordingly take up functions of two or more variables in Chapter 9, and substantially extend the range of problems that we can handle. The technique introduced in this chapter, however, is very powerful, and enables us to derive the implications of many important hypotheses.

In the first paragraph we referred to firms, households, and governments as 'decision-taking units'. The notion of a 'decision-taker' is a very useful one. We may refer to any economic unit, faced with a problem of choice, as a *decision-taker*; and, as we are interested in the behaviour of economic units, we shall formulate hypotheses about their decisions. The familiar hypothesis, or class of hypotheses, is that decision-takers maximise 'something'; and this has led to a good deal of misunderstanding. It is sometimes said in defence of one or other of the maximisation hypotheses that the

---

[1] This chapter is very close to Chapter VIII of R. G. D. Allen, *Mathematical Analysis for Economists*, which is well worth reading at this stage as a rather more rigorous supplement to this chapter.

maximisation of the 'something' is 'rational'. The hypothesis of profit-maximisation is sometimes defended by such arguments as 'Why else would a man be in business?' or 'The object of business is to make money: it would be absurd not to maximise profits'. This sort of attempt to settle *a priori* what is a matter of fact invites the reply that economists still predicate a creature called 'economic man', who never existed and never will, merely because it makes the mathematics convenient! Even worse, it provokes – or provides an excuse for – the sceptic to retreat into descriptive institutionalism. The whole argument is completely wrong-headed. 'Rationality' is to be understood as the consistent choice of action calculated to achieve what is desired, given the possibilities. The decision to maximise one thing rather than another depends on what is desired, and that is neither rational nor irrational, but depends on the tastes and beliefs of the decision-takers.

The question of rationality or irrationality is therefore a question of the appropriateness of the means, given the ends, and neither requires nor implies any judgement about the ends. Thus if an entrepreneur decides that he desires some combination of profit and leisure, rather than profit only, with leisure ignored, it is our business to see what follows if he acts rationally, given these ends. Certainly the assumption that something is maximised makes the mathematics convenient, but any consistently purposeful action can be seen as maximising *something*: the question is *what*. We might say that it is the business of the creative theoretician to suggest the hypothesis that the behaviour of some decision-taker, or class of decision-takers, will be found comprehensible and predictable if it is assumed that they endeavour to maximise some particular function; that it is the business of the analyst (probably the same person) to work out just what behaviour is predicted by the hypothesis in question; and that it is the business of the empirical worker, or econometrician, to find out just how well the predictions do fit the facts. Whether or not a particular hypothesis, such as profit maximisation, should be accepted, at least provisionally, depends, of course, on the correspondence we find between prediction and observation, rather than on any *a priori* argument about rationality or the objects of modern corporations. Before we can test, however, we must derive the predictions of the theory, and to do this we must develop the necessary mathematical technique. Thus we are in no way committed to the notion that it is peculiarly 'rational' to maximise profit instead of power, or holiday-time, or some combination of all three. We do, however, recognise the possibility that the profit motive is so strong that a hypothesis that ignores other goals will, nonetheless, prove to fit the facts pretty well; and if we want to explore such a possibility, then we must be equipped to work out the implications of the hypothesis.

7.2   Necessary and Sufficient Conditions

In many of the examples of the last chapter we came very close to looking
for a maximum value to some function or other when we asked if its rate of
change with respect to some parameter or variable in which we were interested was positive or negative. If the rate of change is always one or the
other, the dependent variable is said to be a monotonic increasing, or decreasing, function of the independent variable, as the case may be. But we
may encounter cases in which it is first increasing and then decreasing, as
we did in 6.4. It will be recalled that the case we had there was a competitive market with linear supply and demand curves. We expressed tax yield

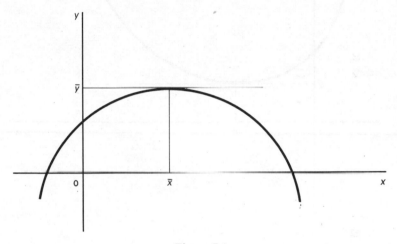

Figure 7.1

(tax rate times quantity sold) as a function of tax rate, and found it to be a
quadratic, so that the yield was an increasing function of the rate for some
values of the rate, and a decreasing function for other, higher, values. Intuition suggests that if a function first increases and then decreases, there must
be a point at which it has a maximum value. (Indeed, in Chapter 3, we saw
that a ∩-shaped quadratic has a maximum at a value of x half-way between
its two intercepts with the x-axis.) We express this a little more formally:
if $y = f(x)$, and y increases as x increases to some value[1] $\bar{x}$, and decreases
thereafter, then y has a maximum value at $x = \bar{x}$. This is illustrated in
Figure 7.1, where y has the maximum value $\bar{y}$ at $x = \bar{x}$.

---

[1] We have previously used the bar to denote either the equilibrium value of a variable or
some constant value, and we discussed the possibility of ambiguity in notation in footnote 1,
p. 138. In this chapter the bar is used exclusively to denote the value of x at which either the
maximum or some other stated value of $f(x)$ occurs.

Now consider the tangent slope or derivative, dy/dx. So long as this is positive, y increases with x; where it is negative, y decreases with x; and where $dy/dx = 0$, y can neither increase nor decrease for (small) changes in x. This is the crucial notion: the derivative must be zero at $x = \bar{x}$, and we have found a *necessary condition* for a maximum. The derivative, of course, measures the tangent slope to the function, and it is clear in Figure 7.1 that a tangent to the curve has a positive slope for all $x < \bar{x}$, a negative slope for all $x > \bar{x}$, and is horizontal – has zero slope – at the maximum value at $\bar{x}$.

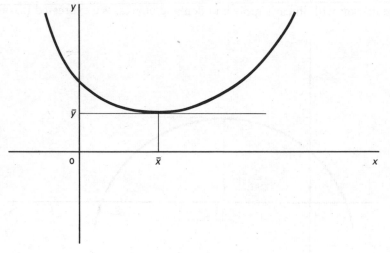

Figure 7.2

We have already got the basic idea of a maximum, which indeed follows very naturally from what we have already done with derivatives. Now consider Figure 7.2, where the function $y = f(x)$ has a *minimum* value at $x = \bar{x}$. Evidently the tangent slope to the function is zero at $x = \bar{x}$. Thus the condition that the first derivative of the function be zero is not *sufficient* to distinguish a maximum from a minimum: it only tells us that we have what is called a *stationary value*. A stationary value is a new idea, and requires a definition, and some thought. If $y = f(x)$, and y neither increases nor decreases for small changes in x in the neighbourhood of $\bar{x}$, then y has a *stationary value* at $x = \bar{x}$. In terms of a graph, this simply means that $f(x)$ is horizontal at $x = \bar{x}$, where the first derivative $f'(x)$ is zero, and this is true both if $\bar{x}$ gives a maximum value of y and if it gives a minimum. We may illustrate this by looking for the maximum or minimum of a quadratic,

$$y = ax^2 + bx + c. \tag{1}$$

The first derivative is

$$\frac{dy}{dx} = 2ax + b. \tag{2}$$

We find a stationary value by finding a value of x at which the tangent slope is zero; that is, a stationary value occurs at that value of x at which

$$\frac{dy}{dx} = 2ax + b = 0 \tag{3}$$

or

$$x = \frac{-b}{2a}.$$

This gives the value of x at which a quadratic has a stationary value, and, we saw in Chapter 3, a quadratic has only one stationary value; but is it a maximum or a minimum?

What we now want is a means of distinguishing between a maximum and a minimum once we have found a stationary value. If we have plotted the graph of the function it will, of course, be perfectly obvious which is which. As usual, we prefer an algebraic method which saves us from plotting graphs and allows us to obtain accurate numerical results when required without depending on the sharpness of a pencil lead. Inspection of Figures 7.1 and 7.2 provides the necessary clue. Consider the tangent slope to $f(x)$ in Figure 7.2. At values of x less than $\bar{x}$, where the minimum occurs, the tangent slope is negative; and at values of x greater than $\bar{x}$ it is positive. As x approaches $\bar{x}$, the tangent slope becomes flatter, or 'less negative'; as x increases beyond $\bar{x}$, the tangent slope becomes steeper or 'more positive'. Compare this with the behaviour of the tangent slope in Figure 7.1, where we have a maximum. For $x < \bar{x}$, the tangent slope is positive but decreasing as x approaches $\bar{x}$; for $x > \bar{x}$, the tangent slope is negative, and increasingly negative as x increases beyond $\bar{x}$. Thus we have:

(i) in the case of a *minimum*, the tangent slope is increasing as x increases in the neighbourhood of $x = \bar{x}$; and

(ii) in the case of a *maximum*, the tangent slope is decreasing as x increases in the neighbourhood of $x = \bar{x}$.

All we have to do now is to express this distinction in terms of derivatives. The tangent slope, dy/dx, is itself a function of x. Its direction of change as x varies depends upon its derivative with respect to x: if its derivative is positive, then the tangent slope is increasing, and we have a minimum, whereas if its derivative is negative, the tangent slope is decreasing and we have a maximum. Since the tangent slope, however, is

$$\frac{dy}{dx} = f'(x)$$

its derivative is

$$\frac{d}{dx}\left(\frac{dy}{dx}\right) = f''(x). \tag{4}$$

Thus we may distinguish between a maximum and a minimum value of the function $f(x)$ by looking at the *direction of change* of the first derivative, which is most easily accomplished by looking at the *sign of the second derivative* of $f(x)$. We may correspondingly state our conditions:

(i) if, where $f(x)$ has a stationary value $[f'(x)=0]$, $f''(x)>0$, the stationary value is a *minimum*, whereas

(ii) if $f''(x)<0$, the stationary value is a *maximum*.

We remarked above that the condition $f'(x)=0$ was a *necessary* condition for a maximum. Since, however, it only identifies a stationary value, it cannot be *sufficient*. The two conditions, $f'(x)=0$ and $f''(x)\gtrless0$, as the case may be, are *necessary and sufficient* to establish maxima or minima.

Since we have necessary and sufficient conditions, we are now able to locate maxima or minima for ourselves. We may try a few illustrative examples. First, let us return to the general quadratic,

$$y = ax^2+bx+c$$

whose first derivative is $2ax+b$. The second derivative is

$$\frac{d^2y}{dx^2} = 2a. \tag{5}$$

Hence if a is positive, the quadratic has a minimum, i.e., is concave from above, whereas if a is negative the quadratic has a maximum, is convex from above. This is confirmed by inspection of the quadratic: x^2 is the 'most powerful' term, and is always positive, so whether the function eventually increases or decreases must depend on the sign of the coefficient, a. If a is positive, then for large enough absolute values of x the function must be increasing, hence it must have a minimum at smaller x; and if a is negative the function must decrease for large enough x, and correspondingly must have a maximum at a smaller x. (This is a good moment to do Exercise 1.)

A numerical example will help to illustrate these ideas. Consider the quadratic

$$y = 10x^2-5x+1. \tag{6}$$

The first derivative is given by

$$\frac{dy}{dx} = 20x-5. \tag{7}$$

We find the value of x that satisfies

$$\frac{\mathrm{d}y}{\mathrm{d}x} = 0 \tag{8}$$

i.e., if $20x - 5 = 0$, it is necessary that

$$x = \tfrac{5}{20} = \tfrac{1}{4}.$$

From inspection, it is clear that this is a minimum value – the coefficient of x^2 is positive; but let us follow up our analysis by taking the second derivative:

$$\frac{\mathrm{d}^2 y}{\mathrm{d}x^2} = 20. \tag{9}$$

This is positive, and indeed is positive for *any* x. Recall, however, the general quadratic $y = ax^2 + bx + c$, whose second derivative is $2a$: this has the sign of a whatever the value of x. This simply means that the tangent slope of a quadratic always changes in one direction: the quadratic is either one 'way up' or the other, and has either a maximum or a minimum, but not one of each. In this numerical example, of course, the coefficient a is 10, and naturally $2a = 20$, positive: $x = \tfrac{1}{4}$ gives the minimum value of the function. (This is a good moment to do Exercise 2.)

7.3 Points of Inflexion

Now we know that, to find maxima or minima, we look at the first two derivatives, and
  (i) if $f'(x) = 0$ at $x = \bar{x}$ we have a stationary value at $\bar{x}$;
  (ii) if $f''(x) > 0$ at $x = \bar{x}$ the stationary value is a minimum; and
      if $f''(x) < 0$ at $x = \bar{x}$ the stationary value is a maximum.
There is, however, an awkward possibility we have overlooked: what happens if, where $f'(x) = 0$, $f''(x) = 0$ too? We have a stationary value, but we have not satisfied the conditions for either a maximum or a minimum. Maxima and minima are known collectively as *extreme values*, or *extrema*. What we have discovered is that there may be *stationary values that are not extrema*. Let us investigate such values. We have:
  (i) $f'(x) = 0$ at $x = \bar{x}$: $f(x)$ has a constant value in the neighbourhood of $\bar{x}$;
  (ii) $f''(x) = 0$ at $x = \bar{x}$: the tangent slope $f'(x)$ also has a constant value in the neighbourhood of $\bar{x}$.
  Now the tangent slope is neither decreasing nor increasing as x goes through the value $\bar{x}$, so that, although the function is stationary, it has not

6

got an extreme value. All that is left is a 'wriggle', illustrated in Figure 7.3, where the function is horizontal in the neighbourhood of $\bar{x}$. Such a 'wriggle' is known as a *point of inflexion*. The function is stationary at $x = \bar{x}$, where its tangent slope is zero, but is positively sloped on both sides of $\bar{x}$, which is to say that y is an increasing function of x both for values of $x < \bar{x}$ and for values of $x > \bar{x}$. (You should be able to illustrate for yourself the case of an inflexional point such that $f'(x)$ is negative on both sides of $\bar{x}$.)

We have already seen that the second derivative of a quadratic is every-

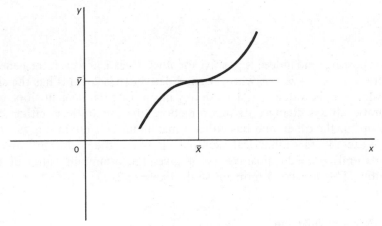

Figure 7.3

where positive or everywhere negative. It follows that a quadratic cannot have a point of inflexion. To illustrate an inflexional point we must there-fore choose from some other class of functions; and the simplest example of a point of inflexion of this sort is afforded by a cubic. Let

$$y = x^3 + 3x^2 + 3x, \tag{10}$$

whence

$$\frac{dy}{dx} = 3x^2 + 6x + 3 \tag{11}$$

and

$$\frac{d^2y}{dx^2} = 6x + 6. \tag{12}$$

We seek a value of x, if there is one, such that both derivatives are zero. The second is obviously zero if $x = -1$. Also, dividing (11) by 3, and setting it equal to zero, we obtain

$$x^2 + 2x + 1 = 0$$

which is satisfied by $x=-1$ and by no other value of x. Hence y has a stationary value which is not an extreme value at $x=-1$ (where $y=-1$), and has no other stationary values. (It is a good idea to plot the function for a few values of x, and see how it behaves.)

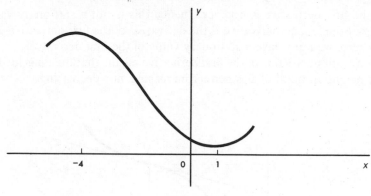

Figure 7.4

Of course, not all cubics behave like this. Let us find the stationary values of

$$y = \tfrac{1}{3}x^3 + \tfrac{3}{2}x^2 - 4x + 10. \tag{13}$$

Set the first derivative equal to zero:

$$\frac{dy}{dx} = x^2 + 3x - 4 = 0, \tag{14}$$

which factors into

$$(x+4)(x-1) = 0, \tag{15}$$

so stationary values occur at $x=-4$ and $x=1$. To discover what sort of stationary values they are, we look at the second derivative,

$$\frac{d^2y}{dx^2} = 2x+3 = \begin{cases} -5 & \text{if } x = -4 \\ 5 & \text{if } x = 1. \end{cases} \tag{16}$$

Thus we have a maximum at $x=-4$, and a minimum at $x=1$, and no stationary value which is not an extreme value. This function is sketched in Figure 7.4, but it is a good idea to plot a few values for yourself, and satisfy yourself that you understand how it behaves.

7.4   Non-Stationary Points of Inflexion

We discovered points of inflexion by asking what happened at a point at which the second derivative as well as the first was zero. There remains yet another possible case: what happens if the second derivative is zero while the first is not? We may sort this out as follows:

(i) the first derivative is non-zero, hence this is not a stationary value;

(ii) but the second derivative is the derivative of the first derivative, and, if it is zero, we must have a stationary value of the first derivative;

(iii) a stationary value of the first derivative means that the tangent slope in the neighbourhood of $\bar{x}$ is neither increasing nor decreasing.

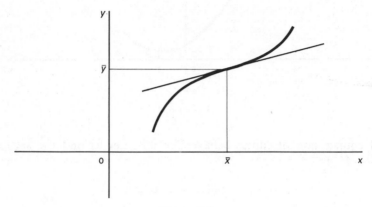

Figure 7.5

Figure 7.5 illustrates a point with these properties. The function $f(x)$ is convex from above up to $x=\bar{x}$, and concave from above thereafter. The tangent slope decreases up to $x=\bar{x}$, and increases thereafter: it has a minimum at $x=\bar{x}$, where the tangent is drawn in Figure 7.5. Inspection of the figure shows that the function 'crosses its tangent' at $x=\bar{x}$, and such a point is called *a non-stationary point of inflexion*. Comparison of Figures 7.1, 7.2, 7.3, 7.4, and 7.5 reveals that at inflexional points the function changes from convex to concave or vice-versa, whether they are stationary values or not, whereas at extreme points there is no change of curvature of this nature. An example of a function with a non-stationary point of inflexion is afforded by

$$y = \tfrac{1}{3}x^3 + \tfrac{1}{2}x^2 + x + 10. \tag{17}$$

Evaluating the derivatives,

$$\frac{dy}{dx} = x^2 + x + 1, \tag{18}$$

and

$$\frac{d^2y}{dx^2} = 2x+1. \tag{19}$$

Setting the second equal to zero, we obtain $x=-\frac{1}{2}$. At this value of x

$$\frac{dy}{dx} = \frac{1}{4}-\frac{1}{2}+1 = \frac{3}{4} > 0.$$

(This function is considered further in 7.6 below.)

We have already noticed that, at a point of inflexion, a function 'crosses its tangent', and that in Figure 7.5 the tangent slope itself has an extreme value (in this case, a minimum) at $x=\bar{x}$. The distinguishing feature of a non-stationary inflexional point is that the second derivative is zero at $x=\bar{x}$, and the tangent slope itself has a stationary value where its derivative is zero. If we wish to know whether a function is changing from convex to concave (from above) or vice-versa, we must find out whether the tangent slope has a minimum or a maximum value at the point of inflexion. This calls for inspection of the sign of its second derivative, which is the third derivative of the original function. The question would then arise: what if the third derivative were zero? Clearly the second derivative would have a stationary value, and we should have to go to the fourth to discover what sort. And so on. Obviously we have not yet got a complete treatment, but we have all we need for our purposes.

7.5 Some Awkward Cases

We may summarise the points that really concern us. An extreme value is stationary, but a stationary value is not necessarily extreme. At a stationary value, $f'(x)=0$. Thus $f'(x)$ is necessary but not sufficient for an extreme value. A sufficient condition for a stationary value to be a maximum is $f''(x)<0$, and for it to be a minimum is $f''(x)>0$. If $f'(x)=f''(x)=0$, the stationary value is a point of inflexion. If $f''(x)=0$, but $f'(x)\neq0$, we have a non-stationary inflexional point. If we wish to know 'which way round' the curvature of the function is changing, we require the sign of $f'''(x)$, etc. This may be set out in schematic form[1]:

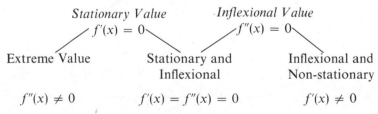

[1] Following R. G. D. Allen, *Mathematical Analysis for Economists, op. cit.*, p. 194.

Now consider the function illustrated in Figure 7.6A. It clearly has a 'peak' – some sort of maximum – at Q. What it has *not* got at Q is a unique first derivative. At Q, the function has a 'kink', and the consequence of this is that, although the function itself is continuous, in the sense that one can draw it without lifting pencil from paper, the first derivative is not continuous. We can see that this is so by considering the behaviour of the tangent to the function in the neighbourhood of Q. As x approaches $\bar{x}$, the slope of the tangent, which is positive, is increasing; as x increases beyond $\bar{x}$, the slope of the tangent, which is now negative, is again increasing; and there is *no unique tangent at $\bar{x}$*: the slope of the tangent 'jumps' between $x < \bar{x}$ and $x > \bar{x}$, and at $\bar{x}$ an infinite number of lines will serve as 'tangents'.

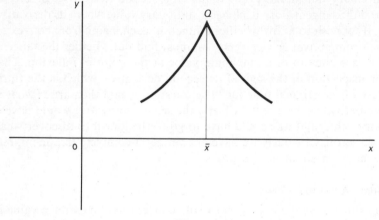

Figure 7.6A

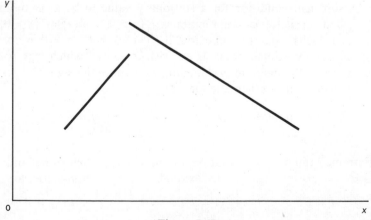

Figure 7.6B

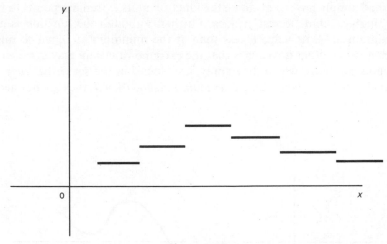

Figure 7.6C

This means that the first derivative 'jumps' discontinuously over $\bar{x}$, and is undefined at this value. Hence we should not be able to find Q by applying the methods considered here – there is no first derivative to set equal to zero at $\bar{x}$. This illustrates the fact that the methods of this chapter are to be applied only to functions that have continuous first and second derivatives. As further examples of functions to which the methods of this chapter do not apply, consider the discontinuous functions illustrated in Figures 7.6B and C. Both functions have 'gaps', and neither has continuous first, or second, derivatives. Both have constant first derivatives (all zero in the case of 6.C) along their 'branches' interrupted by 'jumps'.

Notice that the existence of derivatives, which we require for calculus methods to work, is a separate question from their value. If a derivative is zero, this does *not* mean that it does not exist. Thus consider a straight line, $y = ax + b$. Its first derivative obviously exists and so do its second and higher-order derivatives, but all save the first are everywhere zero: a straight line has no stationary values, no points of inflexion, and never changes in slope – which is to say that it is a straight line!

Finally, it should be borne in mind that a function may have several stationary values, which includes the possibility of two or more maxima, and/or two or more minima. Thus consider Figure 7.7, which has two maxima, at A and B, and two minima, at C and D. (It also has three points of inflexion. You should be able to find them, and say which sort each is.) Our non-graphical methods allow us to distinguish between the maxima, A and B, and the minima, C and D, but neither to say which of A or B is the greater, nor of C or D is the less. Hence if there are several extreme values, we shall simply have to evaluate the function at its extremum points to find the 'highest' and 'lowest' values. Further, although the function is at a maximum at A, its value is less than at the minimum at D, which might seem absurd. What it means is that the extreme values we may discover by calculus methods, where they apply, are 'local' in the sense that *they are greater – or less – than other values in the neighbourhood*: they are not neces-

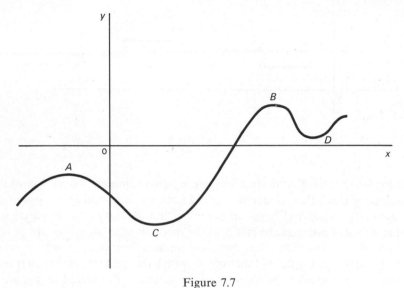

Figure 7.7

sarily the *global* maxima or minima, i.e., the 'highest' or 'lowest' values the functions take on anywhere.

7.6   Some Examples

We have said all we need to about the theory of extreme values, and are equipped to deal with an enormous variety of problems. The difficulty is that, while one may follow the argument step by step, there seems to be a bewilderingly large number of possible cases to remember. The solution is *not* to try to memorise them, but to work a few examples, referring back to the summary in the last section when necessary. After a little practice, you will find that you could reproduce the summary yourself, and that there is no need to tax the memory. This is a characteristic of a logical structure: once it is thoroughly understood, one can reconstruct it at any time for oneself without wasting any effort on 'memorisation'. This sort of familiarity and understanding will come with practice. We shall work some examples in this section, and then go on to economic applications in the next chapter.

(1) We seek an extreme value for

$$y = 10x^2 - 5x + 10 \tag{20}$$

and wish to know if it is a maximum or a minimum. Set the first derivative equal to zero:

$$20x - 5 = 0 \tag{21}$$

whence an extreme value occurs at $x = \frac{5}{20} = \frac{1}{4}$. The second derivative is

$$\frac{d^2y}{dx^2} = 20 \tag{22}$$

which is positive everywhere: $x = \frac{1}{4}$ is a minimum. This example illustrates two familiar points. First, the value of the tangent slope to a U-shaped function is everywhere increasing. Second, compare this example with that of 7.2 above, equation (6), $y = 10x^2 - 5x + 1$. Equations (6) and (20) differ only in the value of the constant term, which has the effect of shifting the function up or down vertically, thus changing the value of y at its extreme point, but not the value of x at which it occurs. This in fact follows from equation (3) in 7.2, where we found that, for the general quadratic, the extreme value occurs at $x = -b/2a$, which is independent of the intercept, c.

(2) Now let us try to find an extreme value for

$$y = 3x^2 \tag{23}$$

the simple power function ax^n with $a = 3$ and $n = 2$. We can look on this as a quadratic in which b and c are both zero. If we put the first derivative equal to zero, we have

$$6x = 0 \tag{24}$$

which can only be true where $x = 0$. The second derivative, 6, is positive, so this function has a minimum at the origin, which is what we should expect of a quadratic with zero intercept and the linear term suppressed.

(3) A little rearrangement is often all that is required to reduce a difficult-looking expression to a standard form that is easily dealt with. Thus consider

$$y = \frac{4 + x^2}{x}. \tag{25}$$

We separate the two terms, and express each in index form, obtaining

$$y = 4x^{-1} + x. \tag{26}$$

6*

Setting the first derivative equal to zero we have

$$\frac{dy}{dx} = -4x^{-2} + 1 = 0, \tag{27}$$

whence

$$x^{-2} = \tfrac{1}{4},$$

$$x^2 = 4, \tag{28}$$

and

$$x = \pm 2.$$

So we have two stationary values. Now

$$\frac{d^2y}{dx^2} = 8x^{-3}. \tag{29}$$

If $x = 2$, we have

$$\frac{d^2y}{dx^2} = \frac{8}{8} = 1 > 0, \tag{30.1}$$

a minimum, whereas if $x = -2$

$$\frac{d^2y}{dx^2} = \frac{8}{-8} = -1 < 0, \tag{30.2}$$

a maximum.

(4) Equation (17) of 7.4 was a cubic with a non-stationary point of inflexion. Let us now discover if it has extreme values as well. The function is

$$y = \tfrac{1}{3}x^3 + \tfrac{1}{2}x^2 + x + 10 \tag{31}$$

whence

$$\frac{dy}{dx} = x^2 + x + 1 \tag{32}$$

and

$$\frac{d^2y}{dx^2} = 2x + 1. \tag{33}$$

In 7.4, we were interested in the inflexional point at which $d^2y/dx^2 = 0$ but $dy/dx \neq 0$. To find out if the function has extreme values, we must solve the equation

$$\frac{dy}{dx} = x^2 + x + 1 = 0. \tag{34}$$

This does not factor, so we must use the quadratic formula

$$x = \frac{-B \pm \sqrt{B^2 - 4AC}}{2A}.$$

Substituting in,

$$x = \frac{-1 \pm \sqrt{1-4}}{2}$$

$$= \frac{-1 \pm \sqrt{-3}}{2}$$

$$= -\frac{1}{2} \pm \frac{\sqrt{3}}{2}\sqrt{-1}. \tag{35}$$

Here we have the mysterious 'square root of minus one', usually denoted by i. But its interpretation here causes no trouble at all. The result is that the equation $dy/dx=0$ only has 'imaginary roots' (roots involving i): it has no real roots. This means that there is no real value of x for which the function $y=\frac{1}{3}x^3+\frac{1}{2}x^2+x+10$ has a stationary value, and there is nothing mysterious about that! It has, as we have already seen, a non-stationary point of inflexion at $x=-\frac{1}{2}$.

(5) Let us now look at a cubic which does have extreme values. We take

$$y = 4x^3 - 6x^2 - 24x + 120. \tag{36}$$

Setting the first derivative equal to zero,

$$12x^2 - 12x - 24 = 0. \tag{37}$$

We can divide through by 12, to obtain

$$x^2 - x - 2 = 0$$

which factors into

$$(x-2)(x+1) = 0 \tag{38}$$

so there are extreme values at $x=2$ and $x=-1$. Taking the second derivative, we find

$$\frac{d^2y}{dx^2} = 24x - 12 = 12(2x-1). \tag{39}$$

Evidently we need only worry about the sign of $2x-1$, an expression which we could have obtained directly by taking the derivative of x^2-x-2. (39) is positive at $x=2$, and negative at $x=-1$, so we have a minimum and a maximum respectively. A little thought, or geometrical experiment, however, suggests that if a maximum point and a minimum point are to be 'connected up' by a continuous function, a point of inflexion in between is called for. It will have to be non-stationary to do the trick; and we have already found all the stationary values of this function anyhow. To find the required point of inflexion, put

$$\frac{d^2y}{dx^2} = 24x - 12 = 0 \tag{40}$$

which is satisfied by $x = \frac{1}{2}$, a value which lies between $x = -1$ and $x = 2$, as we expected. (You now have all the information required to sketch the function. You will necessarily discover, in the process of sketching, where it is convex from above and where concave. Notice that you can check curvature from the third derivative if you wish. Thus at $x = \frac{1}{2}$, the non-stationary point of inflexion, $d^3y/dx^3 = 24 > 0$.)

(6) Our examples so far are of 'polynomials': quadratics, cubics, and, if we like, quartics, quintics, and so on. Rather than going on with higher-order polynomials, introducing no new principles, let us just consider the general function

$$y = ax^n \tag{41}$$

with derivatives

$$\frac{dy}{dx} = anx^{n-1} \tag{42}$$

$$\frac{d^2y}{dx^2} = an(n-1)x^{n-2} \tag{43}$$

etc.

We can now distinguish four possible cases:

(i) n a positive integer, such as 1, 2, 3, ...
(ii) n a negative integer,
(iii) n a positive fraction,
(iv) n a negative fraction.

The first case is familiar. In example (2) above, we had $a = 3$, $n = 2$, and found a minimum at the origin. If n were 3, we should have

$$\frac{dy}{dx} = 3ax^2 = 0 \tag{44}$$

and again a stationary value at the origin: whether it was a maximum or a minimum would depend on the sign of a. The cases $n = 4$, $n = 5$, etc., are analogous.

Case (ii), however, is a little difficult. Let $n = -2$, and we have

$$y = \frac{a}{x^2}, \tag{45}$$

$$\frac{dy}{dx} = \frac{-2a}{x^3}, \tag{46}$$

and
$$\frac{d^2y}{dx^2} = \frac{6a}{x^4}. \tag{47}$$

If we try to set (46) equal to zero, we cannot solve it: putting $x=0$ leaves both (46) and (47) undefined. From (47), however, we see that the second derivative has everywhere the same sign, given by the sign of a as usual. This seems a little mysterious, but the mystery is easily resolved by plotting a few values. For an example, take $a=1$, and $x = \pm 1, \pm 2, \pm 3, \pm 4$. We get

$$x = \quad -4 \quad -3 \quad -2 \quad -1 \qquad +1 \quad +2 \quad +3 \quad +4$$
$$y = \quad \tfrac{1}{16} \quad \tfrac{1}{9} \quad \tfrac{1}{4} \quad 1 \qquad\quad 1 \quad \tfrac{1}{4} \quad \tfrac{1}{9} \quad \tfrac{1}{16}.$$

Thus the function has two branches, which are illustrated in Figure 7.8A. The tangent slope is everywhere increasing as x increases to zero, and everywhere decreasing as x increases above zero, as may be seen from (46), but there is no defined maximum, and the derivatives are undefined at $x=0$. We should find the same thing true for all negative integers in ax^n.

Case (iii) also requires some thought. Suppose that $n = \tfrac{1}{2}$ and we have

$$y = ax^{1/2} = a\sqrt{x} \tag{48}$$

$$\frac{dy}{dx} = \tfrac{1}{2}ax^{-1/2} = \frac{a}{2\sqrt{x}} \tag{49}$$

$$\frac{d^2y}{dx^2} = -\tfrac{1}{4}ax^{-3/2} = \frac{-a}{4\sqrt{x^3}}. \tag{50}$$

In the first place, if we allow x to take on negative values, we are involved with the roots of negative numbers, i again. We shall therefore confine ourselves to positive x, where we can see what is happening. Here the sign of the second derivative is everywhere the same, determined by a, but we cannot solve

$$\tfrac{1}{2}ax^{-1/2} = 0$$

so for $x>0$ the function is monotonic increasing or decreasing, depending on a, and has no defined maximum. Substitution of $x=0$ into (48) gives $y = 0$, however, so this function starts at the origin. It is sketched for $a>0$

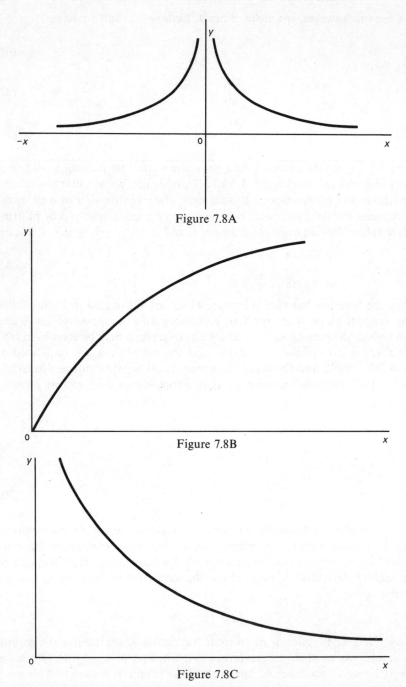

Figure 7.8A

Figure 7.8B

Figure 7.8C

in Figure 7.8B. Notice that in Figure 7.8B, the slope of the function, although everywhere positive, continuously decreases. This is because, as illustrated in (49) and (50), the first and second derivatives of a function of this type are of opposite sign. In general, if

$$y = ax^n$$

$$\frac{dy}{dx} = anx^{n-1},$$

and

$$\frac{d^2y}{dx^2} = a(n-1)nx^{n-2},$$

so that if n is a proper positive fraction $(0 < n < 1)$, $n - 1 < 0$, and n and $n - 1$ are of opposite signs.

We now have case (iv), negative fractions. Let $n = -\frac{1}{2}$, and we have

$$y = ax^{-1/2} = \frac{a}{\sqrt{x}}, \tag{51}$$

$$\frac{dy}{dx} = -\tfrac{1}{2}ax^{-3/2} = \frac{-a}{2\sqrt{x^3}}, \tag{52}$$

and

$$\frac{d^2y}{dx^2} = \tfrac{3}{4}ax^{-5/2} = \frac{3a}{4\sqrt{x^5}}. \tag{53}$$

Once again in order to avoid i, we shall consider this function only over positive values of x. Once again, we cannot define a stationary value by setting (52) equal to zero. The first derivative has everywhere the same sign, so the function is monotonically increasing or decreasing for $x > 0$ according to the sign of a. It is sketched for positive a in Figure 7.8C. Notice that in (52) and (53) the first and second derivatives are of opposite sign. This generalises: if n and $(n-1)$ are both negative, $n(n-1)$ is positive.

These four cases are a little exhausting and awkward! It turns out, however, that negative and fractional indices occur very frequently in important classes of applications, and it is helpful to have some knowledge of the behaviour of the functions.

Exercises

1 The quadratic $y = ax^2 + bx + c$ has either a maximum or a minimum at $x = -b/2a$. What determines the quadrant in which this value occurs?

2 Find the values of x which give extreme values of the following functions, and determine whether they are maxima or minima:

(i) $y = 10x - 0 \cdot 2x^2$

(ii) $y = 100 - 2x + 0 \cdot 01x^2$

(iii) $y = 5 + 10x - x^2$

(iv) $y = 5 + 10x + x^2.$

3 Find the maximum and minimum of

$$y = \frac{1}{15}x^3 - \frac{3}{10}x^2 - 2x + 10.$$

Has it a non-stationary inflexional point? Draw a rough sketch of the function.

4 Find the stationary and inflexional value(s) of

(i) $y = \frac{1}{3}x^3 + x^2 + x + 1$

(ii) $y = \frac{1}{3}x^3 - x + 10$

(iii) $y = \dfrac{x^3 + 4x^2 + 5x + 2}{x + 1}$

(iv) $y = (x^2 - 1)^2$

(v) $y = \dfrac{1 + x}{x^2}$

(vi) $y = x^3 + 2x^2 - 7x + 1.$

CHAPTER 8

ECONOMIC APPLICATIONS OF MAXIMA AND MINIMA

8.1 Average and Marginal Relations

We will start by applying our new techniques to some familiar propositions. We will then return to our two basic linear models, of a perfect market and of income determination, and extend the analysis to problems that we could not previously solve. We then take up an entirely new topic, profit maximisation, and, after deriving the equilibrium conditions, attempt some comparative static analysis. This proves to be easy enough when we take linear examples, but ambitious in the general case, so that section 8.7 is starred.

First, let us demonstrate that a marginal product curve passes through the maximum point of the average product curve. If output is given by

$$q = g(l) \tag{1}$$

then average product is given by

$$\frac{q}{l} = \frac{g(l)}{l} \tag{2}$$

and marginal product by

$$\frac{dq}{dl} = g'(l). \tag{3}$$

To find the maximum point on the AP curve, we set

$$\frac{d}{dl}\left(\frac{q}{l}\right) = 0.$$

Applying the quotient rule to (2), we have

$$\frac{lg'(l) - g(l)}{l^2} = 0. \tag{4}$$

Multiplying both sides of (4) by l^2 we obtain

$$lg'(l) - g(l) = 0,$$

or
$$\frac{g(l)}{l} = g'(l),$$

i.e.,
$$AP = MP. \tag{5}$$

This simple and elegant demonstration may be compared with the relatively laborious and clumsy proof given in Chapter 2, pages 23–26.

(The proof that MC passes through the minimum point on AC – if the latter has a minimum – is similar, and is left to Exercise 1.)

Now consider the maximum point on a revenue function. If the demand curve is given by $p=f(q)$ we may write $R(q)=q.f(q)$. To find the maximum, set the derivative equal to zero:

$$\frac{\mathrm{d}R(q)}{\mathrm{d}q} = q.f'(q)+f(q) = 0 \tag{6}$$

whence, at the maximum

$$f'(q) = -\frac{f(q)}{q} = \frac{-p}{q}. \tag{7}$$

But the elasticity of demand is defined by

$$\eta = \frac{\mathrm{d}q}{\mathrm{d}p}.\frac{p}{q}. \tag{8}$$

Substituting for $f'(q)$ from equation (7), we find that at the maximum point on $R(q)$

$$\eta = \frac{-q}{p}.\frac{p}{q} = -1. \tag{9}$$

This is yet another general result, and yet another example of the power of notation. In obtaining (9) we have used the first-order conditions for a maximum, the definition of η, and the assumption that there is a value of q that satisfies (6), i.e., that the revenue function has a maximum. We have demonstrated that (9) will hold for *any* demand function such that the revenue function does have a maximum.

(This is a good moment to do Exercise 2.)

8.2   Maximising the Yield of an Excise Tax

In 6.4 we investigated the effect on tax yield of changes in tax rate (specific excise tax; competitive market; linear demand and supply) and obtained the expression (equation 6.29, page 138)

$$\frac{\mathrm{d}T}{\mathrm{d}t} = \frac{ad-bc}{d-b}+\frac{2bdt}{d-b}$$

which we found to be positive for some values of t and negative for others. We can now show that there is indeed a unique tax rate that maximises yield. Setting $dT/dt = 0$, we obtain

$$\frac{2bdt}{d-b} = -\frac{ad-bc}{d-b}$$

whence

$$t = \frac{bc-ad}{d-b} \cdot \frac{d-b}{2bd}$$

$$= \frac{bc-ad}{2bd}. \tag{10}$$

We must make sure that the maximum occurs at a positive value of t, and that it is a maximum rather than a minimum. Our standard assumptions are $b < 0$, $d > 0$, $0 < c < a$, which ensure $t > 0$. (bc is negative, ad positive, hence the numerator of (10) is negative; but the denominator is negative because b is negative, so (10) is positive.) Further,

$$\frac{d^2 T}{dt^2} = \frac{2bd}{d-b} < 0 \tag{11}$$

so we do indeed have a maximum.

We get a striking result if we manipulate the expression for the value of t that maximises T. In our supply and demand functions, we took q as the dependent variable, although in the conventional Marshallian diagram q appears on the horizontal axis. Let us see what happens if we treat p as the dependent variable. We now read the demand equation as showing the price at which consumers will clear the market of each quantity, and the supply equation as showing the price required to induce suppliers to put each quantity on the market. Thus instead of the q^d and q^s of our earlier treatment, we shall have p^d and p^s, which we may call demand price and supply price respectively. In the linear case, demand price is given by

$$p^d = \alpha + \beta q \tag{12}$$

and supply price by

$$p^s = \gamma + \delta q. \tag{13}$$

We also have the equilibrium condition

$$p^d = p^s + t. \tag{14}$$

Substituting,

$$\alpha + \beta q = \gamma + \delta q + t \tag{15}$$

whence

$$q = \frac{\gamma - \alpha}{\beta - \delta} + \frac{t}{\beta - \delta} \tag{16}$$

(notice that, if the demand curve slopes down and the supply curve up, $\beta - \delta < 0$, but we must also have $\alpha > \gamma$, i.e., $\gamma - \alpha < 0$).

Now

$$T = tq = \frac{\gamma - \alpha}{\beta - \delta} t + \frac{t^2}{\beta - \delta}. \tag{17}$$

For maximum yield we put

$$\frac{\mathrm{d}T}{\mathrm{d}t} = \frac{\gamma - \alpha}{\beta - \delta} + \frac{2t}{\beta - \delta} = 0 \tag{18}$$

whence

$$t = \frac{1}{2} \frac{(\alpha - \gamma)}{(\beta - \delta)} (\beta - \delta)$$

$$= \frac{1}{2} (\alpha - \gamma) \tag{19}$$

or one-half difference of the intercepts on the price axis, i.e., *t is independent of the slope coefficients β and δ*. We may consider this result rather striking, since relations of this sort usually turn out to depend on elasticities, and since the slope coefficients are absent from (19), this result cannot be expressed in terms of elasticities.

It remains to be shown that we did get the same result earlier in equation (10), i.e., that

$$\frac{bc - ad}{bd} = \alpha - \gamma.$$

This simply requires rearranging the demand and supply functions:

$$q^d = a + bp$$

or

$$p^d = \frac{-a}{b} + \frac{q}{b};$$

$$q^s = c + dp$$

or

$$p^s = \frac{-c}{d} + \frac{q}{d}$$

So we put

$$\left.\begin{aligned} \alpha &= -\frac{a}{b} \\[6pt] \beta &= \frac{1}{b} \\[6pt] \gamma &= -\frac{c}{d} \\[6pt] \delta &= \frac{1}{d} \end{aligned}\right\} \tag{20}$$

when we want to work with p as dependent variable. Checking,

$$\alpha - \gamma = \left(-\frac{a}{b} - \frac{-c}{d}\right).$$

$$= \frac{bc - ad}{bd}.$$

The price-axis intercepts, α and γ, depend, as can be seen from (20), on the quantity intercepts, a and c, *and* on the slope coefficients b and d; but once we have found the price-axis intercepts, we can express the yield-maximising tax rate directly as half their difference, without further consideration of the slope coefficients.

8.3   Maximising the Yield of an Income Tax

We have now followed our regular practice of applying each new piece of technique in turn to the solution of a problem in our linear model of a perfect market. Following the same practice, we should now take up our linear macro-model. We shall, however, find few examples of the application of maxima and minima to elementary macro-economics. The reason is quite simple. If we are only trying to maximise income or employment, we proceed to the full-employment ceiling, illustrated in Figure 4B.1, without requiring the maximisation technique: we go as far in one direction as we can. If, on the other hand, we are trying to make an optimal choice on a frontier between, e.g., ΔY and ΔB (see Figure 4B.2) we are dealing with a more complicated problem than we yet have the technique for, a problem of choice in two variables where the possibilities are limited or constrained by a function of two variables, Y and B. In micro-economics, on the other hand, the assumption that firms try to maximise profits obviously invites us to apply the techniques of the last chapter. There is, however, one straightforward application of the theory of maxima to macro-economics which we may take up first.

A plausible-sounding intuitive argument goes as follows: the higher the rate of income tax, the lower is income, given autonomous spending, but the more yield is obtained from taxing any given income; trading one effect off against the other, we should find a rate of income tax that maximises tax yield. With the analytical tools we now have, we can show that, at least in our simple linear model of income determination, this is a fallacy. For the closed economy, we have

$$T = tY = tkZ \tag{21}$$

where

$$k = \frac{1}{1 - c(1 - t)}$$

and Z is the sum of autonomous expenditures. Differentiating (21),

$$\frac{\mathrm{d}T}{\mathrm{d}t} = \left(t\frac{\mathrm{d}k}{\mathrm{d}t} + k \right) Z \tag{22}$$

by the product rule. We have already found (in Chapter 6.6, equation (32)) that

$$\frac{\mathrm{d}k}{\mathrm{d}t} = -ck^2$$

so we substitute this into (22). Necessary conditions for a maximum require

$$-ctk^2 + k = 0$$

or

$$k(1 - ctk) = 0 \tag{23}$$

(since Z cannot be zero, this must be true if the whole derivative is to be zero). (23) is only satisfied if either k or $(1 - ctk)$ is zero; but neither is possible if we assume $0 < c < 1$ and $0 < t < 1$, as we have done (see 6.6). If we put $1 - ctk = 0$, we obtain $t = 1/ck$. Substituting this value into the expression for k,

$$k = \frac{1}{1 - c\left(1 - \dfrac{1}{ck}\right)}$$

$$= \frac{1}{1 - c + 1/k}$$

so
$$k = \frac{k}{k(1-c)+1}$$

or
$$k(1-c)+1 = 1$$

or
$$k(1-c) = 0$$

which again requires $k=0$, or $1-c=0$ which will not do. What this amounts to is simply that the function $T = tkZ$ does not have a maximum if $0<c<1$ and $0<t<1$. If, of course, we permit $t=1$, $k=1/[1-c(1-t)]=1$, and T simply equals Z: 100% taxation takes all autonomous income (expenditure), and leaves no induced income. Any reduction in taxation below 100% reduces yield because the increase in taxable income is not offset by the reduction in rate. Indeed, values of t in excess of unity make no economic sense: people do not have unlimited resources out of which to pay taxes in excess of their incomes. We may complete the mathematical analysis, nonetheless, and will find that taxes in excess of 100% would, if they were possible, actually increase tax yield, as may be confirmed by numerical experiment in (21). We assume, of course, that autonomous expenditure is unaffected by taxation. Thus consider the condition $k=0$, or

$$\frac{1}{1-c(1-t)} = 0.$$

Multiplying both sides by $1-c(1-t)$ we get the absurd result $1=0$; but we can see that the value of the left-hand side diminishes towards zero as t increases, although the equation cannot be exactly satisfied at any finite value of t. We may conclude that in this model T is not maximised by any value of t short of infinity, where the maximum is not defined, which is why we cannot solve the equation $dT/dt=0$.

We could in fact, have obtained this result directly from 6.6 where we examined equation (35),

$$\frac{d}{dt}\Delta D = k(ctk-1).$$

and showed this to be negative. If the deficit is a monotonic *decreasing* function of the tax rate, tax yield is a monotonic *increasing* function, and obviously

$$\frac{dT}{dt} = \frac{-d}{dt}\Delta D$$

if G is constant. Monotonic functions do not have extreme values short of infinity, and that is that.

This result may in fact be a little surprising: the intuitive argument which suggests that there should be a maximum seems convincing. But remember that, if we have two offsetting effects, there is no reason why there should always be an extreme value or point of balance between the two effects – it is perfectly possible that one is always stronger than the other, and we found other examples of this in Chapter 6. We have, of course, a very simple static model here. We have neglected any incentive or disincentive effects of changed tax rates; and by taking all investment to be autonomous we have ignored the direct effects of taxation on investment as well as any accelerator effects via the change in income. We may, however, conclude that, if anyone still believes the intuitive argument that there is a yield-maximising rate short of infinity, the burden of proof is on him to produce a less simplified model in which this is true. It would not be an easy task!

8.4   Profit Maximisation

We may now take up the important topic of profit-maximisation. We have already discussed some of the properties of cost and revenue functions, and even in Chapter 2, with the clumsy methods then available, we got as far as $MC = MR$, but the technique introduced in the last chapter permits a more thorough analysis. We also discussed at the beginning of the last chapter some methodological aspects of the maximising hypothesis. We now address ourselves directly to the maximising conditions as a preparation for the comparative static analysis from which we hope to obtain some testable predictions.

We define profit, Π, as the difference between revenue, R, and costs, C. If we can contrive to express revenue and costs as functions of quantity, then $\Pi = \Pi(q) = R(q) - C(q)$. This we can manage since $R = pq$, and we can take p either as a constant (perfect competition), or as a function of the quantity (non-perfect competition). Thus we are able to reduce the problem to a problem in one variable, just as we did in the competitive market example of 4A.1, where, by substitution, we were able to solve a single equation for equilibrium quantity, and then substitute into either the demand or the supply equation to find the corresponding price. Now if

$$\Pi = R(q) - C(q), \tag{24}$$

to find profit-maximising output we set the first derivative equal to zero, so we require the q that satisfies

$$\frac{d\Pi}{dq} = \frac{dR}{dq} - \frac{dC}{dq} = 0. \tag{25}$$

(If $p = f(q)$, we have already seen that $dR/dq = qf'(q) + f(q)$. (25) is the necessary condition; for sufficiency we also require

$$\frac{d^2\Pi}{dq^2} = \frac{d^2R}{dq^2} - \frac{d^2C}{dq^2} < 0. \tag{26}$$

These conditions are very familiar: the first requires equality of marginal cost and marginal revenue; the second requires that the marginal cost curve cuts the marginal revenue curve from beneath, i.e., that $MC > MR$ to the right of the equilibrium value $\bar{q}$. Unless we have the actual cost and revenue functions, however, we cannot find $\bar{q}$ explicitly from equation (25). If we have $\bar{q}$, we may also substitute back into the demand function to find price (in cases in which it is not a constant).

Our aim is, of course, to obtain some comparative static predictions but, in the general non-linear case, this proves to be rather difficult. If, however, we assume that the demand and cost functions are linear, it is quite easy. We shall therefore start by working out two examples, one linear and one not, in this section and the next. Then in 8.6 we shall subject the linear example to some comparative static analysis. The analysis of the general non-linear case, in which our knowledge is confined to qualitative restrictions, is left to 8.7 which is starred to indicate that it is difficult and may be omitted on a first reading.

To construct a linear model of a firm in non-perfect competition (a monopolist) we assume that

$$C = k + cq \tag{27}$$

and[1]

$$p = a - bq \tag{28}$$

whence

$$R = pq = aq - bq^2 \tag{29}$$

(it is by (29) that we are able to reduce the problem to one in a single variable). Now

$$\Pi = R - C = aq - bq^2 - k - cq. \tag{30}$$

We set the first derivative equal to zero,

$$\frac{d\Pi}{dq} = a - 2bq - c = 0, \tag{31}$$

whence

$$2bq = a - c$$

or

$$q = \frac{a-c}{2b}, \tag{32}$$

---

[1] Notice that we now write $-bq$ in the demand function instead of $+bq$. This simply means that the condition for the demand curve to slope down is now that b is a *positive* number.

and to find p we substitute from (32) into (28):

$$p = a - b\frac{(a-c)}{2b}$$

or
$$p = \frac{a+c}{2}. \tag{33}$$

Equation (33) gives the surprising result that the profit-maximising price is independent of the slope of the demand curve. This may remind us of our earlier result in 8.2, equation (19) above, that the yield-maximising excise tax was independent of the slopes of the demand and supply curves. We saw that (19) was the result of taking price as dependent variable, whereupon the price-axis intercepts actually depend on the slope coefficients. What is the reason for the analogous result in (33)? We have constant marginal cost, c, which must be equal to marginal revenue, so equilibrium requires the same marginal revenue whatever the slope of the demand curve. If, however, $p = a - bq$ and we keep the intercept, a, constant, varying the slope, b, we trace out a family of iso-elastic demand curves,[1] and two demand curves with the same elasticity at a given price give the same marginal revenue at that price. So, in the case of a linear demand curve *and* constant marginal cost, price *is* independent of the slope of the demand curve. (You should illustrate this result geometrically, and satisfy yourself that it makes sense.)

It remains to check what seems obvious in the linear case, that we have found a maximum and not a minimum. Differentiating (31),

$$\frac{d^2\Pi}{dq^2} = -2b < 0 \tag{34}$$

as required.

8.5 A Non-Linear Example

Before going on to comparative statics, it seems prudent to be sure that we can manage a non-linear example. This once again involves us in non-

[1] In case the notion of iso-elastic demand curves is unfamiliar, we explain it here: we say that two demand curves are iso-elastic when they have the same elasticity at every common price. To show that a family of linear demand curves with a common intercept are iso-elastic, take an arbitrary price $\bar{p}$. Since $p = a - bq$, we can write $b = (a-\bar{p})/q$. Substituting into $\eta = (dq/dp)(p/q)$ and using $dq/dp = 1/(dp/dq) = 1/-b = -q/a-p$, we obtain

$$\eta = \frac{-q}{a-p}\cdot\frac{\bar{p}}{q} = -\frac{\bar{p}}{a-p}.$$

This says that if we fix a and $\bar{p}$, η is given independently of the slope coefficient. This is a good moment to work out for yourself, if you do not already happen to know it, that all linear supply curves through the origin have the same elasticity (unity).

linear cost functions. Construction of a cost function with a prescribed list of characteristics is quite an exacting task.

We have already seen in 6.1 that a U-shaped marginal cost curve must be of at least second degree (a quadratic). Consideration of the rule for taking the derivative of a power function, $d(ax^n)/dx = anx^{n-1}$, makes it clear that the total cost function must be one degree higher, at least a cubic. If its first derivative is to fall and then rise, however, the total cost function must have a point of inflexion, and we can show that this point occurs where marginal cost is at a minimum. If we want a particular function to serve as an illustration of a possible cost function, however, we require some other characteristics. We certainly expect total cost to be a monotonic increasing function of output, and this means that the function must increase for all (positive) values of q: if it has a point of inflexion, it must not be a stationary value. We also require that marginal cost be everywhere positive. Now, we saw in the last chapter that, at a non-stationary point of inflexion, the first derivative is non-zero, but the second is; and this is precisely what we require. Where marginal cost is positive but at a minimum, its derivative, which is the second derivative of total cost, is zero, and here is our non-stationary point of inflexion, dividing the region of increasing returns to the variable factor from that of decreasing returns.

A cost function with the required properties is

$$C = \tfrac{1}{3}q^3 - 5q^2 + 30q + 10 \qquad (35)$$

and it is a good exercise to check for yourself that it does have the properties claimed. If you set the first derivative of (35) equal to zero, you will find an equation with no real roots – application of the formula for solving a quadratic will lead to an expression involving $\sqrt{-1}$. This means, of course, that the marginal cost curve does *not* cross the horizontal axis, which is as it should be.

The cost function (35) is consistent with perfect competition, so we may as well complete the illustration for practice, setting $p = \bar{p} = 6$. Now

$$\Pi = 6q - \tfrac{1}{3}q^3 + 5q^2 - 30q - 10. \qquad (36)$$

We require the value of q that satisfies

$$\frac{d\Pi}{dq} = 6 - q^2 + 10q - 30 = 0, \qquad (37)$$

or, rearranging, that satisfies

$$q^2 - 10q + 24 = 0.$$

This factors into

$$(q-6)(q-4) = 0.$$

Hence (37) is solved by $q=4$ or 6. We expect that at the smaller value Π is at a minimum, and at the larger it is at a maximum. This is confirmed by inspecting

$$\frac{d^2\Pi}{dq^2} = -2q+10 \tag{38}$$

which is negative if $q>5$, as expected. (This is a good moment to do Exercise 5.)

8.6 Comparative Statics in the Linear Case

In Chapter 4 we first discussed comparative statics, and the idea of looking for qualitative predictions, which proved, in general, to mean looking for the signs of the derivatives of endogenous variables with respect to exogenous variables or parameters. To start our comparative static analysis of the profit-maximising model, we need something that we can use as an exogenous variable, or a 'shift parameter' such as the price of an input, or a tax-rate. It is easier to introduce a tax-rate than an input price, and we shall use this example for the moment. Inspection of equations (25), (31), or (37) confirms the well-known result that a lump-sum tax on a producer cannot affect his short-run maximising output, since marginal cost is independent of all costs that do not depend on the level of output. Hence we shall introduce an excise tax – as usual – to the linear-monopoly case of 8.4. If a specific tax is imposed at t per unit, we may regard this as an addition to variable costs, so the cost function becomes

$$C = k+cq+tq \tag{39}$$

and

$$\Pi = aq-bq^2-k-cq-tq \tag{40}$$

if we retain the demand function of (28). We solve for q the equation

$$\frac{d\Pi}{dq} = a-2bq-c-t = 0$$

whence

$$q = \frac{a-(c+t)}{2b}. \tag{41}$$

Comparison of (41) with (32) shows that we have merely moved the MC curve up by the amount of the tax. We expect that the effect of the tax is to reduce q, and this is confirmed: differentiating (41), we find $dq/dt = -1/2b < 0$. We also expect to find an increase in price. Substituting (41) into the demand equation (28) we find

$$p = a-b\frac{(a-c-t)}{2b}$$

$$= \frac{a+c+t}{2} \tag{42}$$

which is evidently larger than $(a+c)/2$. (42) is what we want: it expresses the endogenous variable, p, as a function of the shift parameter, t. It is a simple linear relationship and obviously

$$\frac{dp}{dt} = \tfrac{1}{2} > 0. \tag{43}$$

(43) is signed, which is a success: we have proved that increasing the tax does indeed increase price. That it does so by half the tax change is due to our choice of linear functions. (Notice that $AR = a - bq$ and $MR = a - 2bq$. This is a good moment to do Exercise 6.)

8.7*   Qualitative Comparative Statics and Second-Order Conditions

This is an ambitious section, which may be omitted at a first reading. It is important, but it will stretch our available technique to the limit. What we want to do is to generalise our result by proving $dp/dt > 0$ where we do not have specific functions, but only assume qualitative restrictions such as a downward sloping demand curve. It turns out that we can produce a general proof, and an important one, since it is an example of a class of results which is of great generality.

Suppose we merely have

$$R = q f(q) \tag{44}$$

$$C = g(q) + tq \tag{45}$$

and the qualitative knowledge that the demand curve slopes down and that marginal cost is everywhere positive. We proceed in the usual way, obtaining

$$\frac{d\Pi}{dq} = qf'(q) + f(q) - g'(q) - t = 0. \tag{46}$$

This gives

$$q = \frac{g'(q) + t - f(q)}{f'(q)}. \tag{47}$$

It would be tempting to conclude that $dq/dt = 1/f'(q)$, and quite wrong. The change in tax leads to a change in equilibrium price, so $f(q)$ changes, and with it $f'(q)$; and as q changes so will $g'(q)$. The equilibrium values of price, quantity, marginal revenue, and marginal cost are all interdependent, and if we disturb equilibrium by changing the tax, we have to sort out simultaneously the changes required for a new equilibrium. We have, of course, done this in our linear examples, but the general case is more subtle than anything we have done so far.

It helps to consider the form of the relationship we now have between the endogenous variable q and the shift parameter t. A simple rearrangement of (46) gives

$$q.f'(q)+f(q)-g'(q) = t. \tag{48}$$

The left-hand side of (48) is a function of q, which we may write as $F(q)$. The equilibrium condition is that (46) – or (48) – *must* be satisfied if profits are to be maximised, whatever the value of t, and we can express the equilibrium condition in the form of (48) as

$$F(q) = t. \tag{48a}$$

Solution of (48a) gives the equilibrium value, $\bar{q}$, for any t, and we can look on it as merely another form of the function relating an endogenous to an exogenous variable. In our earlier examples, we have always been able to express the dependent variable as an explicit function of the shift parameter, but the difference between (48) and an earlier example is only the difference between an expression of the form $q=h(t)$ and of the form $F(q)=t$. Evidently we can only expect to obtain the explicit form $q=h(t)$ where we have the actual functions. We have, however, consistently taken as our goal the discovery of general qualitative comparative static predictions; and, in general, we do not have the functions specified, and therefore can only get forms like $F(q)=t$. If, therefore, we can make headway in this case, we have made a big step forward in extending the scope and generality of our comparative static analysis.

It turns out that, given the assumption that equilibrium conditions are satisfied, systematic appeal to the chain rule will do the trick for us. Notice that, if $F(q)=t$ is our equilibrium condition, it must still be satisfied by an appropriate value of q if t is changed to, say, t': for equilibrium, we must still find q such that $F(q)=t'$. But if this is the case, then it must be true that

$$\frac{dF(q)}{dt} = \frac{dt}{dt}$$

or
$$\frac{d}{dt}\left[qf'(q)+f(q)-g'(q)\right] = 1 \tag{49}$$

and all we have to do now is take the derivative indicated in (49). This in fact is not too troublesome, since, by the rule for taking the derivative of a sum of functions, we may proceed term by term.

Consider first the second term, $f(q)$. Now, $f(q)=p$, and, by the chain rule, we must have

$$\frac{dp}{dt} = \frac{dp}{dq}.\frac{dq}{dt},$$

i.e.,
$$\frac{\mathrm{d}f(q)}{\mathrm{d}t} = f'(q) \cdot \frac{\mathrm{d}q}{\mathrm{d}t},$$
(50.1)

whatever $\mathrm{d}q/\mathrm{d}t$ may turn out to be. This is encouragingly simple, and we go on to $g'(q)$. Now, $g'(q)$ is marginal cost, and, whatever $\mathrm{d}q/\mathrm{d}t$ may turn out to be, we have, again by the chain rule,

$$\frac{\mathrm{d}MC}{\mathrm{d}t} = \frac{\mathrm{d}MC}{\mathrm{d}q} \cdot \frac{\mathrm{d}q}{\mathrm{d}t},$$

i.e.,
$$\frac{\mathrm{d}g'(q)}{\mathrm{d}t} = g''(q) \frac{\mathrm{d}q}{\mathrm{d}t}.$$
(50.2)

In case (50.2) looks like sleight of hand, let us consider the economic interpretation. If the tax changes, output changes; if output changes MC changes; hence the rate of change of MC with respect to the tax rate is equal to the rate of change of MC with respect to output times the rate of change of output with respect to tax rate, whatever the latter may prove to be.

This leaves the more complicated term, $qf'(q)$, to which we shall have to apply the product rule:

$$\frac{\mathrm{d}}{\mathrm{d}t} qf'(q) = q \cdot \frac{\mathrm{d}}{\mathrm{d}t} f'(q) + f'(q) \cdot \frac{\mathrm{d}q}{\mathrm{d}t}.$$

Using the chain rule again,

$$\frac{\mathrm{d}}{\mathrm{d}t} f'(q) = \frac{\mathrm{d}}{\mathrm{d}q} f'(q) \cdot \frac{\mathrm{d}q}{\mathrm{d}t}$$

$$= f''(q) \cdot \frac{\mathrm{d}q}{\mathrm{d}t}$$

so

$$\frac{\mathrm{d}}{\mathrm{d}t} qf'(q) = q \cdot f''(q) \frac{\mathrm{d}q}{\mathrm{d}t} + f'(q) \frac{\mathrm{d}q}{\mathrm{d}t}.$$
(50.3)

We now collect up (50.1), (50.2), and (50.3), and substitute into (49) to obtain

$$q \cdot f''(q) \frac{\mathrm{d}q}{\mathrm{d}t} + f'(q) \frac{\mathrm{d}q}{\mathrm{d}t} + f'(q) \frac{\mathrm{d}q}{\mathrm{d}t} - g''(q) \frac{\mathrm{d}q}{\mathrm{d}t} = 1.$$
(51)

This simplifies readily:

$$\frac{\mathrm{d}q}{\mathrm{d}t} [q \cdot f''(q) + 2f'(q) - g''(q)] = 1$$
(52)

Now dq/dt is what we are looking for, and rearranging (52) we have

$$\frac{dq}{dt} = \frac{1}{q.f''(q)+2f'(q)-g''(q)}. \tag{53}$$

Comparing (53) with (49), we can see that what we have done is find $dF(q)/dt$, and that, by the chain rule, this is nothing but $F'(q)\,dq/dt$, which is what we have in (52). Simple rearrangement then gives us

$$\frac{dq}{dt} = \frac{1}{F'(q)},$$

which we have in (53).

What this means is that (53) gives us the rate of change of *equilibrium q*, or $\bar{q}$, the value of q that satisfies (46) – or (47), or (48) – with respect to the shift parameter t. We may again compare (49) with some of our earlier exercises in comparative statics, where we expressed some endogenous variable, say, y, as a function of some exogenous variable, say z, and then found $d\bar{y}/dz$. In our earlier cases we had simple relations of the form $y=h(z)$, whereas this time we have had a rather complicated expression in the form $F(y)=z$; but there is no difference in principle.

We may recall that the object of the exercise was to prove $dp/dt>0$. Hence the step required now is obviously to prove $dq/dt<0$. Thus we want to show, if we can, that (53) is negative. This looks a little unpromising: (53) is rather complicated. Furthermore, we do not get much encouragement from inspecting it term by term. $f''(q)$ is the rate of change of the slope of the demand curve, and we have made no general assumption about that; and while $f'(q)$ must be negative, $g''(q)$, the slope of the marginal cost curve, can have any sign at equilibrium in non-perfect competition. Nonetheless, we can make progress, and we shall discover an example of one of the most important theorems of comparative statics. The equilibrium value $\bar{q}$ is found by solving for q equation (46), the first-order maximum condition. We require, however, the second-order condition too, and differentiating (46) a second time, we find

$$\frac{d^2\Pi}{dq^2} = q.f'(q)+2f'(q)-g''(q). \tag{54}$$

If we assume that q *is* at the value $\bar{q}$ that yields maximum profit, then (54) must be negative. But inspection now reveals a remarkable circumstance: the right-hand side of (54) is identical to the denominator of (53), hence if $\bar{q}$ is the profit-maximising value of q, (53) is negative too, and we have our proof. It is easily completed by remembering that, with $p = f(q)$, we must have

$$\frac{\mathrm{d}\bar{p}}{\mathrm{d}t} = f'(q)\frac{\mathrm{d}\bar{q}}{\mathrm{d}t} \qquad (55)$$

by the chain rule again, and since both $f'(q)$ and $\mathrm{d}\bar{q}/\mathrm{d}t$ are negative $\mathrm{d}\bar{p}/\mathrm{d}t > 0$.

We set out to prove $\mathrm{d}\bar{p}/\mathrm{d}t > 0$ in the general case, without specific functions, using only the assumptions that the demand curve slopes down and that marginal cost is positive. It turns out, not surprisingly, that we also have to assume that equilibrium conditions *are* satisfied, just as we did in the linear models of a perfect market or of income determination. In the case of a maximisation hypothesis, however, the assumption that equilibrium obtains requires not only that the necessary, or first-order, conditions are satisfied, but also that the second-order conditions are satisfied. Then the assumption that the values of q and p are such as to satisfy the *sufficient conditions* for a maximum *after* equilibrium has been disturbed is itself sufficient to tell us their direction of change with respect to a shift parameter, that is, to sign (53) and (55) which give the rates of change of *equilibrium* values with respect to the shift parameter. This is an example of one of the most important results in the theory of maximising models, that the assumption that the solution *is* a maximum can be sufficient, under certain conditions, to yield qualitative comparative static predictions. What we have just done, in deriving (53), and obtaining its sign from (54), is an example of what is called 'the qualitative calculus'. Much of Samuelson's great book, *The Foundations of Economic Analysis*, is devoted to the qualitative calculus, that is, to the differentiation of equilibrium conditions with respect to shift parameters, and the search for predictions about directions of change. The book itself requires a good deal more technique, but we now have the principles. It is by the application of the qualitative calculus that we find the predictions, if any, that follow from our model. Indeed, we have applied it frequently in this book already, and many of the best known results in standard micro-economics are examples of the qualitative calculus, proved by the methods we have just used.

This is a starred section, and it seems appropriate to address a remark to the reader who has persisted with it. You might reflect upon the extraordinary power of the analytical tools which have allowed us to provide so general a proof: it has, after all, been managed with little more than repeated applications of the chain rule, and the assumption that the conditions for a maximum are satisfied, i.e., that we are talking about equilibrium behaviour. You might also reflect that, if you have come this far, you have proved what we asserted at the beginning, that if you can do economics you can do mathematical economics.

It would be nice to be able to generalise further, and apply our comparative static analysis in the case of other shift parameters besides our rather overworked excise tax. Thus demand might be shifted by some parameter such as income, or costs might be made to depend on output and the price of an input, such as the wage rate. The appropriate functions would then be

$$p = f(q, \alpha)$$

and

$$C = g(q, w).$$

Evidently we cannot go further in this direction unless we can handle functions of two or more variables, which are the subject of the next chapter. Before going on, however, we might wonder why we were able to handle the tax case, since this gives

$$C = C(q, t)$$

as the general cost function. The reason is that the tax is simply to be *added* to the other costs, so that this becomes

$$C = g(q) + qt$$

and C is linear in t. The derivative of C with respect to q is obviously $g'(q)$ *plus* t; and the derivative of C with respect to t is obviously q. We now seek more general methods of handling functions of two or more variables that we can use when we do not have these simple additive cases.

Exercises

1 Prove that $MC = AC$ at the minimum point on the latter (if it exists).

2 Prove that a monopolist who has zero marginal cost maximises profit by setting the price at which the elasticity of demand is unity. (This is the famous 'mineral springs' case, proved by the French mathematical economist Cournot in 1838 in his *Récherches sur les Principes Mathematiques de la Théorie des Richesses*.)[1]

3 (i) Suppose that an employer's demand for labour is given by

$$l^d = 100 - 2w$$

where w is the wage-rate. If a union wishes to maximise the total pay of its membership, and is not concerned with redundancy, what wage rate will it ask for? What wage rate will it ask for if the members adopt a work- and wage-sharing scheme. Is this result dependent on the demand curve being linear? Try to generalise.

[1] This is available in English as *Researches into the Mathematical Principles of the Theory of Wealth*, translated by A. M. Kelly, Reprints of Economic Classics, New York, 1960.

(ii) A pay-roll tax of $0 \cdot 1w$ is now imposed. Find the wage-rate that maximises total pay to employees. (*Hint :* The union wishes to maximise wl; due to the pay-roll tax, $w = 0 \cdot 9\ \bar{w}$ where $\bar{w}$ is the total price paid by the employer.) Do you regard the answer as freakish, or general? Who would you say 'bears the tax' in this case?

4 In a competitive market, demand and supply are given by

$$q^d = 1200 - 2p$$

$$q^s = 4p.$$

Find the tax rate which maximises tax yield. (This is the numerical example of 4A.1.)

5 (i) In the example of 8·5, find whether an output of 6 actually exceeds the output at which average variable cost is at a minimum; and determine whether it pays better to produce 6 or nothing.

(ii) Sketch the average and marginal cost curves, and illustrate your answer to (i).

6 (i) Assume that $p = a - bq$, as in the example of 8·4 and 8·6, but that cost is given by

$$C = k + cq + dq^2.$$

Find the expressions for profit maximising p and q. What restrictions will you put on the value of the coefficient d?

(ii) Now suppose that an excise tax is levied at rate t. Find $d\bar{p}/dt$, and compare your result with the result of the text, where marginal cost was constant.

7 Assume that a firm has the following demand and cost functions

$$p = 150 - 0 \cdot 5q$$

$$C = 100 + 3q + 7q^2$$

and that a subsidy is paid of 3 per unit.

(i) Find profit-maximising price and quantity.

(ii) Would anything be produced in the absence of the subsidy?

(iii) Find the rates of change of equilibrium price and quantity with respect to the subsidy.

CHAPTER 9

FUNCTIONS OF TWO OR MORE VARIABLES

9.1 Partial Derivatives

So far, we have confined ourselves to functions of one variable, but this is in fact very restrictive, as the following examples illustrate. We expect the quantity demanded of a good to depend on income, and perhaps on prices of substitutes, as well as on the price of the good in question; cost is a function of such variables as wage rates as well as output; and we do not wish to be confined to assuming always that wages are constant when output and employment change. The values of our multipliers also depend on several parameters, any one of which may change. Thus in the multiplier

$$k = \frac{1}{1-(c-m)(1-t)} \tag{1}$$

we could ask what happened to k if c or m changed as well as if t changed. Previously we dealt with this (see pages 139–40) by assuming that m and c were constants while we varied t. We cannot always adopt so simple an approach and it is now time to investigate a function of more than one variable in which all the variables can change. We shall deal here with functions of two variables ($y = f(x, z)$), but the techniques developed extend in an obvious manner to functions of more than two variables.

Consider the very simple case of a household's demand function containing only two independent variables,

$$q^d = D(p, y), \tag{2}$$

where q^d is the household's demand for some commodity, p is the price of the commodity, and y is the household's income. (2) is a function of two variables and we wish to study its properties. First, we wish to know how demand changes as price changes, income held constant, and how demand changes as income changes, price held constant. Later, we shall wish to ask such questions as 'is the reaction of q^d to a change in price itself altered by a change in income?' or 'is the reaction of q^d to a change in income itself altered by a change in the price of the commodity?'. We need a technique to handle these and other related questions. When we dealt with the multiplier, restated in (1) above, our method was to assume c and m to be constant while we found the reaction of k to changes in t. We could also (although we did not have occasion to do so) have assumed t and c to be constant in order to find the reaction of k to changes in the value of m, and so on. We can now use this method systematically to attack functions of many variables.

To begin with let us consider the following demand function as a specific example of a function of two variables:

$$q^d = 10y^2 + 2y^4 p^{-2} - 3p^3. \tag{3}$$

As we are only going to consider the demand function, there is no risk of confusion between quantity demanded and quantity supplied, and we may accordingly suppress the superscript on q in this chapter. If p is held constant we can treat it just as we would any constant in a function of one variable, and we can obtain the derivative of q with respect to y in the ordinary way. If you do this you will find that its value is $20y + 8y^3 p^{-2}$. We can also hold y constant, treat it as we would a constant in simple differentiation, and obtain the derivative of q with respect to p. If this is done we obtain $-4y^4 p^{-3} - 9p^2$.

Now consider what we have done. Notice that we have obtained two different derivatives from (3), and in each case we need to specify the variable with respect to which we have taken the derivative. In the first case we asked how demand changed as income changed, price held constant, and to answer this we found the derivative of q *with respect to y*. In the second case we asked how q changed as price changed, income held constant, and to answer this we found the derivative of q *with respect to p*. To remind us that when we take the derivative of a function of two or more variables with respect to one of its arguments, we hold the other arguments constant, we speak of *partial derivatives* or just partials for short. Partial derivatives are denoted by 'curly d's', ∂, in place of ordinary Roman d's. Thus from (3) above we have derived two partial derivatives which we write

$$\frac{\partial q}{\partial y} = 20y + 8y^3 p^{-2} \tag{4}$$

and

$$\frac{\partial q}{\partial p} = -4y^4 p^{-3} - 9p^2. \tag{5}$$

Partials may be denoted in at least three ways. To illustrate the notation we write the partials of $y = f(x, z)$:

$$f_x = \frac{\partial y}{\partial x} = \frac{\partial f(x, z)}{\partial x}\bigg|_{z \text{ constant}} \qquad (6)$$

$$f_z = \frac{\partial y}{\partial z} = \frac{\partial f(x, z)}{\partial z}\bigg|_{x \text{ constant.}} \qquad (7)$$

All three expressions in (6) are read 'the partial derivative of y with respect to x', and all three in (7) are read 'the partial derivative of y with respect to z'.

Now let us give a formal definition of partial derivatives. Consider the general function $y = f(x, z)$. The partial of y with respect to x is defined as[1]

$$\lim_{\Delta x \to 0} \frac{\Delta y}{\Delta x} = \frac{f(x + \Delta x, z) - f(x, z)}{\Delta x} = \frac{\partial y}{\partial x} \qquad (8)$$

and the partial of y with respect to z is

$$\lim_{\Delta z \to 0} \frac{\Delta y}{\Delta z} = \frac{f(x, z + \Delta z) - f(x, z)}{\Delta z} = \frac{\partial y}{\partial z}. \qquad (9)$$

In both (8) and (9) the change in the value of the function is the result of a change in only one of the independent variables. In (8) the value of the function changes because x changes by Δx, and in (9) it changes because z changes by Δz.

Notice that you have now learned a new technique in the space of a very few pages and with a minimum of effort. If you recall the problems encountered in learning simple differentiation in Chapter 5 you may wish to remark on the ease with which this new and very important technique has been mastered.

Now let us return to the example of the demand function of (3) and to its two partial derivatives in (4) and (5). The partial of the quantity demanded with respect to price was

$$\frac{\partial q}{\partial p} = -4y^4 p^{-3} - 9p^2. \qquad (5)$$

Notice that this expression for the partial of demand with respect to price has income as an argument. Thus $\partial q / \partial p$ is a function not only of p but also of y. This partial derivative can be given a specific value only if a specific

---

[1] This type of definition was first used in Chapter 5 and if you are at all uncertain about it you should re-read page 110 now.

value of the other argument (income in this case) is stated. This should not seem too surprising since it is necessary to hold income constant when finding $\partial q/\partial p$. The fact that $\partial q/\partial p$ depends not only on p but also on y suggests that we consider what happens to the reaction of q to p as y changes. We could ask, for example, if the demand for the commodity becomes more or less responsive to a change in its price as the household's income rises. Formally, we are asking what happens to $\partial q/\partial p$ as y varies. We can write this as $\partial(\partial q/\partial p)/\partial y$ which denotes the partial derivative with respect to a change in income of the partial derivative of quantity demanded with respect to a change in price. Although this sounds very complex it expresses in formal terms a very simple question: 'how does the responsiveness of q to a change in p vary as y varies?'.

We can easily discover the answer for the demand function in (3) by differentiating (5) with respect to y to give

$$\frac{\partial\left(\frac{\partial q}{\partial p}\right)}{\partial y} = \frac{-16y^3}{p^3}. \tag{10}$$

We may notice that for p and y positive (10) is always negative: the response of q to changes in p declines as y rises.

We can also ask how the response of q to y varies as p varies, and to do this we differentiate (4) with respect to p obtaining

$$\frac{\partial\left(\frac{\partial q}{\partial y}\right)}{\partial p} = \frac{-16y^3}{p^3}. \tag{11}$$

This expression tells how the response of demand to a change in income varies as price varies. The notation on the left hand side of (10) and (11) is rather clumsy although descriptive and the following notation is usual:

$$\frac{\partial\left(\frac{\partial q}{\partial p}\right)}{\partial y} = \frac{\partial^2 q}{\partial p\,\partial y} = f_{py}. \tag{12}$$

The first term in (12) has been used already and it is to be read as directing us to take the partial of q with respect to p (equation (5)) and differentiate it with respect to y (equation (10)). The 'two' in the numerator of the second expression indicates that the function has been differentiated twice, while the terms in the denominator indicate that the process of partial differentiation has been carried out once with respect to p and once with respect to y. The third expression in (10) is the most compact notation: it indicates that the function f has been differentiated first with respect to p and then with respect to y.

Applying this notation to (11) we have analogously

$$\frac{\partial\left(\dfrac{\partial q}{\partial y}\right)}{\partial p} = \frac{\partial^2 q}{\partial y\,\partial p} = f_{yp}. \tag{13}$$

These terms are referred to as *second-order cross-partial* derivatives, or 'cross-partials' for short. A cross-partial measures the rate of change in a first-order partial as one of the variables originally held constant changes.

A comparison of (10) and (11) shows that $f_{py}=f_{yp}$. Indeed, this is no accident. The order in which we do the differentiation is of no consequence, and it is always true that for any function $f(x, z)$

$$f_{xz} = f_{zx}.$$

We shall not attempt to prove this important result here but its proof can be found in any standard text book on mathematics.[1]

It seemed obvious to pose the question that we have just considered: what happens to $\partial q/\partial p$ as y changes, and what happens to $\partial q/\partial y$ as p changes. There is also another related question we could ask: what happens to $\partial q/\partial p$ as p itself changes. Now we are wondering if the reaction of q to p is different when price is high from what it is when price is low. No student who is familiar with the elementary proposition that demand elasticity varies over the range of most demand curves will be surprised by this question. To answer it we merely differentiate (5) once again with respect to price and we get

$$\frac{\partial\left(\dfrac{\partial q}{\partial p}\right)}{\partial p} = 12y^4 p^{-4} - 18p. \tag{14}$$

We adopt the following notation:

$$\frac{\partial\left(\dfrac{q}{p}\right)}{\partial p} = \frac{\partial^2 q}{\partial p^2} = f_{pp}. \tag{15}$$

[1] See, for example, Courant, *Differential and Integral Calculus*, Vol. II (1936), pp. 55–7. The proof requires that the function is smooth and differentiable at the point in question. But we have already confined our attention to such 'well-behaved' functions. See Chapter 5, pp. 125–27.

This is called the second-order partial derivative of q with respect to price, and it is found by differentiating the original function twice with respect to price. What it tells us is how the reaction of q to a change in price, income held constant, is itself changing as we change price. The sign of the second partial f_{pp} tells us if the slope of the demand curve is increasing or diminishing as we move up the curve.

A similar question could be asked about q and y, and is answered by differentiating (4) with respect to y to give

$$\frac{\partial\left(\frac{\partial q}{\partial y}\right)}{\partial y} = 20 + 24y^2p^{-2}. \qquad (16)$$

The notation in this case is

$$\frac{\partial\left(\frac{\partial q}{\partial y}\right)}{\partial y} = \frac{\partial^2 q}{\partial y^2} = f_{yy}. \qquad (17)$$

This is called the second-order partial derivative of q with respect to income. It tells us how the response of q to a change in y is itself changing as y changes.

9.2 Summary

We may now summarise the results obtained so far for the case of a function $y = f(x, z)$.

(1) There are two first order partial derivatives of the function which are written: f_x and f_z or $\partial y/\partial x$ and $\partial y/\partial z$. They are obtained by differentiating the function with respect to the relevant variable, holding the other variable constant.

(2) There are two direct second-order partial derivatives, f_{xx} and f_{zz} which are also often written as $\partial^2 y/\partial x^2$ and $\partial^2 y/\partial z^2$. These are obtained by differentiating $f(x, z)$ twice with respect to x in the first case and twice with respect to z in the second case.

(3) There are two second-order cross partial derivatives f_{xz} and f_{zx} which are also often written as $\partial^2 y/\partial x\, \partial z$ and $\partial^2 y/\partial z\, \partial x$. These are obtained by differentiating $f(x, z)$ first with respect to x and then with respect to z in one case, and first with respect to z and then with respect to x in the other case. In fact, the order of differentiation turns out not to matter so that $f_{xz} = f_{zx}$;

7*

9.3 An Example

Now let us draw together the results for our specific demand function to see what we can learn about its behaviour.

$$q = 10y^2 + 2y^4p^{-2} - 3p^3 \tag{3}$$

$$f_y = 20y + 8y^3p^{-2} \tag{4}$$

$$f_p = -4y^4p^{-3} - 9p^2 \tag{5}$$

$$f_{yp} = f_{py} = -16y^3p^{-3} \tag{10 and 11}$$

$$f_{pp} = 12y^4p^{-4} - 18p \tag{14}$$

$$f_{yy} = 20 + 24y^2p^{-2}. \tag{16}$$

Let us now see if we can sign each of the first- and second-order partial derivatives. Inspection reveals the following for both $y, p > 0$: (i) $f_y > 0$ which shows that the good is non-inferior at all levels of income, (ii) $f_p < 0$ which shows that the demand curve for the commodity slopes downwards at each level of income, (iii) $f_{pp} \gtrless 0$ according to the values of y and p. This shows that the responsiveness of demand to increases in price itself increases as price increases at some price-income combinations, and decreases as price increases for other price-income combinations, (iv) $f_{yy} > 0$. This shows that the responsiveness of demand to a change in income increases as income increases, and (v) $f_{yp} = f_{py} < 0$. This shows both that the responsiveness of demand to a change in income decreases as price increases, and that the responsiveness of demand to a change in price decreases as income increases. Evidently, although it is a simple matter to take the five first- and second-order partial derivatives of a function of two variables, they reveal a great deal of rather complex information about the behaviour of the function. (This is a good time to do Exercise 1.)

9.4 Separable Functions

Consider the household demand function

$$q = 4y + 3y^5 - 20p^2 - 100p^{-8}. \tag{18}$$

This function differs fundamentally from the demand function in (3) above in that in (18) there are no terms involving both y and p while in (3) there is such a term, $2y^4p^{-2}$. We shall see the importance of this if we calculate the first- and second-order partial derivatives for the function in (18):

$$f_y = 4 + 15y^4 \tag{19}$$

$$f_p = -40p + 800p^{-9} \tag{20}$$

$$f_{yy} = 60y^3 \tag{21}$$

$$f_{pp} = -40 - 7200p^{-10} \tag{22}$$

$$f_{yp} = f_{py} = 0. \tag{23}$$

Because there are no terms involving both y and p it follows that the reaction of demand to price is independent of the level of income, and also that the reaction of demand to changes in income is independent of the level of price. Formally this is shown by the fact that the cross-partials are zero. Whenever the cross-partials are zero it follows that the value of the function is determined by the sum of the separate effects of the independent variables in question and that there is no 'interaction' between the variables. This is why in the last chapter we could get along easily when we could write the cost function $C = C(q, t)$ as a separable function $C = f(q) + g(t)$ but were stuck when we could not assume the cost function was separable and could only write $C = C(q, w)$.

9.5 Geometrical Interpretation of Partial Derivatives

In Figure 9.1 we have drawn a three-dimensional 'surface' which is a graphical representation of a particular function $z = f(x, y)$. You should try to visualise the surface as being concave to the origin, i.e., as bulging out towards you. We must now try to give a geometrical interpretation to the partial derivatives that we have identified so far. Consider first $\partial z/\partial x$ evaluated at some point, Q on the surface (i.e., at some specific value for each of x, y, and z). This partial derivative measures the slope in the x-z plane of the tangent to the curve at Q. This tangent is the line T_x in Figure 9.1. In order to see what is meant by the x-z plane, imagine taking a knife and cutting the surface open along a line perpendicular to the y axis. This will expose a new surface which was formerly in the interior such as the cross-hatched one in Figure 9.2a and, if you look at this end-on you will see the curve of its outer edge, which is shown in Figure 9.2b. The slope of the tangent to the curve in 9.2b is the partial derivative $\partial z/\partial x$, measured at the value of y at which we cut open the surface. If we take our knife and again cut the surface open perpendicular to the y-axis but at a different level of y we will expose a new curve in the x-z plane, and there is no guarantee that it will have the same shape and thus the same tangent slope at corresponding points as the curve first exposed.

The second order partial derivative $\partial^2 z/\partial x^2$ indicates what is happening to $\partial z/\partial x$ as we increase x holding y constant. Figure 9.2b shows that this second order partial must be negative throughout because the slope of the tangent (i.e., $\partial z/\partial x$) diminishes as x increases. (The tangent-slope is negative and its absolute value is increasing as x increases.)

Next consider the partial derivative $\partial z/\partial y$ evaluated at Q. We are now interested in the tangent slope in the y-z plane which is the slope of the surface when it is cut open perpendicular to the x axis. This tangent slope is shown in Figure 9.1 by the line T_y. The second-order partial $\partial^2 z/\partial y^2$ measures the rate of change of this tangent slope as we slide it around in the z-y plane holding z constant.

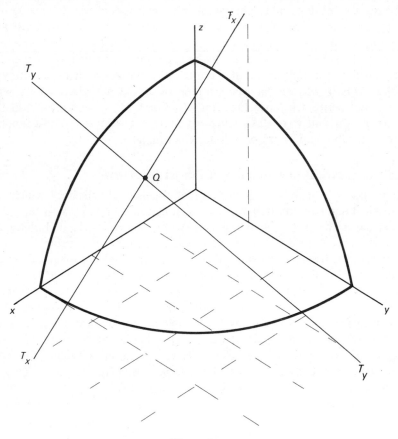

Figure 9.1

It will be evident from inspection of Figures 9.1 and 9.2 that the words 'the partial derivative *evaluated at Q*' are not idle pedantry. The tangent slopes vary as we move about the surface, and each is changed by a change in the other variable: hence the existence of cross-partial derivatives. Thus $\partial^2 z/\partial x\, \partial y$ measures the rate of change in the tangent slope T_x as we slide Q towards y, and similarly $\partial^2 z/\partial y\, \partial x$ measures the rate of change in T_y as we

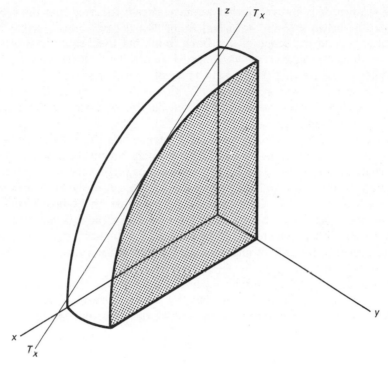

Figure 9.2a

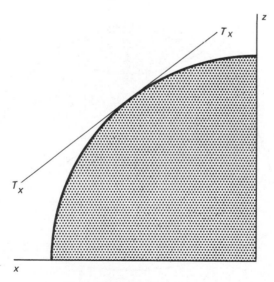

Figure 9.2b

slide Q towards x. But recall that we have already asserted that the cross-partials are always equal. A formal proof that the two cross-partials are equal is beyond the scope of this book, but what their equality shows is that it does not matter in which order one differentiates. In terms of Figure 9.1 it means that the rate of change of T_x with respect to y is identical with that of T_y with respect to x. With a little bit of geometrical intuition – or experiment – some readers will be able to convince themselves that this is reasonable.

Inspection of Figure 9.1 reveals the existence of a third plane that can be cut out of the function. We can take our knife and cut the function open perpendicularly to the z axis, revealing a surface such as the shaded one in Figure 9.3a. If you look at this surface straight on, i.e., in the x-y plane, you will see the curve of its outer edge which is drawn in Figure 9.3b. This shows how x and y vary with each other when z is held constant at the value of z at which we cut open the surface. The tangent gradient to this curve measures the rate of change required of y when x changes if z is to remain constant.

A familiar device in economic analysis is to convert a three-dimensional function to a two-dimensional surface by plotting 'iso-bars' each one of which shows all those combinations of two variables that keep the value

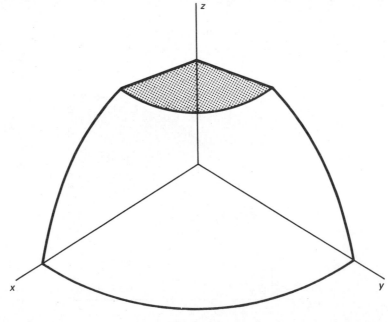

Figure 9.3a

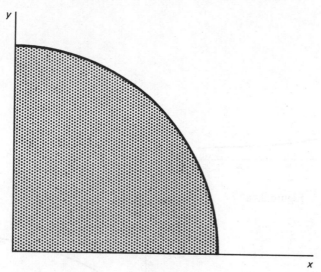

Figure 9.3b

of the function constant at a particular value. Each iso-bar is distinguished from the others by the different value at which the function is held constant. The curve in Figure 9.3b is an example. An indifference curve which shows all those combinations of two goods that keep utility constant, and an iso-quant which shows all those combinations of two inputs that keep output constant, are examples commonly encountered in economics. We shall refer to these curves by the general name 'iso-f' curves: any one such curve tells us all the combinations of two variables that keep the value of the function constant at some stated level.

We may illustrate each of the planes we have been discussing by plotting in Figure 9.4 three relations derived from our demand function in (3) above. Figure 9.4a shows the curve relating q and p, with y held constant at 10. Figure 9.4b shows the curve relating q and y with p held constant at 5. Figure 9.4b shows the curve relating p and y for q held constant at 100. The first two curves are self explanatory. The third curve shows how price and income are to be changed so that their separate effects on q are to offset each other so as to keep q constant at 100. It is another example of an iso-f curve.

9.6 The Slope of the Iso-f curve

We have already evaluated $\partial q/\partial p$ and $\partial q/\partial y$ and it remains to evaluate the slope in the third plane. This slope, illustrated in Figure 9.3 is the slope of the iso-f curve. The method of evaluating it is not easy to discover, although fortunately it proves to be easy to apply once we have developed it.

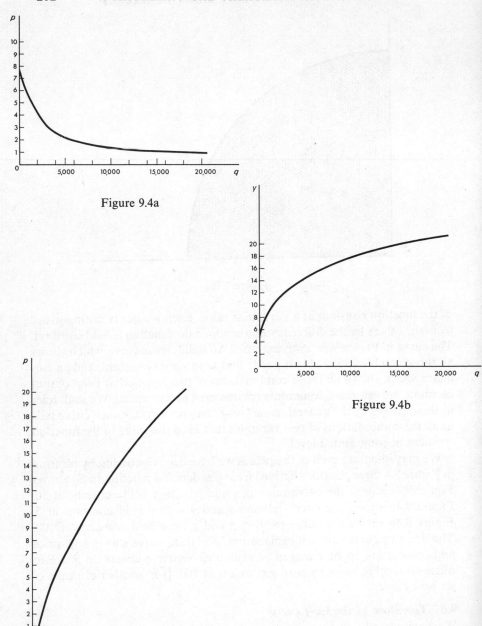

Figure 9.4a

Figure 9.4b

Figure 9.4c

We are obliged to persist with this development by the importance of the slope of the iso-*f* curve in economic applications.

We proceed in two steps. We first ask how q varies when *both* p and y vary. This will give us $\Delta q = f(\Delta p, \Delta y)$. When we have an expression for this we can, as a second step, hold q constant and discover what Δy *must be* for a given Δp if $\Delta q = 0$.

Step One   The change in q when both p and y vary is given by

$$\Delta q = f(y + \Delta y, p + \Delta p) - f(y, p). \tag{24}$$

This merely says that if y increases by Δy and p increases by Δp, the change in q is found by discovering the value of q when the new values of y and p are inserted into the function, and subtracting the value of q given by the original value of y and p.

We now play a few tricks with this function to get it into the form we require. As is so often the case, each step may appear arbitrary, but the object is the familiar one of transforming an expression into a form that reveals the relation in which we are interested. The first step is to add $f(y, p + \Delta p)$ to the right hand side of (24) *and* subtract it as well, an operation which, of course, leaves the equality unaffected. (24) now becomes

$$\Delta q = f(v + \Delta y, p + \Delta p) - f(y, p + \Delta p) + f(y, p + \Delta p) - f(y, p). \tag{25}$$

Next we multiply the first two terms in (25) by $\Delta y / \Delta y$ and the last two terms by $\Delta p / \Delta p$. Since both of these expressions are equal to unity, neither of the operations affects the value of the right hand side of (25). These operations give us

$$\Delta q = \frac{[f(y + \Delta y, p + \Delta p) - f(y, p + \Delta p)] \, \Delta y}{\Delta y}$$

$$+ \frac{[f(y, p + \Delta p) - f(y, p)] \, \Delta p}{\Delta p}. \tag{26}$$

We now have Δq as the sum of two terms, the first being the ratio of a complicated expression to the change in y and the second the ratio of a complicated expression to the change in p.

We now proceed as we did with simple derivatives: we try to find the limit of these two ratios as the change in y and the change in p get smaller and smaller, indeed as Δy and $\Delta p \rightarrow 0$. First we consider the behaviour of the first term, *leaving aside momentarily the Δy in the numerator*. What we wish to find is

$$\lim_{\Delta y \to 0} \frac{f(y + \Delta y, p + \Delta p) - f(y, p + \Delta p)}{\Delta y}. \tag{27}$$

From the definition of a partial derivative (see equation (8) above) we see that this is the partial derivative of q with respect to y evaluated at the point $(y, p + \Delta p)$. We therefore see that (27) is

$$\frac{\partial}{\partial y} f(y, p + \Delta p) = f_y. \tag{28}$$

As Δp approaches zero this will approach f_y evaluated at the point y, p.

We now consider the second term in (26), *leaving aside momentarily the Δp in the numerator*. We wish to find

$$\lim_{\Delta p \to 0} \frac{f(y, p + \Delta p) - f(y, p)}{\Delta p}. \tag{29}$$

Equation (8) tells us that (29) is the partial derivative of q with respect to p evaluated at the point (y, p). So we see that (29) is

$$\frac{\partial q}{\partial p} f(y, p) = f_p.$$

We have now taken the limits of the two terms on the right hand side of (26). Replacing the terms Δy and Δp in the numerators, which we had temporarily left aside, we see that

$$\lim_{\Delta k, \Delta y \to 0} \Delta q = f_y \, \Delta y + f_p \, \Delta p. \tag{30}$$

This is a result of fundamental importance and we must stop and consider how we have arrived at it. In (24) we wrote down the exact definition of Δq, and we then manipulated the expression to arrive at (26). Substitution of values for y, Δy, p, and Δp into (26) would always give the correct value of Δq. In going from (26) to (31) we substituted in f_y and f_x which are the values approached by the two expressions in the right hand side of (26) as the changes in p and y get smaller and smaller. Thus (31) gives us an approximation to the correct value of Δq as p and y change together, the approximation getting closer and closer to the correct result as the changes in p and y get closer and closer to zero. Thus we can write $\Delta q = f_y \, \Delta y + f_p \, \Delta p$ plus an error that can be made as small as is desired by taking Δx and Δy appropriately close to zero. To indicate that we are dealing with arbitrarily small increments in y and p, not just increments of any size, we write dy in place of Δy, dp in place of Δp and dq in place of Δq. With this change we have arrived at what is called *the total differential of the function*:

$$dq = f_y \, dy + f_p \, dp. \tag{31a}$$

Using the alternative notation for the partial derivatives we can write this as

$$dq = \frac{\partial q}{\partial y}\,dy + \frac{\partial q}{\partial p}\,dp. \tag{31b}$$

This is a remarkable and very powerful result. It says that we can approximate the change in the value of a function when there are small changes in all of the independent variables by multiplying the (small) change in each of the variables by the partial derivative of the function with respect to that variable and summing the result even though each partial was evaluated holding the other variable constant.

9.7 A Geometrical Interpretation of the Total Differential

Consider first taking a function of one variable, $y = f(x)$, and approximating the change in y in response to a change in x by

$$dy = f'(x)\,dx. \tag{32}$$

If we evaluate $f'(x)$ at a particular point on the function we obtain the slope of the line tangent to the curve at that point. (32) is thus a linear function relating dy to dx by a constant which is the slope of the tangent. Hence when we use (32) to estimate dy for a given dx we are estimating dy by moving along the tangent instead of obtaining dy exactly by moving along the curve which graphs the actual function. The procedure clearly involves an error, the magnitude of which is indicated by ε in Figure 9.5. It should be clear from an inspection of the figure that the error gets smaller and smaller as dx is taken smaller and smaller. Indeed as $dx \to 0$ the error, ε, $\to 0$.

With functions of two variables the total differential measures movements along the plane that is tangent to the surface at the point at which the differential is evaluated. This is illustrated in Figure. 9.6. The plane in this figure is assumed to be the plane that is tangent to the function in Figure 9.1 at the point Q. Measuring dq according to (31) is equivalent to measuring it along the tangent plane for given changes in y and p. Clearly, if the surface is curved, there will be an error involved, but an error that can be made as small as is desired by letting dy and dp become appropriately small.

Let us now find the total differential for our demand function given in (3)

$$q = 10y^2 + 2y^4p^{-2} - 3p^3.$$

We know from (4) and (5) what the partials are and we can write the total differential as

$$dq = (20y + 8y^3p^{-2})\,dy + (-4y^4p^{-3} - 9p^2)\,dp. \tag{33}$$

We now have a expression that tells us (approximately) how q changes as both y and p change.

Step Two In trying to evaluate the slope of the iso-f curve you will recall that we set out to find how y would have to change if p were changed with q held constant. As a first step we developed an expression, the total differential, showing how q changed when both y and p changed. We can now make use of this result to discover how y must change as p changes if

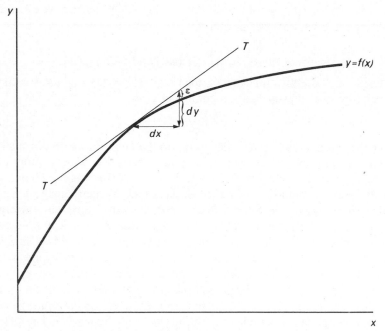

Figure 9.5

q is to remain constant. If q is to be constant, the total differential must be zero. Thus we merely take the expression in (31) and set it equal to zero:

$$dq = f_y\,dy + f_p\,dp = 0.$$

Now we rearrange this by subtracting $f_p\,dp$ from both sides:

$$f_y\,dy = -f_p\,dp.$$

Since dp is an arbitrarily small increment in p we can divide both sides by dp. We also divide both sides by f_y and obtain

$$\frac{dy}{dp} = -\frac{f_p}{f_y}. \tag{34}$$

On the left hand side of (34) we have the ratio of two small increments, one in p and the one in y necessary to keep q constant. We now regard this ratio as the derivative of y with respect to p. We have seen earlier that the derivative is the limit of the corresponding incremental ratio so we should not be disturbed to encounter this idea here. We will, nevertheless, say a bit more about it after we have completed the present argument. If we interpret dy/dp in (34) as a derivative, we have the result we require. We see from it

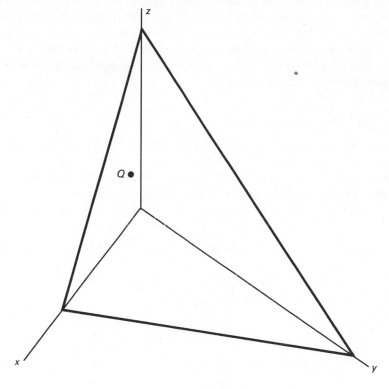

Figure 9.6

that the tangent slope dy/dp with q held constant is minus the ratio of the two partial derivatives of p and y. The general result has a strong intuitive appeal. To see this consider a numerical example. If a unit change in y causes demand to change in the same direction by, say, $\frac{1}{2}$ a unit, and if a unit change in price causes demand to change in the opposite direction by, say, 0·25, then a rise in income of 1 unit will have to be met by a rise in price of 2 units if demand is to be unchanged.

We now return to the example of equation (3). We can use the partials from (4) and (5) to substitute into (34) and obtain

$$\frac{dy}{dp} = -\left(\frac{20y+8y^3p^{-2}}{-4y^4p^{-3}-9p^2}\right).$$ (35)

This expression tells us how much y must be changed to compensate for a change in p if q is held constant. Geometrically it is the slope of the curve obtained by slicing the function open in the p–y plane. Such a curve is shown for q held constant at 100 in Figure 9.4(a) and (35) is the expression that allows us to determine the slope of this curve at any p–y point. If you inspect (35) you will see that for $y, p > 0$ the whole expression is positive. This shows that if price is raised (*ceteris paribus*, this *lowers* demand) income must also be raised (*ceteris paribus* this *raises* demand) if quantity demanded is to remain unchanged.

9.8   The Differential Coefficient

In step two above we read the dy/dp in (33) as 'the derivative of y with respect to p'. In fact we obtain it by taking dp, which was an arbitrarily small increment in p, and dividing it into dy which was a small increment in y necessary to keep q constant. Were we correct in interpreting this ratio as a derivative? To see that we were, take the total differential from (31a) above,

$$dq = f_y \, dy + f_p \, dp,$$ (31a)

and let $dp = 0$ so that only y influences the change in the value of the function (i.e., p is a constant). This gives us

$$dq = f_y \, dy$$

or
$$\frac{dq}{dy} = f_y.$$ (36)

This tells us that we can regard the derivative, f_y as the ratio of the change in q to the arbitrarily small increment in y (i.e., the ratio as the d's get smaller and smaller). These small increments are called *differentials* and, since the derivative may be regarded as the ratio of two of them, it is sometimes called a 'differential ratio' or a 'differential coefficient'.

This is a good point at which to read or re-read the starred paragraph 8.7 of the last chapter. In fact, we used there the notion of a total differential, and if this is realised, equation (25) of Chapter 8 may be more comprehensible.

9.9 Functions of Functions and Total Differentials

Finally we need one more very powerful result that is quite easily established. We ask what happens if both y and p are functions of some other variable, say t. We seek the effect on q of an arbitrarily small increment in t. In doing this we shall assume without proving it that the function-of-a-function rule can be applied to partial derivatives of functions of more than one variable in just the same way as it is applied to derivatives of functions of one variable. In Chapter 5 (see page 116) we established that if $x=x(y)$ and $y=y(z)$ then $dx/dz=dx/dy \cdot dy/dz$. We now assume that we can also show that, for any single valued function, if $x=f(y, z)$ and $y=y(t)$ then [1]

$$\frac{\partial x}{\partial t} = \frac{\partial x}{\partial y} \cdot \frac{dy}{dt}. \tag{37}$$

We can now set up our present problem as follows. We have

$$q = D(y, p)$$
$$y = y(t)$$
$$p = p(t)$$

and we wish to find dq/dt. Applying the function-of-a-function rule gives us

$$\frac{dq}{dt} = \frac{\partial q}{\partial y} \cdot \frac{dy}{dt} + \frac{\partial q}{\partial p} \cdot \frac{dp}{dt}$$

$$= f_y \cdot \frac{dy}{dt} + f_p \cdot \frac{dp}{dt}. \tag{37}$$

We already know from (31), however, that the total differential of q is $f_y\, dy + f_p\, dp$, so we can see that, for practical purposes, all we need to do is to take the total differential and divide it through by dt. This result is tremendously important and will be used many times in subsequent treatments.

9.10 Some Examples

As usual, there are exercises at the end of this chapter but we shall work through two more examples before going on.

(1) Consider a production function, $f(L, C)$, where L and C are the quantities of labour and capital used. Let the function be

$$q = L^{3/4}C^{1/4}. \tag{38}$$

[1] For a proof see R. D. G. Allen, *Mathematical Analysis, op. cit.,* p. 333.

We wish to discover the slope of the iso-quants that show how capital and labour can be substituted for each other keeping output constant. We do this in the following steps:

$$\frac{\partial q}{\partial L} = \frac{3}{4} L^{-1/4} C^{1/4} \tag{39}$$

$$\frac{\partial q}{\partial C} = \frac{1}{4} L^{3/4} C^{-3/4}. \tag{40}$$

Now we have the two partial derivatives of the function with respect to C and L. In order to find the partial of L with respect to C *holding q constant* we make use of (34) to write

$$\frac{dC}{dL} = -\frac{f_L}{f_C} = -\frac{\frac{3}{4}L^{-1/4}C^{1/4}}{\frac{1}{4}L^{3/4}C^{-3/4}}$$

$$= -\frac{3C}{L}. \tag{41}$$

This tells us that the slope of the iso-quant depends only on the ratio of labour to capital and not on the absolute levels of the two factors. In this production function the slope of the iso-quant for a given factor ratio is thus the same for all scales of output. This is an important property of any production function with constant returns to scale, of which the above is an example. Much use is made of this property in production theory and we shall return to it in Chapter 10, Section 2.

(2) Now let us assume that both L and C are functions of time, t. Possibly both the population and the capital stock are increasing over time. Equation (31) tells us how to write the total differential of this function:

$$dq = f_L \, dL + f_C \, dC. \tag{42}$$

Now we can make use of the result in (37) to handle the case in which $L = L(t)$ and $C = C(t)$:

$$\frac{dq}{dt} = f_L \frac{dL}{dt} + f_C \frac{dC}{dt}. \tag{43}$$

This expression tells us the rate at which production is increasing over time, given the production function and the rate at which labour and capital are increasing over time.

9.11   Maximum and Minimum Values of Functions of Two or More Variables

Our final task in this chapter is to learn how to find stationary values of functions of more than one variable. Of course not all functions of two or more variables will have stationary values. A plane, for example, is the three-dimensional equivalent of a straight line, and just as a linear function has neither a maximum nor a minimum value (it goes on increasing indefinitely in one direction and decreasing in the other) so a plane has neither a maximum nor a minimum. Inspection of Figure 9.1 (see page 198) suggests that the function illustrated there has no stationary value either, at least in the range of positive x, y, and z. But the thimble-shaped function

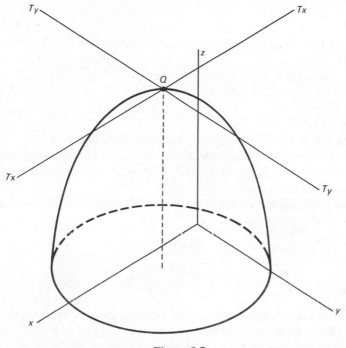

Figure 9.7

in Figure 9.7 has an obvious maximum at Q, where the two tangents, T_x and T_y are both horizontal. We may assert at once that a *necessary condition* for a maximum is that both partial derivatives are zero. This says that we cannot be at a maximum if we can increase the value of the function by changing either of its arguments, the other held constant. We can be quite sure that these two conditions are not sufficient: if the thimble were turned upside down, we should have a minimum where the slopes of the two tangents were also horizontal. Thus, as with the case of functions of one variable, we require second-order conditions to distinguish maxima from minima. Furthermore, we must expect stationary values that are not extreme values. The possibilities of non-extreme stationary values and non-stationary inflexion points in three dimensions become quite complex. Fortunately, it is not necessary to consider them here.

Second-order conditions for distinguishing minima from maxima in functions of more than one variable are not too difficult but they do require that we develop a second-order total differential of the function. We shall put off doing this until we need it on the grounds that this is already an overly-long chapter and it is time to see if we can get any return from the heavy investment in techniques that we have already made.

Exercises

1 Find the first- and second-order partial derivatives of the following functions:

(i) $z = 3x^2 + 4xy + y^2$
(ii) $z = x^3 + x^2y + 2y^2x + 2y^3$
(iii) $z = ax/y^2$
(iv) $z = 1/xy$.

Show that the general result $f_{xy} = f_{yx}$ holds in these cases.

2 Find an expression for the slope of the iso-z curves for (iv), and evaluate the slope at $x = 5$, $y = 10$, and at $x = 15$, $y = 30$. What do you conclude about the slopes of the iso-z curves?

3 Find the total differential dz/dt for each of the functions in Exercise 1, if

$$x = 3t$$

and

$$y = 2t^2.$$

4 If

$$k = \frac{1}{1 - (c - m)(1 - t)}$$

find the first- and second-order partial derivatives of k with respect to c, m, and t. (*Hint:* Express the first-order partials in terms of k and calculate the second-order partials without expanding powers of k.)

5 A consumer has a utility function

$$U = x^\alpha y^\beta$$

where x and y are the quantities that he consumes of the only two goods available to him, where $0 < \alpha, \beta < 1$ and where U is an ordinal index of utility. When we say U is an ordinal index of utility we mean that its value of U allows us to say which of two $x - y$ combinations is preferred (that yielding the higher U), but the function does not allow us to measure utility to the extent of saying by *how much* one is preferred to the other.

(i) Show that there is diminishing marginal utility to increased consumption of either commodity when the consumption of the other is held constant. (*Hint:* This requires both first order partial derivatives.)

(ii) Show that the indifference curves have a negative slope.

(iii) What happens to the marginal utility of x as y is increased? (*Hint:* You need a cross partial here.)

(iv) Do you need any further calculation to discover what happens to the marginal utility of y as x is increased?

(v) Does the marginal utility of x or y ever reach zero for finite quantities of x or y?

CHAPTER 10

APPLICATIONS OF PARTIAL DERIVATIVES

10.1 Partial Derivatives and Elasticities

In Chapter 5 we dealt with price elasticity of demand first using incremental ratios and then using derivatives. At that time we considered the simple function $q^d = D(p)$, where q^d is the quantity demanded of some commodity and p is its price. The more general hypothesis used in economics is that the demand for the ith commodity depends on the price of that commodity, on all other prices, on income, and on tastes. We write this[1]

$$q_i^d = D_i(p_1, \ldots, p_i, \ldots, p_n, y). \tag{1}$$

This is read 'the quantity demanded of the ith commodity is a function of the prices of all n commodities, including the ith one, and of income'. We now define price elasticity of demand as

$$\frac{\partial q_i^d}{\partial p_i} \cdot \frac{p_i}{q_i^d}. \tag{2}$$

Thus, elasticity involves the partial derivative of the quantity demanded with respect to price. We must take a partial derivative because the demand for a commodity depends on things other than its own price and price elasticity refers to what happens when price changes *all other things held constant*.

We can also define cross elasticity between the ith and the jth goods as

$$\frac{\partial q_i^d}{\partial p_j} \cdot \frac{p_j}{q_i^d}. \tag{3}$$

[1] Notice tastes are not introduced as an argument in the function: they are usually thought of as determining the form of the function. Thus if $q_i^d = 2p_1^2 - 3p_2^3 \ldots$ a change in tastes might cause the function to shift, e.g., to $q_i^d = 1 \cdot 9p_1^2 - 3 \cdot 2p_2^{2 \cdot 9} \ldots$. The omission of tastes from the function is made because we have no measure of tastes and so are unable to enter them explicitly into the function. This approach, however, raises many difficulties when we come to test demand theory. See Lipsey, *Positive Economics, op. cit.*, pp. 206–209.

Finally we define income elasticity of demand as

$$\frac{\partial q_i^d}{\partial y} \cdot \frac{y}{q_i^d}. \tag{4}$$

In each of these cases we are using a partial derivative. We are asking, therefore, what happens to demand as one of the terms in the demand function varies *all other terms being held constant*. Students are often upset by the frequent use of *ceteris-paribus* arguments in economics. We have seen that there is a well-established mathematical tool of proven value for handling such arguments. Indeed *ceteris-paribus* arguments in elementary economics are usually only a verbal translation of a treatment which, when expressed formally, relies on partial derivatives. There is nothing mysterious about the technique: it involves nothing more than discovering how the dependant variable changes as one of the independent variables changes while all the others are held constant. Once we have mastered the tool of total differentials we can deal with simultaneous changes in many variables if we wish to do so, but it is often appropriate to deal with *ceteris-paribus* changes taking one variable at a time.

10.2   The Cobb-Douglas Production Function

In production theory we assume that the output of a firm is related to its inputs of factors of production. We refer to this relation as a production function and we write it:

$$q = q(x_1, x_2, \ldots, x_m) \tag{5}$$

where q is the quantity produced per period of time and x_1 to x_m are the quantities of m factors of production used by the firm over the same period of time.

A great deal of effort has been expended over the last thirty years in trying to estimate from empirical data the precise form of production functions for individual firms or for whole industries. One function that appears to describe much observed behaviour is the so-called Cobb-Douglas production function, an example of which we met on page 209,

$$q = Ax_1^\alpha x_2^\beta \ldots x_m^\eta \tag{6}$$

where $\alpha + \beta + \cdots + \eta = 1$ and $0 < \alpha, \beta, \ldots, \eta < 1$. This says that output is given by the *product* of all the inputs each raised to a positive fractional power, the result multiplied by some number A, and with the added restriction that all the powers should sum to unity.

We do not need to worry here about the problems – which can be formidable – of estimating such functions statistically, nor do we need to take sides on the debate about the degree to which the evidence does support the hypothesis that many, if not all, industries do have Cobb-Douglas production functions. For purposes of the present exercise we can *assume* that the econometricians have told us that the Cobb-Douglas production function does seem to provide a reasonable description of production behaviour in many industries, and our job as economic theorists is to discover the implications of this. We ask ourselves the question: if this function does hold, what other things can we expect to hold as well? This is a typical task of the economic theorist. He takes it that certain things are true of the world and seeks to discover what other things must also be true. A good economist will be able to suggest immediately a 'shopping list' of relevant questions when presented with a problem such as this one. In this case our shopping list must include such questions as, what are the shapes of the total, average, and marginal product and cost curves as one factor is varied in the short run? what are the returns to scale when all factors are varied in the long run? what will be the effects on factor earnings of variations in factor supplies? Other interesting questions may suggest themselves as the analysis proceeds, but we start with a list of questions that consideration of standard theory suggests we should ask about any production function that we wish to take seriously.

We shall work with a two-factor production function, identifying the two inputs as labour (L) and capital (C). The argument easily generalises to any number of factors. The student should follow the general reasoning for the two factor cases by working with a numerical example of his own. The function $q = L^{3/4}C^{1/4}$ is one we suggest you use, and, if you check each of the results for this function yourself, you will find it easier to follow the more general argument in the text. The general function for two inputs with which we shall work is

$$q = AL^{\alpha}C^{\beta} \tag{7}$$

where $\alpha + \beta = 1$, A is a constant, and L and C are the quantities used of two factors of production, labour and capital.

It is often convenient to remove the constant A. This can always be done with any multiplicative function merely by dividing through by the constant. This gives

$$\frac{q}{A} = L^{\alpha}C^{\beta} \tag{8}$$

and merely by defining a new unit of measurement

$$q^* = \frac{q}{A} \tag{9}$$

we can write

$$q^* = L^\alpha C^\beta. \tag{10}$$

Thus we see that the value of A depends on the units chosen, and a change in unit chosen will cause a change in A. It follows that it is always possible to pick a unit in which to make our measurements such that $A = 1$. We can also make use of the restriction that α and β add to unity to rewrite (10) as

$$q^* = L^\alpha C^{1-\alpha}. \tag{11}$$

For various reasons it is convenient in the present treatment to retain the constant, and so we shall use the production function in the form given by (7).

We start by taking capital as fixed and ask how production varies as inputs of labour are varied. To show that capital is being held constant for the present exercises we put a bar over the variable C:

$$q = AL^\alpha \bar{C}^\beta. \tag{12}$$

This shows how total product varies as labour input varies, capital being held constant at some level $\bar{C}$. Since $\bar{C}^\beta$ will be a constant, we can define a new constant $b = A\bar{C}^\beta$ and write

$$q = bL^\alpha. \tag{13}$$

Equation (13) defines the text-book total-product curve with output as a function of the input of the variable factor of production.

The average product is found by dividing total product by the number of units of labour used:

$$AP = \frac{q}{L} = \frac{bL^\alpha}{L}, \tag{14}$$

$$= bL^{\alpha-1}. \tag{15}$$

Since $0 < \alpha < 1$ it follows that $-1 < \alpha - 1 < 0$, and to emphasise this we write

$$AP = \frac{b}{L^{1-\alpha}}. \tag{16}$$

(16) shows that average product is always positive, but that it declines continuously as labour input rises. In case we are not sure of this from inspection of (16), or by recalling page 169, we can differentiate it as follows:

$$\frac{\partial AP}{\partial L} = b(\alpha - 1)L^{\alpha-2}. \tag{17}$$

Since $0 < \alpha < 1$ it follows that (17) is negative for any positive value of L.

This proves formally what our inspection of (16) suggested, that the AP declines continuously as labour input is increased.

The marginal product of labour is $\partial q/\partial L$. Differentiating (13) this is

$$MP = \frac{\partial Q}{\partial L} = \alpha b L^{\alpha - 1}. \qquad (18)$$

We know that the exponent on L is negative, so that L appears in the denominator of this expression. This tells us that marginal product declines

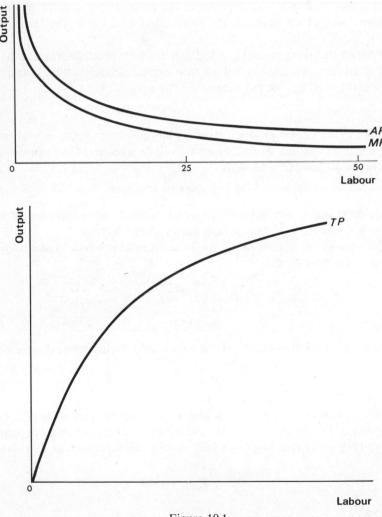

Figure 10.1

continuously as labour inputs increase but that it never becomes negative.[1]
(To check that MP declines continuously you should calculate $\partial MP/\partial L$
and check that it is negative for all positive values of L.)

These product curves are plotted in Figure 10.1 for the particular numerical values stated in the figure. We have now made our first discovery about
this production function: marginal and average products decline from the
outset. In the production function usually shown in text books, the marginal and average products rise at first and only decline eventually. The
type of curves usually assumed in elementary production theory are illustrated in Figure 10.2.

Now let us consider costs. If we let w and r stand for the prices of labour
and capital respectively, we can write

$$TC = wL + rC. \tag{19}$$

We want TC as a function of q. We can get total short run cost very easily
since C is fixed at $\bar{C}$ and only L varies. Thus q is a simple function of L and
so also is TC. First we must slightly transpose our basic short-run production function

$$q = bL^{\alpha} \tag{20}$$

in the following simple way:

$$L^{\alpha} = \frac{q}{b} \tag{21}$$

or

$$L = \frac{q^{1/\alpha}}{b^{1/\alpha}}. \tag{22}$$

---

[1] We have said that the student should check his understanding of the general Cobb-
Douglas results obtained in the text by carrying out similar manipulations for the function
$q = L^{3/4}C^{1/4}$. To show what is required we shall quickly obtain the results so far established
for the case of this specific function. Assume capital is held constant at 16 units and use (13):

$$q = 2L^{3/4}$$

$$AP = \frac{2L^{3/4}}{L} = \frac{2}{L^{1/4}} = 2L^{-1/4}$$

$$\frac{\partial AP}{\partial L} = -\frac{1}{2}L^{-5/4} = -\frac{1}{2L^{5/4}}$$

$$MP_L = \frac{1 \cdot 5}{L^{1/4}} = 1 \cdot 5L^{-1/4}$$

$$\frac{\partial MP}{\partial L} = 0 \cdot 375L^{-5/4}.$$

We now substitute L from (22) into the total cost expression in (19). This gives

$$TC = \frac{wq^{1/\alpha}}{b^{1/\alpha}} + r\bar{C}. \qquad (23)$$

In the short run capital is fixed, and so also is the cost of capital: $r\bar{C} = F$ is

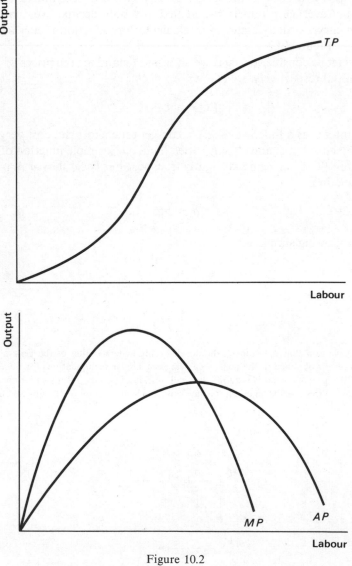

Figure 10.2

fixed costs. If the firm buys its labour in a competitive market we can assume that the price of labour, w, is a constant. We now have total cost in (23) and can calculate average cost merely by dividing by q:

$$AC = \frac{TC}{q} = \frac{wq^{1/\alpha}}{b^{1/\alpha}q} + \frac{F}{q} \tag{24}$$

$$= \frac{wq^{\frac{1}{\alpha}-1}}{b^{1/\alpha}} + \frac{F}{q}. \tag{25}$$

Since $1/\alpha > 1$ it follows that $(1/\alpha) - 1 > 0$. Thus the exponent on q is positive and average cost must rise continuously as output rises. Average fixed cost, however, declines as the fixed capital cost, F, is spread over a larger and larger number of units. The average total cost curve declines at first and then rises.[1]

The marginal cost curve is also easily calculated by differentiating (23):

$$MC = \frac{dTC}{dq} = \frac{wq^{\frac{1}{\alpha}-1}}{\alpha b^{1/\alpha}}. \tag{26}$$

Since $(1/\alpha) - 1$ is positive marginal cost rises continuously as output is increased.

The fact that the average and marginal cost curves do not have the text-book U-shape is a consequence of the shape of the average and marginal product curves on which we have already commented. The ATC curve does have the usually assumed 'U-shape' because of the influence of overhead costs.

We have already discovered some interesting facts. With a production function that is not inconsistent with observed data, the cost curves do not have the shape they are usually assumed to have in standard text-books. This is a very interesting observation and indeed it turns out to hold for all constant-returns-to-scale production functions. We now investigate returns to scale, that is long-run production behaviour. The basic production function written with the units chosen so that the constant $A = 1$ is

$$q = L^\alpha C^\beta \tag{27}$$

which, because $\alpha + \beta = 1$, can be rewritten as

$$q = L^\alpha C^{1-\alpha}. \tag{28}$$

[1] The student may wish to gain some practice in differentiation by proving for himself that the level of output for which the AC curve is a minimum is given by the following expression:

$$q = b\left(\frac{F}{w}\right)^\alpha \frac{1}{\left(\frac{1}{\alpha}-1\right)^\alpha}.$$

Let us investigate long-run returns to scale by first trying the experiment of doubling both inputs:

$$q = (2L)^\alpha (2C)^{1-\alpha}$$
$$= 2^\alpha L^\alpha 2^{1-\alpha} C^{1-\alpha}$$
$$= 2L^\alpha C^{1-\alpha}. \tag{29}$$

Since before we doubled our inputs q was given by $q = L^\alpha C^{1-\alpha}$ we see that doubling our inputs doubles our output. Possibly this was just an accident holding when we doubled our inputs but not for other changes. We are, of course, interested in any proportional change that we might make in all of our inputs. To investigate this more general problem we multiply all inputs by some constant λ. This gives us

$$q = (\lambda L)^\alpha (\lambda C)^{1-\alpha}$$
$$= \lambda^\alpha L^\alpha \lambda^{1-\alpha} C^{1-\alpha}$$
$$= \lambda L^\alpha C^{1-\alpha} \tag{30}$$

and, since $L^\alpha C^{1-\alpha}$ is our original output before we multiplied inputs by λ, it follows that multiplying all our inputs by some amount, λ, multiplies our output by the same amount, λ. Evidently the Cobb-Douglas production function displays constant returns to scale throughout its whole range.

10.3 A Digression on Homogeneous Functions

The Cobb-Douglas production function is an example of a function that is homogeneous of degree one or, as it is sometimes called, a linear homogeneous function. In general, we say that a function is homogeneous of degree n if multiplying all the arguments in the function by the same constant, λ, multiplies the value of the function by λ to the power n, i.e., by λ^n.

First consider some examples:

$$q = LC \tag{31}$$

is homogeneous of degree 2 since

$$\lambda L \lambda C = \lambda^2 LC, \tag{32}$$

while

$$q = L^{1/4} C^{1/4} \tag{33}$$

is homogeneous of degree $\frac{1}{2}$ since

$$(\lambda L)^{1/4} (\lambda C)^{1/4} = \lambda^{1/2} L^{1/4} C^{1/4}. \tag{34}$$

Indeed the function

$$Y = X^n Z^m \tag{35}$$

is homogeneous of degree $n+m$ since

$$(\lambda X)^n (\lambda Z)^m = \lambda^{n+m} X^n Z^m. \tag{36}$$

Of course not all functions are homogeneous. Any of the previous examples can be rendered non-homogeneous by giving them an additive constant. For example

$$q = L^{1/2} C^{1/2} + a \tag{37}$$

is not homogeneous in L and C. If you multiply L and C by λ you do not multiply q by λ. This is because the constant is unchanged when you change L and C so that doubling L and C is not sufficient to double the output. Thus

$$\lambda L \lambda C + a = \lambda^2 LC + a \tag{38}$$

cannot be derived by multiplying $q = LC + a$ by any power of λ. In other words, if we have any function $y = y(x, z) + A$, where A is a constant, we cannot obtain the new value of the function resulting from multiplying x and z by λ by multiplying the original value by λ raised to any power: there is no n such that $\lambda^n y = y(x\lambda, z\lambda) + A$. Since any additive constant renders a function non-homogeneous it follows that homogeneous functions have the property that their value must be zero when all the variables in the function are zero. If Y is a homogeneous function of X then a graph of the function must pass through the origin. Formally we write this as follows: $f(0) = 0$.

10.4 Optimum Factor Proportions

The 'optimum factor proportion' means that combination of factors that is best from the point of view of minimising costs. We can pose the problem of discovering the optimum combination in more than one way. First, we can discover for any given level of output the factor inputs that minimise total cost. This is equivalent to finding the lowest budget line that touches a particular iso-quant. Secondly, we can take a given level of expenditure and find the factor combination that gives the highest total output. Graphically, in this case, we are moving along a given budget line looking for the highest attainable iso-quant. Our elementary theory tells us that in both cases we shall arrive at a point at which an iso-quant and a budget line are tangent to each other. If we repeat the operation for each level of output or expenditure and join up all the points so defined, we shall obtain an expansion path showing how factor inputs vary as total output changes. Three such paths are shown in Figure 10.3. In path (1) the ratio L/C rises as output expands, in (3) it falls, and in (2) it is constant. Thus on path (2) the optimum ratio in which to combine the factors depends only on relative prices and does not change as the scale of output changes.

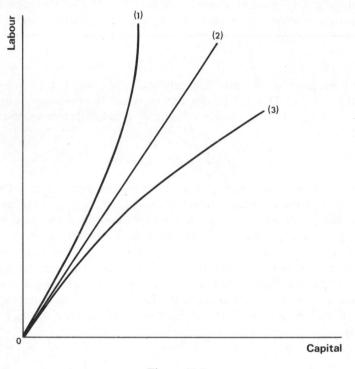

Figure 10.3

The path for the Cobb-Douglas production function is the linear path (2). Thus the optimum factor combination is independent of the scale of operations and depends only on relative prices. We must, however, leave the derivation of this important result until we have one further technique at our command, that of constrained maxima, which we shall study in Chapter 11.

We can, however, get close to the result if we calculate the expression for the slope of the iso-quants of this function. In the case of production functions, the iso-f curves show combinations of the two factors L and C that keep q constant, and the slope of the curves show the rate of substitution between the two factors necessary to keep q constant. The slope of the iso-quant is easily calculated by recalling the result in the previous chapter (see pages 206–207):

$$\frac{dL}{dC} = -\frac{\dfrac{\partial q}{\partial C}}{\dfrac{\partial q}{\partial L}} = -\frac{\beta L^{\alpha} C^{\beta - 1}}{\alpha L^{\alpha - 1} C^{\beta}} = -\frac{\beta L}{\alpha C}. \tag{39}$$

Thus we see that the slope of the iso-quant depends only on the *ratio* in which the two factors are used and not on the absolute levels of either. (This is a generalisation of the result found in example 1 in page 210 of the previous chapter.) This suggests, as we shall prove formally in a subsequent chapter, that the factor proportions that minimise costs with respect to given factor prices are the same whatever the scale of production. If this is so, then optimum factor proportions for given factor prices are the same at all levels of output: all expansion paths are linear.

10.5 The Distribution of the Total Product

Early Classical economists such as Smith and Ricardo felt that one of the most important problems of political economy was to discover the laws that governed the distribution of the national product between the three classes of society, the labourers, the capitalists, and the landlords. Gradually, towards the latter part of the nineteenth century, the marginal productivity theory gained ascendance. According to this theory each factor received a payment, per unit of time worked, equal to the value of the marginal product of that factor. Thus if one more labourer added to the existing labour force would add 10 bushels of wheat per month to the product, then the wage rate for *all* workers would be 10 bushels of wheat per month, and the total monthly wage bill would be 10 bushels multiplied by the number of labourers employed. Similarly for each other factor. The marginal productivity theory explained only the demand curve for a factor, and supply had to be explained by other considerations. In equilibrium, however, price and quantity must be at some point on the demand curve (the point where the curve is cut by the supply curve) whence it is a prediction of the theory that in equilibrium the price of every factor will be equal to the value of its marginal product.

The theory posed two major problems. The first was a purely theoretical one and was usually called the *adding-up problem*. The question here was: if each factor is paid at a rate equal to its marginal product, will the total payments to all factors be equal to total production? If total payment exactly exhausts the product there is no problem, but, if these payments are greater than or less than total production, problems must arise. Clearly, it is logically impossible to pay to factors a real amount in excess of what is produced while, if less than what is produced is paid out, the problem is: who gets the surplus and how? If payment according to marginal product was impossible because sufficient production would not be available, the marginal productivity theory would be in real trouble. Indeed, it would be refuted on purely logical grounds, since it would be impossible to fulfil the conditions of the theory that each factor should be paid a rate equal to its marginal product.

Now let us consider the adding-up problem in the case of the Cobb-Douglas production function. The function was written in (7)

$$q = AL^{\alpha}C^{\beta}.$$

We have seen (pages 222–23) that this function is homogeneous and if we assume that $\alpha + \beta = 1$ the function is linear and homogeneous (i.e., it has constant returns to scale).

If we wish to study the distribution of the total product, we must first determine the marginal products of the two factors:

$$\frac{\partial q}{\partial L} = A\alpha L^{\alpha-1}C^{\beta} \tag{40}$$

$$\frac{\partial q}{\partial C} = A\beta L^{\alpha}C^{\beta-1}. \tag{41}$$

The total payment to each factor is, of course, the rate of pay per unit *times* the number of units employed. This is

$$Y_L = \frac{\partial q}{\partial L}\cdot L = A\alpha L^{\alpha-1}C^{\beta}L \tag{42}$$

$$= A\alpha L^{\alpha}C^{\beta} \tag{43}$$

where Y_L stands for the real income of labour.[1] But from (7) we know that $AL^{\alpha}C^{\beta}$ is the total product, q. Therefore we can write (43) as

$$Y_L = \alpha q. \tag{44}$$

---

[1] Notice that we have expressed the wage in real units. If we wished we could multiply by the price of the product and obtain the wage in money units. Our problem would then be to discover if the money value of payments to factors equalled the money value of the product. This is of course the same as discovering if the real payment to all factors equals real output.

Similarly for capital

$$Y_C = \frac{\partial q}{\partial C} \cdot C$$

$$= \beta a L^x C^{\beta - 1} C$$

$$= \beta a L^x C^{\beta}$$

$$= \beta q. \tag{45}$$

The total income paid to all factors is the sum of the payments to each factor. Thus we have

$$Y = Y_L + Y_C = \alpha q + \beta q$$

$$= (\alpha + \beta)q. \tag{46}$$

In the Cobb-Douglas case we have $\alpha + \beta = 1$. Thus (46) reduces to $Y = q$ and this tells us that the total product is just exhausted by income payments if both factors are paid at a rate equal to the value of their marginal products.

There are two other cases to be considered. If $\alpha + \beta < 1$ the production function is homogeneous of degree less than one: there are decreasing returns to scale. According to (46) $Y < q$, when both factors are paid the values of their respective marginal products. In this case there is a surplus equal to $(1 - \alpha - \beta)q$ remaining after all income payments have been made and there is nothing in the theory to show who should get it.

Consider the case in which $\alpha + \beta > 1$. The production function is homogeneous of degree greater than one: there are increasing returns to scale since doubling all inputs more than doubles the output. In this case (46) shows $Y > q$ so that it is impossible to pay each factor a wage equal to the value of its marginal product since there is not enough product to go around.

When we depart from the Cobb-Douglas function we find that the general case of homogeneous functions is handled with a theorem called Euler's Theorem (pronounced Oiler's Theorem!). This theorem is now well within the technical grasp of the readers of this book but we shall not present its proof here.[1] The general statement of the theorem is as follows. If

$$y = f(x_1, x_2, \ldots, x_n)$$

is a homogeneous function of degree one then it is true that

$$y = \frac{\partial y}{\partial x_1} \cdot x_1 + \frac{\partial y}{\partial x_2} \cdot x_2 + \cdots + \frac{\partial y}{\partial x_n} \cdot x_n. \tag{47}$$

[1] See Allen, *Mathematical Analysis, op. cit.*, pp. 317–19.

8*

Euler's theorem shows that for any linear homogeneous function (constant returns to scale) the value of the function is exactly equal to the sum of the partial derivatives with respect to each variable in the function each multiplied by the value of the variable in question. This shows that the adding-up problem is solved for constant returns production functions but not for increasing or decreasing returns ones. Of course if there is one factor that is hypothesised to earn a rent not related to the value of its marginal product then the adding up problem does not occur in such a severe form. In this case $n-1$ factors can be paid the value of their marginal products and the nth merely gets whatever is left over.

The second problem that arose with marginal productivity theory stemmed from the observation of what was thought to be a constancy in the relative shares of national income going to the various factors. When reasonably reliable data on distribution were first studied in the interwar period, the investigators observed what appeared to them to be a remarkable constancy in the distribution of income between labour and capital. What people had expected was never made too clear, but some economists seemed to have felt that the great increase in the capital stock over the previous 100 years should have increased the share of total income going to capital. Others felt that, because of the effect of diminishing returns, the distribution of income should have changed in some direction or another in response to changes in relative factor proportions, and that the persistance of a constancy must mean that, contrary to the prediction of marginal productivity theory, relative factor shares did not respond to relative factor proportions.

As economic theorists we can suppose that we have been presented with the following situation:

(1) we assume that marginal productivity theory holds; and
(2) we accept that over the last 100 years the total quantity of capital has increased faster than the total quantity of labour (i.e., C/L has risen).

We then ask ourselves:

(1) do we have any prediction to offer regarding the relative shares of income going to labour and to capital (i.e., about the ratio Y_C/Y_L)? and
(2) specifically, would the observation of a constant Y_C/Y_L over an extended period of time refute any prediction of the marginal productivity theory of distribution?

Let us consider what the answers to these questions would be if the production function were Cobb-Douglas. We have already determined the total quantity of the product going to labour and capital in equations (43) and (45):

$$Y_L = A\alpha L^\alpha C^\beta$$

and $$Y_C = A\beta L^\alpha C^\beta.$$

Thus the ratio of wages to gross profit is

$$\frac{Y_L}{Y_C} = \frac{A\alpha L^\alpha C^\beta}{A\beta L^\alpha C^\beta}$$

$$= \frac{\alpha}{\beta}. \tag{48}$$

The fraction of total income going to each factor is

$$\frac{Y_L}{Y} = \frac{A\alpha L^\alpha C^\beta}{AL^\alpha C^\beta} = \alpha \tag{49}$$

$$\frac{Y_C}{Y} = \frac{A\beta L^\alpha C^\beta}{AL^\alpha C^\beta} = \beta. \tag{50}$$

Thus the proportion of income going to labour and capital depends only on the coefficients α and β and is quite independent of the size of the labour force, L, and of the size of the capital stock, C. This is a most remarkable and interesting result, and we would have been unlikely to have discovered it by unaided verbal analysis. Yet the result follows from a routine application of a simple mathematical technique to the production function, and one does not have to be gifted with great theoretical insight to discover it for oneself, once the necessary mathematical technique has been mastered.

We have seen that the combination of marginal productivity theory with the Cobb-Douglas production function predicts that factor shares will remain constant in the face of changing factor supplies. The reason for this is that an increase in the quantity of one factor drives its marginal product and hence its price down *in proportion to the increase in quantity* so that the factor's share remains constant. Investigation of the Cobb-Douglas production functions shows that the answer to question (2) is 'no'. Indeed if production functions are Cobb-Douglas we expect the shares of income going to labour and capital to remain constant.

10.6 Imperfect Markets

The results presented so far assumed perfect markets, for only in the case of perfect competition does labour receive the value of its marginal physical product as a wage. Let us now consider very briefly the case in which firms sell their products on non-perfect markets. In this case the wage will be equal to the marginal revenue product of labour, which is the change in revenue due to a marginal change in the labour force. This will be less than the value of the marginal product of labour because an increase in output drives the price down (so that a reduction in revenue is suffered on those units already being produced). We may now write:

$$w = MRP = MPP \times MR \qquad (51)$$

where w is the wage rate. A familiar result allows us to rewrite this as[1]

$$w = MPP\left(1 + \frac{1}{\eta}\right)p. \qquad (52)$$

We now consider the total wage bill, W:

$$W = wL = (MRP)L = L.MPP\left(1 + \frac{1}{\eta}\right)p. \qquad (53)$$

In the Cobb-Douglas case we already know from (43) above that:

$$L.MPP = \alpha L^{\alpha}C^{\beta}$$

$$= \alpha q, \qquad (54)$$

where q is total output. Substitution of (54) into (53) gives

$$W = \alpha q\left(1 + \frac{1}{\eta}\right)p. \qquad (55)$$

Multiplying both sides by $1/pq$ gives

$$\frac{W}{pq} = \alpha\left(1 + \frac{1}{\eta}\right) \qquad (56)$$

where W is already in money units from (51) above and pq gives output

---

[1] In Chapter 6 equation (18) we had

$$MRP = MPP\left(q\frac{dp}{dq} + p\right).$$

We now substitute w for MRP since the wage paid will equal MRP and we factor out the p to get

$$w = MPP\left(\frac{q}{p}.\frac{dp}{dq} + 1\right)p$$

$$= MPP\left(\frac{1}{\eta} + 1\right)p.$$

also in money units. Thus the share of wages will be constant for a given α if η remains constant but will vary if η varies.

We see that, in this case, the share of income going to labour depends partly on the production function and partly also on market conditions. It is worth asking if we can give any meaning to the factor $1/\eta$ that appears in (56). This may be interpreted loosely as showing the degree of monopoly. If a commodity is sold under perfect competition, elasticity to the individual firm is ∞ and $1/\eta = 0$. If there is some product differentiation, but not a great deal – a situation that we might get under monopolistic competition – η is finite but still quite large, and thus $1/\eta$ is still small. As the degree of product differentiation increases each producer becomes more like a monopolist, his own elasticity decreases, and hence $1/\eta$ increases.

Now this begins to look more interesting. It appears that our marginal productivity theory in a world of non-perfect competition gives rise to a theory that distribution depends on the degree of monopoly in the economy. We shall not pursue this topic further here but it does seem that there is some interesting material to be explored along these lines.[1]

10.7 Some General Results for the Model of a Single Competitive Market

Several times throughout this book we have used a linear model of a single competitive market. We are now in a position to handle this model in much more general terms by dropping the assumption, maintained so far, that the demand and supply functions are linear. We write

$$q^d = D(p, \alpha) \tag{57}$$

$$q^s = S(p, \beta) \tag{58}$$

$$D(p, \alpha) = S(p, \beta). \tag{59}$$

Equations (57) and (58) define demand and supply functions as depending on the price of the product and two *shift parameters*, α and β. There are many other factors that affect demand and supply, such as tastes, income, taxes etc. Since a change in any of these factors must shift either the demand or the supply curve (or both), any change can be handled by making an appropriate change in α and/or β. To see how this works let us now consider disturbing the equilibrium by making a small change in α and/or β. In the new equilibrium (59) must still hold, and so it follows that the change

[1] The interested reader might wish to start with N. Kaldor 'Alternative Theories of Distribution', reprinted as Chapter 12 in *Essays on Value and Distribution*, Duckworth, London, 1960.

in q^d must be equal to the change in q^s. Writing this in differential notation we have

$$dq^d = dq^s. \tag{60}$$

We now derive the differentials of q^d and q^s from equations (57) and (58):

$$dq^d = D_p \, dp + D_\alpha \, d\alpha, \tag{61}$$

and

$$dq^s = S_p \, dp + S_\beta \, d\beta. \tag{62}$$

Equation (61) uses the result derived in Chapter 9, and says that the change in q^d is equal to the partial derivative of q^d with respect to price multiplied by the change in price plus the partial derivative of q^d with respect to α multiplied by the change in α. Similarly for equation (62). If you are in any doubt about this you should review pages 204–06 now. Substituting (61) and (62) into (60) we obtain:

$$D_p \, dp + D_\alpha \, d\alpha = S_p \, dp + S_\beta \, d\beta. \tag{63}$$

We are interested in the change in price that is caused by a shift in either the demand or the supply curve so we manipulate (63) as follows:

$$dp(D_p - S_p) = S_\beta \, d\beta - D_\alpha \, d\alpha,$$

whence

$$dp = \frac{S_\beta \, d\beta - D_\alpha \, d\alpha}{D_p - S_p}. \tag{64}$$

Now let us consider the effect on price of a shift in the demand curve alone, the supply curve being held constant. If the supply curve is not to shift $d\beta = 0$ and (64) reduces to

$$dp = -\frac{D_\alpha \, d\alpha}{D_p - S_p}. \tag{65}$$

Consider first an increase in demand. If we put $d\alpha > 0$ then, since a rise in α shifts the demand curve to the right, we must have $D_\alpha > 0$. If the demand curve slopes downward then $D_p < 0$ (i.e., a rise in price lowers q^d). Assuming that the supply curve slopes upward then $S_p > 0$, whence the denominator of (65) is negative. Thus we have a positive quantity over a negative quantity but with a minus sign before the whole so that the expression is positive. Thus we have proved that an increase in demand ($d\alpha > 0$) increases price ($dp > 0$) as long as the demand curve slopes downwards ($D_p < 0$). Next consider a leftward shift in the demand curve. In this case $d\alpha < 0$ and the whole expression for dp becomes negative. Thus a leftward shift in demand lowers price.

The reader is left (see Exercise 4) with the task of proving the analogous propositions for the effect of supply shifts (demand curve constant) on price.

Note how simply these results have been attained and how general they are. We are no longer confined to linear demand and supply functions nor to the particular curve that we just happen to draw on a two-dimensional diagram. We are now able to derive the four basic predictions about the effect on price of shifts in the demand and supply curves (often misleadingly called the laws of demand) using only the basic assumptions that q^d and p vary inversely with each other (i.e., $D_p < 0$) and that q^s and p vary directly with each other (i.e., $S_p > 0$). Since α and β stand for anything that shifts the demand and supply curve we can handle any new case we meet merely by establishing which curve is shifted and in which direction. Once this is done we know the sign of $d\alpha$ or $d\beta$ and we can immediately discover the effect on price and quantity without having to work laboriously through the model each time. This is thus a result of great power and generality.

10.8 Income Determination

We have several times had occasion to consider linear versions of a simple macro-model of the determination of national income. We are now able to drop the restrictive linearity assumption and show how comparative static results can be obtained in the more general case. We shall produce one result as an example and then ask you to derive another in the questions at the end of this chapter.

The simplest model of national income is based on the following relations:

$$C = C(Y, \alpha), \tag{66}$$

$$Y = C + Z, \tag{67}$$

$$Z = Z(\beta). \tag{68}$$

Equation (66) gives the behavioural assumption relating to consumption: consumption depends on income and a lot of other factors such as taxes, income distribution, the introduction of new goods, and credit terms. All of these are assumed to be constant and a change in any one of them can be represented by a change in the parameter α. Equation (67) shows the equilibrium condition that current income should equal the sum of an induced component, current consumption expenditure, and an autonomous expenditure[1] Z. Equation (68) says that current autonomous expenditure, Z, is itself dependent on a large number of factors such as the growth rate,

---

[1] When we say autonomous we mean, of course, independent of income; such expenditure can be a function of other variables.

the rate of interest, and the level of taxes, all of which are constant. A change in any one of these can be represented by a change in the parameter β.

Substitution of (66) and (68) into (67) produces the following expression for income:

$$Y = C(Y, \alpha) + Z(\beta). \tag{69}$$

This is an equilibrium condition and, whatever shifts occur, the new equilibrium level of income must also satisfy this relation. To discover the change in Y consequent on changes in α and β we take the total differential of (69):

$$\mathrm{d}Y = C_Y \, \mathrm{d}Y + C_\alpha \, \mathrm{d}\alpha + Z_\beta \, \mathrm{d}\beta. \tag{70}$$

(70) shows the change in income to be in part a function of itself ($C_Y \, \mathrm{d}Y$). This is, of course, a consequence of the assumption that income affects consumption and consumption affects income.

In order to obtain some results consider the case of a stable consumption function and a change in autonomous expenditure so that $\mathrm{d}\alpha = 0$, $\mathrm{d}\beta \neq 0$. Expression (70) reduces to

$$\mathrm{d}Y = C_Y \, \mathrm{d}Y + Z_\beta \, \mathrm{d}\beta \tag{71}$$

$$\mathrm{d}Y(1 - C_Y) = Z_\beta \, \mathrm{d}\beta \tag{72}$$

$$\frac{\mathrm{d}Y}{\mathrm{d}\beta} = \frac{Z_\beta}{1 - C_Y}. \tag{73}$$

This defines the multiplier as the derivative of Y with respect to β, and shows it to be equal to the change in autonomous expenditure caused by the change in β divided by one minus the partial derivative of consumption with respect to income. Clearly the model can be extended to produce other results but we shall not bother the reader with these here. Some of them are suggested in the questions at the end of the chapter. We have however succeeded, as in the demand-and-supply case, in shedding the assumptions of linearity and in deriving general qualitative predictions from the model of national income that depend only on assumptions about qualitative restrictions that can be put on relevant partial derivatives. From (73) it follows, for example, that the change in income exceeds the change in autonomous expenditure as long as $0 < C_Y < 1$.

We have now gone a long way towards producing general results which do not depend on special, and possibly unreal, assumptions such as linearity in all our functional relations. The total differential is the tool that allows us to do this. We have now illustrated what we asserted in Chapter 1 that,

far from forcing our models to be narrow and restrictive, the use of mathematics allows us to shed restrictions that we were forced to employ not
because we thought them warranted by our knowledge but only because
of the limitations in our verbal and geometrical tools of analysis.

Exercises

1 Check that Euler's theorem (see equation (47)) holds for the function
$y = x^2 z^{-1}$ at the point $x = 2$, $z = 4$. (*Hint:* Calculate y in two ways, first by
substituting into the above function and second by substituting the relevant
values into (47).)

2 Consider the production function

$$q = C^{2/3} L^{2/3}.$$

(i) Does it display decreasing returns to each factor?

(ii) Does it have constant, increasing or decreasing returns to scale?

(iii) Calculate the expression for total payments if both factors get a
price equal to the value of their marginal products.

3 Consider the production function

$$q = AC^{\alpha} L^{\alpha}.$$

(i) Can you discover what the value of α would have to be for each
factor to have constant returns to that factor (the other held constant)?

(ii) Can you give any interpretation of this result?

4 Establish the effects on price and quantity of a leftward and a rightward
shift in the supply curve in a perfectly competitive market. (See equation
(64).)

5 Consider the effects of an upward shift of the consumption function on
the level of national income.

6 The quantity theory determines the price level according to the equilibrium condition

$$kPT = M$$

where P is the price level, T is the volume of transactions, k is the fraction
of the money value of transactions people desire to hold as balances, and
M is the supply of money.

(i) Write P as an explicit function of M, T, and k.

(ii) Investigate the change in P for changes in each of the independent
variables, the others held constant.

(iii) Write the total differential of this function.

CHAPTER 11

CONSTRAINED MAXIMA AND MINIMA

'... Economics brings into full view that conflict of choice which is one of the permanent characteristics of human existence. Your economist is a true tragedian.' Robbins.

11.1 Choice and Economics

In Chapter 4B we encountered the notion of a frontier limiting the quantities of two desired variables that might be had in combination. In Chapter 7 we defined rational action as action chosen consistently to get as near to any desired goal as circumstances permit. A frontier, of course, delimits just what circumstances do permit. Going as far as one can in the desired direction, given the frontier, is known technically as *maximising subject to a constraint*. The idea of maximising subject to a constraint is probably the most important single idea in economics. If economics is the 'science of choice', then its subject-matter is precisely the study of constrained maxima. Just how important constrained maxima are we shall see more clearly in the next chapter in which we consider governmental policy making and entrepreneurial decision taking as well as household behaviour. 'But when time and the means for achieving ends are limited *and* capable of alternative application, *and* the ends are capable of being distinguished in order of importance, then behaviour necessarily assumes the form of choice'.[1]

As in Chapter 7, we confine our discussion to calculus methods, which means that we assume continuity and differentiability.

We have already remarked that there can exist maxima that cannot be found by calculus methods. These are particularly frequent and important in practical cases that arise in trying to find constrained maxima. The modern technique of linear programming is designed to find the maxima in such cases. We might say that linear programming makes the 'science of

[1] Lionel Robbins (Lord Robbins), *An Essay on the Nature and Significance of Economic Science*, 2nd ed., *op. cit.*, p. 14. The whole of Chapters I and II, at least, should be read in this connection.

choice' operational. It is, however, beyond the scope of this book.[1] It should also be emphasised now that this will be about the least rigorous chapter of *this* book. We shall show a method of solving the problem, but there will be little by way of proof.

If one 'good' is independent of all others, there is no problem of choice: we merely take as much as is available, or as affords satiety, whichever is the less. If there are two goods, but they are positively associated, the situation is not materially altered: we take as much as is available, or as affords satiety, of the combination. Thus a problem of choice arises only if there are two or more desired goods, and they are negatively associated in the real world, so that an increase in one involves some sacrifice of the other. We may say that a problem of choice arises when two or more goods are positively desired but negatively associated. We shall give examples later. For the moment, it does not matter what the 'goods' may be, whether income and leisure, present or future consumption, high employment and price stability, growth and exchange stability.

For a constrained maximum problem to arise, there must be two or more goods. There must also be at least two functions connecting them. One is obviously the constraint, or frontier. The other is the *maximand*, that which is to be maximised. The essential characteristic of the maximand is that it is an increasing function of both goods. We shall consider other properties later; but for a constrained maximum we require that the two goods are both desired, and that all alternative combinations of the two goods can be *ranked or ordered* consistently by the decision taker. The function representing this ordering is the function to be maximised, often called the *objective function*. One very familiar objective function is the so-called *utility function* ascribed to the individual consumer. Evidently so long as there *is* a consistently ordered function to be maximised, it is immaterial what we call it. Tradition has it that in the case of the individual consumer the maximand is to be called a utility function, and in other cases merely an objective function. What matters is to realise that, whenever we have a choice problem, we have a constraint (or frontier, or boundary), and a maximand (or objective function, or utility function).

11.2 Tangency Conditions

Suppose now that we have a maximand, $f(x, y)$, and a constraint, $F(x, y)$. In the interests of easy recognition, we shall use here the lowercase f to denote the objective function, and the uppercase F to denote the constraint. Many other notations are used, and will serve. The objective function is

[1] For a lucid introduction which does not presuppose sophisticated mathematical technique, see W.J.Baumol, *Economic Theory and Operations Analysis*, Prentice-Hall, Englewood Cliffs, N.J.

often denoted by U or ψ, and the constraint by virtually any functional symbol.

The easiest case to start with is the familiar one illustrated in Figure 11.1, where the constraint gives a straight-line frontier, BC. The iso-f curves, which connect pairs of values of x and y that give constant values of the function $f(x, y)$, are convex from below, and associated with higher values of $f(x, y)$ the further they are from the origin. (We looked into the properties of iso-f curves in Chapter 9.) In the case of the individual consumer,

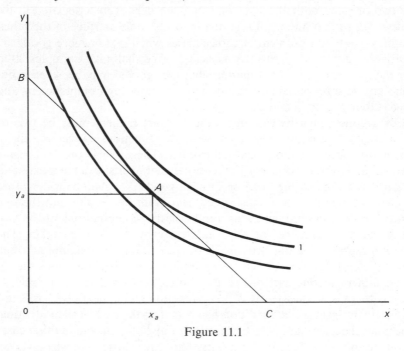

Figure 11.1

whose objective function is usually called a utility function, the iso-f curves are known as indifference curves. Iso-f curves, however, exist *whatever* is being maximised and whatever we call it, so long as the maximand is a continuous, differentiable function; and so much confusion and mystery has been occasioned by the notions of utility, indifference, satisfaction, etc., that it seems wiser to use, for the moment at least, the more neutral terminology of objective function and iso-f curve.

From inspection of Figure 11.1, it is obvious that the highest attainable level of $f(x, y)$ is reached at A, where an iso-f curve is tangential to the frontier. At A, the quantities of the goods obtained are Ox_a and Oy_a. We shall henceforth take it for granted, *without proof*, that tangency is required at a constrained maximum. The problem now is to find an algebraic method which will allow us to *calculate* the values of x and y that give tangency when we are given the functions algebraically or numerically: we do not wish to be reduced to trial-and-error approximate methods with ruler and compass, which, incidentally, would be impossible in cases of more than two variables.

First of all, let us write the constraint as

$$F(x, y) = B - cx - dy = 0 \qquad (1)$$

which turns out to be a convenience. This is just a rearrangement of $B = cx + dy$, where B may be thought of as a constant 'income', and c and d are two 'prices'. A further rearrangement of equation (1) gives

$$y = \frac{B}{d} - \frac{c}{d} x \qquad (2)$$

which is the equation of BC in Figure 11.1. The ratio $-c/d$ is the slope of the frontier, or trade-off rate. Clearly we could count in units of y, putting $d = 1$ if we chose, but it is helpful to retain the form of equation (1) for the moment. Now, tangency at A means that the slopes of the constraint and the iso-f curve are the same, so let us consider their slopes. We know that the slope of the frontier is $-c/d$, but for the sake of symmetry let us derive this result by the methods of Chapter 9, which we shall have to use to obtain the slope of the objective function. We saw there that, where the value of a function is constant, its total differential is zero, from which we may derive its x, y slope. Hence if

$$F(x, y) = 0 \qquad (3)$$

$$F_x \, dx + F_y \, dy = 0$$

and

$$\frac{dy}{dx} = -\frac{F_x}{F_y}. \qquad (4)$$

We can look on (3) as the equation of an 'iso-B' curve, if we like. In equation (1) we assume that B is a constant, which gives $F(x, y) = 0$ for given B. Different values of B, with c and d unchanged, would give frontiers parallel to BC. Now we merely check that (4) gives the correct slope. Differentiating (1), we have

$$F_x = -c$$

and

$$F_y = -d$$

so the slope of the constraint is $-c/d$. We now apply the same technique to the maximand. Along a contour in Figure 11.1, $f(x, y)$ has a constant value, so its total differential is zero, i.e.,

$$f_x\, dx + f_y\, dy = 0$$

whence

$$\frac{dy}{dx} = -\frac{f_x}{f_y}. \tag{5}$$

But at A, where the two slopes are equal,

$$\left.\frac{dy}{dx}\right|_{\text{constraint}} = \left.\frac{dy}{dx}\right|_{\text{maximand}} \tag{6}$$

or, using (4) and (5),

$$-\frac{f_x}{f_y} = -\frac{F_x}{F_y}. \tag{7}$$

We may give (7) a familiar economic interpretation. If $f(x, y)$ is the consumer's utility function, the partial derivatives f_x and f_y are the marginal utilities, and their ratio is the marginal rate of substitution which is the slope of the indifference curve. Hence (7) is the famous result that the ratio of the marginal utilities, f_x/f_y, must be equal to the price ratio or trade-off rate F_x/F_y, or c/d.

Evidently (7) must be satisfied at a constrained maximum. By rearranging it, we can obtain a clue to the sort of procedure that will solve for equilibrium x and y. Dividing both sides by $-F_x$, and multiplying both sides by f_y, we obtain

$$\frac{f_x}{F_x} = \frac{f_y}{F_y}. \tag{8}$$

(This is the famous result that the ratio of the marginal utility of one good to its price must be equal to the ratio of the marginal utility of the other good to its price.) Equation (8) establishes that the two ratios are equal to each other, but we do not know their value. Let us put them equal to some unknown, λ. In fact since the value of λ is yet to be determined we can just as well put them equal to $-\lambda$ which proves to be convenient. Thus

$$\frac{f_x}{F_x} = \frac{f_y}{F_y} = -\lambda. \tag{9}$$

This appears pointless at present, but we go on a little. Notice that we do not know the value of $-\lambda$, and could just as well have written μ or $\sqrt{\eta}$, if it proved helpful. We can break (9) up into two equations,

$$f_x = -\lambda F_x$$

and

$$f_y = -\lambda F_y$$

or, for greater convenience,

$$f_x + \lambda F_x = 0 \qquad (10.1)$$

$$f_y + \lambda F_y = 0. \qquad (10.2)$$

If we remember that the constraint must always be satisfied, we can add a third equation

$$F(x, y) = 0 \qquad (10.3)$$

and we have three equations in the three unknowns, x, y, and λ. These equations must be satisfied at the point of tangency: they were derived from precisely the requirements of tangency. And if we knew the actual forms of the functions f and F, we could solve the equations (10). The next step is to look for a standard algebraic procedure which will lead directly and quickly to equations (10), and which will have the property that it will extend to cases of more than two variables, which we could not otherwise handle. It turns out that there is a standard procedure, and that, although its development may look a little mysterious, its operation is perfectly straightforward.

We introduce yet another new variable, V, and put

$$V = f(x, y) + \lambda F(x, y). \qquad (11)$$

This is called the Lagrangean equation, and λ an 'undetermined Lagrangean multiplier', after the French mathematician Joseph Louis Lagrange (1736–1813). It appears that we are only complicating the problem, but first V and then λ will drop out again shortly. Let us try to maximise V. V is a function of three variables, x, y, and λ, so we must set all three partial derivatives simultaneously equal to zero. Differentiating (11) with respect to each in turn, we obtain

$$V_x = f_x + \lambda F_x = 0$$

$$V_y = f_y + \lambda F_y = 0$$

$$V_\lambda = F(x, y) = 0$$

and we have reproduced equations (10), our required conditions for tangency! Thus it turns out that introducing the new unknowns, V and λ, and maximising V, produces the three equations which we obtained by manipulating the tangency conditions of equation (7).

11.3   An Example

Before taking a closer look at what is going on, let us work an example. Let the objective function be

$$f(x, y) = 2x^{1/2}y^{1/2} \tag{12}$$

and the constraint be

$$F(x, y) = 100 - 2x - y = 0. \tag{13}$$

We do not wish to try to find an approximate answer by laborious graphical methods, drawing contours of $f(x, y)$, so we obediently carry out our procedures. Put

$$V = 2x^{1/2}y^{1/2} + \lambda(100 - 2x - y) \tag{14}$$

and equate the partial derivatives to zero:

$$V_x = x^{-1/2}y^{1/2} - 2\lambda = 0 \tag{15.1}$$

$$V_y = x^{1/2}y^{-1/2} - \lambda = 0 \tag{15.2}$$

$$V_\lambda = 100 - 2x - y = 0. \tag{15.3}$$

If we can solve these three simultaneous equations, we are home. There exist powerful methods for solving sets of simultaneous equations, but fortunately we do not need them here: a little manipulation will do the trick. From (15.2),

$$\lambda = x^{1/2}y^{-1/2}.$$

Substituting this into (15.1), we have

$$x^{-1/2}y^{1/2} - 2x^{1/2}y^{-1/2} = 0$$

so

$$\frac{y^{1/2}}{x^{1/2}} = 2\frac{x^{1/2}}{y^{1/2}}$$

and, on cross-multiplying,

$$y = 2x.$$

Substituting this into (15.3), we have

$$100 - 2x - 2x = 0$$

so

$$x = 25 \tag{16.1}$$

and

$$y = 100 - 2x = 50. \tag{16.2}$$

It turns out that there is no need here to find the value of the 'undetermined multiplier', λ, any more than there is to find V, but in view of the famous ratio result in equations (8) and (9), it may be of some interest. From (15.2) we get[1]

$$\lambda = \frac{\sqrt{25}}{\sqrt{50}} \simeq \pm\frac{5}{7}.$$

Since the price ratio given by the constraint is $1:2$, it may be worth satisfying ourselves that the iso-f curve has a slope of -2 at $x=25$, $y=50$. We want the ratio of the partial derivatives, $-f_x/f_y$, but we have already found them in (15.1) and (15.2), so we write directly

$$\frac{dy}{dx} = -\frac{x^{-1/2}y^{1/2}}{x^{1/2}y^{-1/2}}$$

$$= -\frac{y}{x} = -2.$$

(You are asked to extend this example in Exercise 1.)

11.4 Justification of the Procedure

In 11.3 we produced a method, via V and λ, which gives our tangency requirements in such a form that we can actually find x and y once we are given particular functions. There may be some suggestion of sleight of hand about the whole operation, however, so we shall consider it a little further. Up through equations (10) we were only manipulating the tangency requirements, which we said were evident from consideration of Figure 11.1. Then we suddenly introduced V, which turned out, on differentiation, to give (10.1), (10.2), and (10.3): that is, maximising V gives the tangency requirements for maximising $f(x, y)$ subject to $F(x, y)=0$. How can this be? Bear in mind that we write the constraint in such a fashion that $F(x, y)$ *does* equal zero (in our example $F(x, y)=100-2x-y$), and equation (11) becomes

$$V = f(x, y) + \lambda(0).$$

It does not follow that we can write $V=f(x, y)$, arguing that $\lambda(0)=0$ and can be dropped, because we have still to *find* values of x and y such that $F(x, y)=0$. Thus if we maximise V we are maximising f and *at the same time* keeping the constraint satisfied, that is, holding $F(x, y)=0$. The difference between maximising f alone and maximising V is that when we

---

[1] Recall that the sign $\simeq$ means 'approximately equal to'.

maximise V we keep the constraint satisfied since the partial derivative $V_\lambda = F(x, y)$, and we bring in the derivative (the slope of the constraint) which we require for tangency. And this is as far as we can go in justifying this subtle but very powerful procedure. Part of its power lies, of course, in the fact that it extends immediately to functions of three or more variables.

11.5* Convexity

We should now say something about second-order conditions but the algebra required for a full treatment is too much for us here. We can, how-

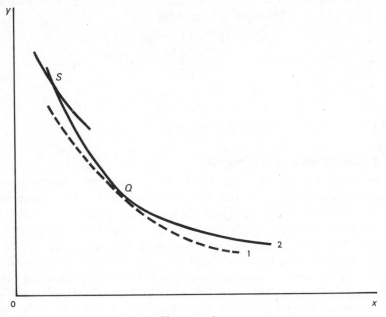

Figure 11.2

ever, make some headway with a geometrical consideration of a simple and common case. Thus in Figure 11.1, it is obvious that A *is* a maximum. But consider Figure 11.2, where the first-order or tangency conditions are satisfied at Q. If the curve labelled 1, the flatter of the two curves, is the constraint, and the curve labelled 2 is an iso-f curve, then all is well. Suppose, however, that 1 were an iso-f curve and that 2 were the constraint: then higher values of the maximand would be attainable, such as that at S, and Q would certainly not be a maximum. In Figure 11.3, the constraint is again the straight line BC, but the objective function is concave towards the origin. Tangency conditions are satisfied at T, but T is a minimum rather than a maximum. The maximum will occur at a 'corner solution' such as B (which cannot be discovered by calculus methods). Comparison of these three figures suggests that, *if* the frontier is a straight line, convexity of the objective function is sufficient to ensure that the tangency occurs at a maximum, in which case the first-order conditions are both necessary *and* sufficient, and it can be proved that this is indeed so. If the frontier is non-linear, however, there are no short-cuts, and a full-dress treatment of second order conditions is required.

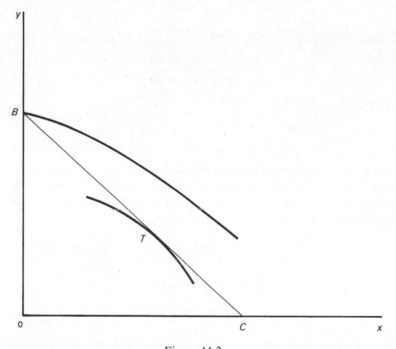

Figure 11.3

Since linear constraints are fairly common in economics, we will conclude by working out the conditions for convexity in the objective function. Let the function be $f(x, y)$, and its slope, which we shall denote by r, the Marginal Rate of Substitution, be given by

$$r = \frac{dy}{dx} = \frac{-f_x}{f_y}. \tag{17}$$

Convexity means that, as x increases, sliding round a curve, the slope itself becomes less steep, or 'less negative'. Thus convexity means that the marginal rate of substitution, or tangent slope, r itself, has a rate of change with respect to x which is *positive*. So the convexity condition is

$$\frac{dr}{dx} > 0. \tag{18}$$

Since r, however, is a function of both variables x and y, we require the total differential

$$dr = \frac{\partial r}{\partial x} dx + \frac{\partial r}{\partial y} dy.$$

Dividing through by dx, this gives

$$\frac{dr}{dx} = \frac{\partial r}{\partial x} + \frac{\partial r}{\partial y} \frac{dy}{dx}$$

or from (17)

$$\frac{dr}{dx} = \frac{\partial}{\partial x}\left(\frac{-f_x}{f_y}\right) + \frac{\partial}{\partial y}\left(\frac{-f_x}{f_y}\right) \cdot \left(\frac{-f_x}{f_y}\right). \tag{19}$$

(Notice that in (19) we have substituted for $dy/dx = r = -f_x/f_y$ in the last term.) To evaluate the two partial derivatives of r we next apply the quotient rule (see pages 114–16) to each in turn, since f_x and f_y are in general both functions of x and y, to obtain

$$\frac{dr}{dx} = -\left(\frac{f_y f_{xx} - f_x f_{xy}}{f_y^2}\right) - \left(\frac{f_y f_{xy} - f_x f_{yy}}{f_y^2}\right)\left(\frac{-f_x}{f_y}\right)$$

which, with a little manipulation, simplifies to

$$\frac{dr}{dx} = -\frac{f_y^2 f_{xx} - 2f_x f_y f_{xy} + f_x^2 f_{yy}}{f_y^3}.$$

Since f_y and therefore f_y^3 are positive, our convexity condition is

$$f_y^2 f_{xx} - 2f_x f_y f_{xy} + f_x^2 f_{yy} < 0. \tag{20}$$

Now f_y and f_x and their squares are all positive, so the inequality (20) is satisfied if, for example, f_{xx} and f_{yy} are both negative and f_{xy} is non-negative (positive or zero). If f_{xy} were negative, then whether or not (20) was satisfied would depend on relative magnitudes, and could not be determined qualitatively. If, however, f_{xx} or f_{yy} were positive, it would still be possible to satisfy (20) if f_{xy} were also positive and sufficiently large. Thus we cannot lay down any very simple conditions for convexity, other than that (20) must be satisfied. In particular, we should notice that our discussion of (20) shows that the condition $f_{xx} < 0$ and $f_{yy} < 0$ is neither necessary *nor* sufficient for convexity, because of the possible effects of the term f_{xy}. This is important because, in the case of a utility function, f_x may be interpreted as marginal utility with respect to x, and $f_{xx} < 0$ as diminishing marginal utility. Since convexity may be interpreted as diminishing marginal substitutability, what we have found is that diminishing marginal utility is neither necessary nor sufficient for diminishing marginal substitutability.[1]

By way of example, we may satisfy ourselves that the function used above, $f(x, y) = 2x^{1/2}y^{1/2}$, satisfies the convexity conditions. We have already found that in this case

$$r = \frac{dy}{dx} = \frac{-y}{x}$$

and the problem is to find dr/dx. We may substitute into the general expression in (20), or proceed directly, which will probably do more for our understanding of what is involved. We have to remember that we are looking at the change in the slope of an iso-quant as we slide round it, so that y can neither be held constant as x varies nor varied independently of x: it must be treated as a function of x. So to differentiate $-y/x$, we rewrite it as $r = -yx^{-1}$, and apply the product rule to obtain the total differential

$$\frac{dr}{dx} = -\left\{ yx^{-2} + x^{-1}\frac{dy}{dx} \right\}.$$

Substituting for dy/dx, we have

$$\frac{dr}{dx} = -\{-yx^{-2} - yx^{-2}\}$$

$$= \frac{2y}{x^2} \tag{21}$$

which is positive as required. Combining this objective function with a linear constraint, first-order conditions will therefore be sufficient to ensure a maximum.

11.6 Constrained Maxima

It remains to say something about constrained minima, but these are now straightforward: the first-order conditions are identical with those for a maximum, and only the second-order conditions are different. Second-order conditions are troublesome, but we can clear up a couple of simple

[1] This is most clearly explained by Hicks, *Value and Capital*, O.U.P. 1939, 2nd ed. 1946, pp. 12–16, who gives the economic interpretation too.

cases. First, suppose that it is desired to minimise $f(x, y)$ subject to a linear constraint, i.e., to get as near as possible to the origin in Figure 11.4. Then, by an obvious reversal of the convexity argument of the last section, the tangency at R gives a minimum provided that the iso-f curve is *concave* from below. Second, suppose that it is desired to minimise a *linear* function $f(x, y)$ subject to a non-linear constraint $F(x, y) = 0$. We may use Figure 11.1 to illustrate this if we think of BC as the objective function, which is to be got as near to the origin as possible, and one of the iso-f

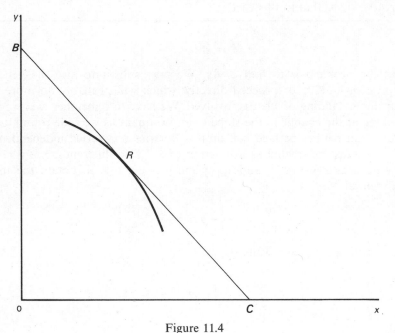

Figure 11.4

curves, say that labelled 1, as now being the constraint. Then evidently tangency is sufficient for a minimum provided that the *constraint* is convex from below.

11.7   Illustrations

A little more illustration of the ideas of this chapter may be helpful. Suppose that we are given an objective function of the form

$$f(x, y) = Ax^{\alpha}y^{\beta} \tag{22}$$

which is to be maximised subject to some linear constraint $F(x, y) = 0$. We ask what restrictions are to be put on the permissible values of the coefficients A, α, and β for this to be a reasonable objective function, and to satisfy the conditions for a tangency being a maximum. First of all, if the function is to be positive, A must be positive. Second, we require that it be an increasing function of both x and y, that is, we require positive first derivatives:

$$f_x = \alpha A x^{\alpha-1} y^\beta > 0 \qquad (23.1)$$

and

$$f_y = \beta A x^\alpha y^{\beta-1} > 0. \qquad (23.2)$$

Thus we must have A, α, and β all positive. Now, we have already seen that negative second derivatives are neither necessary nor sufficient for convexity, but in many contexts they seem sensible. If we interpret f_x and f_y as marginal utilities, as we suggested in our discussion of convexity in 11.5 above, then f_{xx} and f_{yy} are the rates of change of the marginal utilities. The idea of diminishing marginal utility has considerable intuitive appeal, although it is not strictly necessary for equilibrium positions to exist (because, in its absence, we *could* get convexity by sufficient juggling with the second-order cross-partial derivative f_{xy}). It certainly helps to make sense of the idea of utility and scarcity, that it is not the 'absolute' or 'total' utility of a good that determines its value, but its marginal utility, which we expect to be smaller the more of the good is taken, i.e., the less scarce it is. Now if we want

$$f_{xx} = \alpha(\alpha-1)A x^{\alpha-2} y^\beta \qquad (24.1)$$

and

$$f_{yy} = \beta(\beta-1)A x^\alpha y^{\beta-2} \qquad (24.2)$$

to be negative, we must have $\alpha < 1$ and $\beta < 1$. The slope of the iso-f curves is given by

$$\frac{dy}{dx} = \frac{-f_x}{f_y} = \frac{-\alpha A x^{\alpha-1} y^\beta}{\beta A x^\alpha y^{\beta-1}}$$

$$= -\frac{\alpha}{\beta} \frac{y}{x} \qquad (25)$$

which is obviously negative since both first derivatives are positive. Finally, for convexity we require

$$\frac{dr}{dx} > 0.$$

To find dr/dx, we may again substitute into (20), or proceed directly by the methods that led to (21). Following the latter route, we take the total differential of

$$r = -\frac{\alpha}{\beta} yx^{-1}$$

to obtain

$$\frac{dr}{dx} = -\frac{\alpha}{\beta}\left[\frac{-y}{x^2}+\frac{1}{x}\frac{dy}{dx}\right].$$

Substituting for dy/dx, as before, we have

$$\frac{dr}{dx} = -\frac{\alpha}{\beta}\left[\frac{-y}{x^2}-\frac{\alpha}{\beta}\frac{y}{x^2}\right]$$

$$= \frac{y}{x^2}\left(1+\frac{\alpha}{\beta}\right)\frac{\alpha}{\beta} \qquad (26)$$

which is positive as required. (It is a good exercise to check for yourself, by substituting the numerical values, that (21) and (26) are consistent.)

If we are invited to maximise the objective function (22) subject to

$$F(x, y) = B-rx-sy = 0 \qquad (27)$$

we put

$$V = Ax^{\alpha}y^{\beta}+\lambda(B-rx-sy) \qquad (28)$$

and set the partial derivatives equal to zero:

$$V_x = \alpha Ax^{\alpha-1}y^{\beta}-\lambda r = 0 \qquad (29.1)$$

$$V_y = \beta Ax^{\alpha}y^{\beta-1}-\lambda s = 0 \qquad (29.2)$$

$$V_\lambda = B-rx-sy = 0. \qquad (29.3)$$

Solving these equations will be a little more difficult than in the numerical example of 11.4 above, where we had $s=1$, but the general procedure is the same. We start by eliminating λ. From the first equation

$$\lambda = \frac{\alpha Ax^{\alpha-1}y^{\beta}}{r}.$$

Substituting into the second,

$$\beta Ax^{\alpha}y^{\beta-1} = \frac{s}{r}\alpha Ax^{\alpha-1}y^{\beta}.$$

Cancelling A, and dividing both sides by $\beta x^{\alpha-1} y^{\beta-1}$,

$$x = \frac{s}{r} \frac{\alpha}{\beta} y$$

and substituting this into the third equation,

$$B - s \frac{\alpha}{\beta} y - sy = 0$$

whence

$$B - ys \left(\frac{\alpha}{\beta} + 1 \right) = 0$$

or

and

$$y = \frac{B}{s} \left(\frac{\beta}{\alpha + \beta} \right) \tag{30.1}$$

$$x = \frac{B}{r} \left(\frac{\alpha}{\alpha + \beta} \right). \tag{30.2}$$

(As a check on this general result, you should substitute in the numerical values of α, β, r, s, and B from the example in 11.3. Notice that in this case $\alpha/\beta = 1$.)

The solutions in equations (30) are worth attention: they have a number of interesting properties and we shall quickly find that we have in fact established a great deal. First, the terms B/r and B/s may be interpreted as the purchasing power, or real value, of the budget, expressed in each equation in terms of the price of the relevant good. Thus equations (30) say that equilibrium quantities depend on income and relative prices (purchasing power), and on the exponents of the objective function only. Second, notice that if B increases, prices constant, x and y increase in proportion. This means that the *proportion* in which x and y are taken depends on relative prices and is independent of B, as may be confirmed by evaluating

$$\frac{x}{y} = \frac{Br^{-1}}{Bs^{-1}} \left(\frac{\dfrac{\alpha}{\alpha + \beta}}{\dfrac{\beta}{\alpha + \beta}} \right) = \frac{s}{r} \cdot \frac{\alpha}{\beta}.$$

It follows that the expansion path, or 'income-consumption curve', corresponding to changing B with given s/r is a straight line through the origin. This is a property of a *homogeneous* objective function, and we can easily

9

show that (22) is homogeneous of degree $\alpha + \beta$ (see Chapter 9). Finally, notice that if prices and money income (i.e., r, s, and B) all change in proportion, the equilibrium values of x and y given by (30) are unaffected. Thus the demands are said to be free of 'money illusion' or *homogeneous of degree zero* in absolute prices. This is a property required in many models in which we wish to distinguish between 'real' and 'monetary' phenomena.

In Chapter 9, we discussed homogeneous functions, and we have considered an example in the Cobb-Douglas production function. The objective function of (22), $Ax^\alpha y^\beta$, is obviously a close relation to the Cobb-Douglas function. If we make $\alpha + \beta = 1$, we have the first-order homogeneous case; if we do not impose this restriction, we have a homogeneous objective function of order $\alpha + \beta$. If x and y are each increased by some factor μ, which leaves their ratio unchanged, we have $A(\mu x)^\alpha (\mu y)^\beta = A\mu^{\alpha + \beta} x^\alpha y^\beta = \mu^{\alpha + \beta}(Ax^\alpha y^\beta)$.

11.8   Many Variables

We now come to a remarkable demonstration of the power of our calculus methods compared with compass and ruler: we can extend our technique to cases of more than two variables with the greatest possible ease.

Let us start with the case of three variables, x, y, and z, and a single constraint. If we write the objective function $f(x, y, z)$, and the constraint $F(x, y, z) = 0$, all we need do is form the equation

$$V = f(x, y, z) - \lambda F(x, y, z) \tag{31}$$

and set all four partial derivatives equal to zero:

$$V_x = f_x - \lambda F_x = 0 \tag{32.1}$$

$$V_y = f_y - \lambda F_y = 0 \tag{32.2}$$

$$V_z = f_z - \lambda F_z = 0 \tag{32.3}$$

$$V_\lambda = -F(x, y, z) = 0. \tag{32.4}$$

The equations (32) give, by analogy with (10) above, the conditions for tangency between two *surfaces* in three dimensions. If the constraint is linear, and the iso-f surfaces convex, this may be visualised as tangency between an inclined plane (say, the surface of a book suitably tilted) and an iso-f curve shaped like a smooth cup or saucer. Simple rearrangement of (32) gives the usual 'marginal equalities' or tangency conditions,

$$\frac{f_x}{F_x} = \frac{f_y}{F_y} = \frac{f_z}{F_z} = \lambda \tag{33}$$

perfectly analogous with those in two dimensions. If we know that the constraint is linear and the objective function convex, then the first-order conditions in (32) are sufficient as well as necessary for a maximum. (No proof: but consider for yourself the cup and book analogy.) If we do not know this, then second-order conditions are required, and are beyond us.

A useful and simple trick is now to extend this analysis to any number of variables. It is useful because, among the many possible applications of constrained maxima, one is to the case of the individual consumer, facing a large number of consumer goods, and *we do not wish to have to specify, on every separate occasion, how many he faces: we want a general result.* That it is simple we shall now demonstrate: all we need is a little notation. We shall in fact not use the notation subsequently in this book; but as it is very commonly encountered in the economics literature, and as no new mathematical ideas are involved, we for once break our rule of doing no mathematics that we do not use.

Let the number of variables be n, when n is any number greater than or equal to two. Then denote the variables by

$$x_1, x_2, \ldots, x_n.$$

The objective function can accordingly be written as

$$f(x_1, x_2, \ldots, x_n) \tag{34}$$

and the constraint as

$$F(x_1, x_2, \ldots, x_n) = 0. \tag{35}$$

The common case of interest is that of a linear constraint. This can now be written

$$B - \sum_i p_i x_i = 0 \qquad (i = 1, \ldots, n). \tag{36}$$

The very compact notation of (36) is new, and requires explanation. The 'summation sign' (capital sigma) means 'the sum of', so $\sum_i x_i$ means 'the sum of all the x's'. The marginal note '$i = 1, \ldots, n$' (read 'i equals one to n') tells the reader which x's: here $x_1, x_2, \ldots, x_n$. So

$$\sum_i x_i \, (i = 1, \ldots, n) = x_1 + x_2 + x_3 + \cdots + x_n.$$

Instead of using the marginal note with the summation sign, this may be written

$$\sum_{i=1}^{n} x_i$$

which is read 'the sum from i equals one to n of the x_i', and means the same thing. Equation (36) should now be compared with (27), the linear constraint in the two-variable case, where

$$F(x, y) = B - rx - sy = 0$$

$$= B - (rx + sy).$$

In (36), where there may be more than two variables, we have written x_i instead of x, y, z, v, w, etc. In the same way, we have put p_i for the coefficients r, s, etc. Imagine trying to write out (36) without this notation in a case in which $n = 100$: there are not enough letters in the alphabet! The notation $\sum_i p_i x_i$ means that, attached to each x_i, there is a coefficient p_i, and that each x is to be multiplied by its coefficient before the sum is taken. Thus

$$\sum_{i=1}^{n} p_i x_i = p_1 x_1 + p_2 x_2 + \cdots + p_n x_n.$$

As a further simplification of the notation, if there is no room for ambiguity as to the number of x_i to be summed, we may drop the n over the summation sign and the marginal note, writing merely $\sum_i$, as we have just done.

An economic interpretation of (36) is that B is income, the x_i goods, and the p_i their prices: (36) is often known as the 'budget equation' or 'budget constraint'. It is, however, the perfectly general form of an *n-dimensional linear constraint*. And now, indeed, we are in n dimensions, where the geometry of two or three dimensions can aid our intuition but cannot solve our problem.

The solution is, however, quite easy. To maximise (34) subject to (36) we form the usual equation,

$$V = f(x_1, x_2, \ldots, x_n) + \lambda \left(B - \sum_{i=1}^{n} p_i x_i \right) \tag{37}$$

and set all the partial derivatives equal to zero. There are $n + 1$ of them, one for each x and one for λ. Writing all these out is cumbersome, and, anyhow, we still do not wish to be committed to a particular number for n. Again, a notational device is what is needed. At first sight, what now appears is quite terrifying; but no new ideas are involved. All we are doing here is presenting a short-hand which is in common use, and with which one rapidly becomes familiar. We can write

$$
\left.\begin{aligned}
V_{x_1} &= f_{x_1} - \lambda p_1 = 0 \\
V_{x_2} &= f_{x_2} - \lambda p_2 = 0 \\
&\;\vdots \\
V_{x_i} &= f_{x_i} - \lambda p_i = 0 \\
&\;\vdots \qquad \vdots \qquad \vdots \\
V_{x_n} &= f_{x_n} - \lambda p_n = 0 \\
V &= B - \sum_{i=1}^{n} p_i x_i = 0
\end{aligned}\right\} \tag{38}
$$

where the dots indicate that the appropriate number of equations *of identical form* have been omitted and the subscripts x_1, etc., on V indicate as usual the variable with respect to which the partial derivative is taken. To obtain the partial derivatives of the second term in (37), we proceeded as follows:

$$
\frac{\partial}{\partial x_1}\left(\lambda B - \lambda \sum_{i=1}^{n} p_i x_i\right) = \frac{\partial}{\partial x_1}(\lambda B - \lambda p_1 x_1 - \lambda p_2 x_2 - \cdots - \lambda p_n x_n) = -\lambda p_1
$$

and so on for each x_i. An even more compact notation for (38) is

$$
\left.\begin{aligned}
f_{x_i} - \lambda p_i x_i &= 0 \qquad (i = 1, \ldots, n) \\
B - \sum_{i=1}^{n} p_i x_i &= 0
\end{aligned}\right\} \tag{39}
$$

where the marginal note $i = 1, \ldots, n$ tells the reader that there are n equations of identical form to the ith, which is the only one written out. From (38) or from (39) we can derive the marginal equalities

or
$$
\left.\begin{aligned}
\frac{f_{x_i}}{f_{x_j}} &= \frac{p_i}{p_j} \qquad (i, j = 1, \ldots, n) \\
\frac{f_{x_i}}{p_i} &= \frac{f_{x_j}}{p_j} = \lambda
\end{aligned}\right\} \tag{40}
$$

where the subscripts i and j and the marginal note indicate that we can substitute in whichever we like of $1, 2, \ldots, n$: thus we have shown, in the most compact way, that the equalities (40) must be true for *any pair whatever*. In any practical case, solving the n equations in (38) may be quite a chore; but what is very satisfactory is how easily we may obtain the n-dimensional analogue, in (40), of our tangency condition: (40) is perfectly general, true whatever value n may happen to have, and says that we must have equality for each pair of goods between the trade-off rate given by our constraint, p_i/p_j, and the marginal rate of substitution, f_{x_i}/f_{x_j}.

11.9   Multiple Constraints

We have seen that our Lagrangean technique is easily extended to cases of more than two variables. We may now ask whether it extends to cases of more than one constraint. Cases in which there is more than one constraint do arise in economics, as we may briefly illustrate. If a government imposes some sort of rationing scheme – say, of certain consumer goods in war-time – then the individual household is constrained not only by its budget but also by its ration book. Under current University Grants Committee rules, only two-ninths of the non-professorial teaching staff in a university may be Readers or Senior Lecturers: this is therefore a constraint on each university's hiring and promotion policy additional to that imposed by its budget. A manning agreement between a firm and a union, which specifies a certain number of men for a task, irrespective of whether technological advance may have reduced the required number, will operate on the firm's investment policy as an additional constraint to that imposed by its budget. It does not require much imagination to go on multiplying examples.

The extension of our technique to the case of more than two constraints is quite straightforward *on certain conditions*. But the whole subject of multiple constraints is vast and difficult, so what we shall do here is, first, show how easily we can set up the problem, and then show how easily we can manufacture a simple and important example in which the technique does not work. We shall also derive a few general lessons from the example of failure.

Suppose, first, that we have an objective function $f(x, y, z)$, and that x, y, and z are related by two constraints, say

$$H(x, y) = 0$$
$$\text{and} \quad F(y, z) = 0. \quad (41)$$

Then it is easy enough to introduce two Lagrangean multipliers, λ and μ, say, set up the equation

$$V = f(x, y, z) - \lambda H(x, y) - \mu F(y, z), \quad (42)$$

and set equal to zero the partial derivatives with respect to x, y, z, λ, and μ. On the same lines, we can handle a case of n variables and m constraints, obtaining as equilibrium conditions the equation to zero of $n+m$ partial derivatives. It turns out, however, that the solution of even a very simple example of the form of (42) rapidly becomes tiresome, so we shall not work

an example. It is more important to look at the cases in which the method
will not work!

In (42) we have three variables and two constraints. There might, however, be as many constraints as there are variables. We can illustrate this
perfectly well in two dimensions. Thus let the objective function be $f(x, y)$,
one constraint be of the ordinary budget-type, $B-p_x x-p_y y=0$, and a
second be a rationing-constraint, that the amount of x taken may not exceed some fixed amount, say OD in Figure 11.5, where the budget constraint is AB. Since no point outside OAB is attainable, and no point to the
right of the vertical line QD, the effective frontier has become AQD. Now
there are two possible, and quite distinct cases.

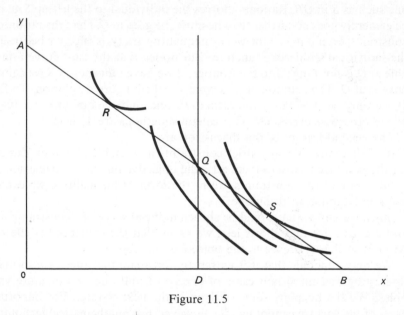

Figure 11.5

Suppose, first, that tangency between an iso-f curve and AB occurs at a
point in AQ such as R. Then the second, or ration, constraint does not
affect the chosen position: it is ineffective. Evidently, then, if we tried to
maximise $f(x, y)$ subject to the budget and the ration constraints, we should
not find R. This is because the rationing constraint is what is called a 'weak
inequality', written

$$x \leqslant OD$$

which is read 'x less than or equal to OD'. In plain words, this means that
the individual does not have to take up his whole ration if he does not wish
to. But there is no place in our calculus techniques for inequalities. If we

want to solve maximising problems of this sort, we require other methods (linear programming methods can handle some of them). If, of course, we insist that the whole ration is taken, the ration constraint becomes an equality; but now the individual is required to be on OD, and as he must be on AB, there is no choice problem: Q is the *only* attainable point. In general, if we insist on the *exact* fulfillment of as many constraints as there are variables, we leave the individual with no choice, but simply require him to be at a point like Q. Notice that it is impossible for the iso-f curve to be tangent to both branches of the frontier at Q, and only by a fluke will it be tangent to even one.

Suppose, second, that in the absence of rationing the chosen position is one such as S in QB. Rationing forces the individual to the left up SA, and he evidently goes no further than he must: he goes to Q. Here the rationing-constraint, even if it is of the weak-inequality variety, is effective because of the individual's objective function. But notice that the iso-f curve attainable at Q is not tangent to the frontier: if we have tangency at S we cannot have it at Q. The solution at Q is what is called a corner solution. To find Q, we only need to know the ration OD and that the amount of x taken would otherwise exceed OD. Our calculus methods are no help.

The general lessons of this discussion are:

(i) if there are as many strict constraints as variables, we look directly for the point that satisfies them all – the objective function is irrelevant;

(ii) if *any* of the constraints are in the form of inequalities, we cannot use our Lagrangean technique;

(iii) if we know what would be chosen in the absence of a constraint, and add a constraint that allows less, we know that the constraint is effective without further reference to the objective function.

We may conclude that it is extremely fortunate that there are so many interesting and important cases of one constraint and two or more variables! We shall explore some of them in the next chapter. For important cases of the sort we cannot handle, however, new mathematical techniques which allow for practical computation are being rapidly developed.

Exercises

1 (i) Find equilibrium x and y if the maximand is that of 11.3, $f(x, y) = 2x^{1/2}y^{1/2}$, but the constraint becomes $F(x, y) = 200 - 2x - y = 0$, i.e., 'income' has doubled. What conclusion does this suggest?

(ii) What difference would it make to equilibrium x and y if $2x^{1/2}y^{1/2}$ were replaced by $10x^{1/2}y^{1/2}$? Or by $2x^{1/2}y^{1/2} + 20$? What conclusion about the form of the maximand does this suggest?

(iii) Evaluate the second-order partial derivatives of $2x^{1/2}y^{1/2}$.

2 (i) Find equilibrium x and y if the objective function is

$$f(x, y) = 20x^{1/2}y^{1/2}$$

and the constraint is

$$F(x, y) = 300 - 2x - 5y = 0.$$

(ii) Show that convexity conditions are satisfied.

3 (i) Find equilibrium x and y if the objective function is

$$f(x, y) = 20xy - (x^2 + y^2)$$

and the constraint is

$$F(x, y) = 229 - 2x - 5y = 0.$$

(ii) How do the 'marginal' utilities behave in the neighbourhood of the equilibrium values of x and y?

4 You are given the objective function

$$f(x, y) = ax + by$$

defined only over non-negative x and y, together with the constraint

$$F(x, y) = C - cx - dy = 0.$$

(i) It may be obvious to you that the methods of this chapter will not work, but try to apply them anyhow. You will obtain

$$\lambda = \frac{a}{c}$$

and

$$\lambda = \frac{b}{d}.$$

Could both be true simultaneously, save by accident? Can these equations be solved for x and y?

(ii) Draw a diagram to illustrate the case. Find the best point by inspection. Is there more than one possibility? Consider the answers to (i) in the light of your diagram, and interpret.

(iii) Suggest an economic interpretation.

9*

CHAPTER 12

APPLICATIONS OF CONSTRAINED MAXIMA AND MINIMA

12.1 The Least-Cost Combination

The best known applications of constrained maxima and minima are the 'classical' ones in micro-economics, to utility theory and production theory. We shall consider the micro-examples first, and then go on to some examples in macro-economics dealing with policy problems.

The first problem is to find the conditions for minimising the cost of a given output. This is the problem of finding the combination of factors which, with given factor prices, makes a given output most cheaply. It is therefore often referred to as the problem of the 'least-cost combination'. We looked at production functions in Chapter 10, and, with the tools now at our disposal, we can solve this problem very easily, and we can do it in either of two ways.

Method 1: We seek to minimise the total cost of the inputs, subject to production being at some predetermined level.

Method 2: We seek to maximise production, subject to costs being at some predetermined level.

These two methods are illustrated in Figure 12.1, where one input, say capital, K, is measured on the vertical axis, and another, labour, L, on the horizontal. Each of the curves convex to the origin, or iso-quants, shows all the combinations of K and L which will produce a given output. Thus we assume that the production function is continuous and twice differentiable (no corners) and, in particular, that we have diminishing marginal substitutability which gives convexity in the iso-quants. We assume given factor prices, the wage rate being fixed at w, and the interest rate at r. The slope of a line such as AB measures the factor price ratio. Now consider what our two methods mean geometrically.

Method 1: We choose an iso-quant, say that corresponding to output X_0, and look for the point on it at which the cost of producing X_0 is minimised.

It is pretty obvious geometrically that this occurs where the iso-quant is tangent to a budget line, e.g., at Q on AB; and this is the tangency condition that we took for granted in the last chapter.

Method 2: We choose a budget line, say, AB, and look for the highest attainable output level. This again gives tangency at Q.

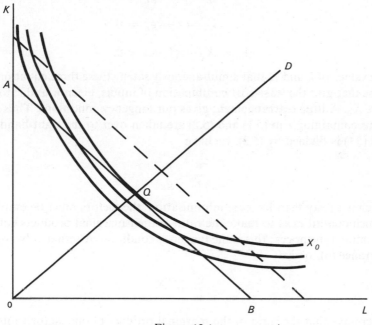

Figure 12.1

It is now quite straightforward to solve the problem analytically, both ways, and to show that the two approaches are completely interchangeable.

Method 1: Since we seek to minimise the cost of a given output, our objective function is total cost, which is simply the sum of the inputs each multiplied by its price:

$$C = wL + rK. \tag{1}$$

The constraint is that output be at a fixed level X_0, so, if the production function is

$$X = g(L, K) \tag{2}$$

we may write the constraint as

$$X_0 - g(L, K) = 0. \tag{3}$$

We now proceed, as we learned in the last chapter, to write

$$V = wL + rK + \lambda[X_0 - g(L, K)] \qquad (4)$$

where λ is our undetermined Lagrangean multiplier, and to find an extreme value we set each of the partial derivatives of (4) equal to zero:

$$V_L = w - \lambda g_L = 0 \qquad (5.1)$$

$$V_K = r - \lambda g_K = 0 \qquad (5.2)$$

$$V_\lambda = X_0 - g(L, K) = 0. \qquad (5.3)$$

The values of L and K that simultaneously satisfy these three equations are those that give the least-cost combination of inputs, given w and r, to produce X_0. A little rearrangement gives our tangency conditions. Thus if the terms containing λ in (5.1) and (5.2) are taken over to the right-hand side, and (5.1) is divided by (5.2), we have

$$\frac{w}{r} = \frac{g_L}{g_K} \qquad (6)$$

which is to say that, for cost minimisation, the factors must be employed in such quantities as to make the ratio of their marginal products equal to the ratio of the prices: this is the tangency condition. Alternatively, we may rearrange (6) to give

$$\frac{g_L}{w} = \frac{g_K}{r} \qquad (7)$$

which says that the ratio of the marginal product of one factor to its unit cost must be equal to that of the other factor. This is the common sense condition that the marginal product of a pound's worth of factor must be the same for all factors. Thus suppose that it were violated, and we had, for example,

$$\frac{g_L}{w} > \frac{g_K}{r}. \qquad (8)$$

Now w and r are expressed in money units, say 10/– an hour for the wage, and £7 per annum for the use of capital. The ratios g_L/w and g_K/r tell us marginal product per pound – or per shilling – spent on the factor. Thus the inequality (8) says that a marginal 'dose' of extra expenditure on labour adds more to output than the same amount spent on capital. It obviously pays to switch from capital to labour, to adopt, that is, a more labour-intensive method of production. Now if we assume diminishing marginal productivity, the use of more labour reduces g_L and the use of less capital increases g_K, so we move in the direction of equality (7). (Remember that we saw, in Chapter 11 above, that negative second derivatives, or diminishing marginal products, are neither necessary nor sufficient for convexity of the iso-quants. If we did not assume diminishing marginal productivity, we should still have equations (5), and hence the alternative conditions (6) and (7), and to explain the movement from (8) to (7), we should appeal to diminishing marginal substitutability, or convexity.)

Method 2: Now our objective function is output, so we seek to maximise

$$X = g(L, K) \tag{2}$$

subject to the constraint of a fixed budget,

$$C_0 - wL - rK = 0. \tag{9}$$

Instead of (4) we simply write

$$V = g(L, K) + \lambda(C_0 - wL - rK) \tag{10}$$

and set the first derivatives equal to zero:

$$V_L = g_L - \lambda w = 0 \tag{11.1}$$

$$V_K = g_K - \lambda r = 0 \tag{11.2}$$

$$V_\lambda = C_0 - wL - rK = 0. \tag{11.3}$$

After our geometrical discussion, the similarity between (11) and (5) is hardly surprising. (6) and (7) can be derived from (11) exactly as from (5), and the derivation is left to the reader.

What we have illustrated here is the extraordinary flexibility of the method of constrained maxima or minima. We also learn something about objective functions and 'utility'. In Method 1 we minimised cost. Now $C = wL + rK$ hardly looks like a 'utility' – or 'disutility' – function, but all we need do is to assume that the producer would rather achieve any output for less cost than for more, and we have an objective function, something that we want to minimise. Similarly, the production function $X = g(L, K)$ is not a utility function; but if we assume that the producer would rather have more output than less, for a given outlay, we have something to maximise. Later on we shall take up the case of the individual consumer, and the objective function will then be a utility function in the ordinary sense; but we may guess now that if 'utility' is looked upon merely as an objective function, much of the mystery often attached to it dissolves; and we may also guess that the technique of constrained maxima may be profitably employed *wherever* something can be discovered of which, *ceteris paribus*, either more or less is desired, giving us an objective function, and there is some frontier or constraint limiting the amounts that may be had.

The next step in a systematic treatment of production is comparative static analysis. That is, we should ask how the least-cost combination is changed when the factor prices, w and r, change. We should hope to obtain the signs of such expressions as

$$\frac{dL}{dw}, \quad \frac{dL}{dr}, \quad \frac{dK}{dw}, \quad \text{and} \quad \frac{dK}{dr}. \tag{12}$$

Since capital is one of our factors, we are dealing with the long-run (by definition) or, as it is sometimes called, the case of 'full-adjustment'. If we had the signs of the expressions in (12), we should have the predicted directions of change of both factors, allowing for full adjustment, in response to a change in either factor price. We have seen in earlier examples in Chapter 8, however, that to obtain directions of change at extremum points we have to make use of second-order conditions; and the second order conditions to go with (5) or (11) require a good deal more technique than we now have. So we shall leave the general case here, and take up again the particular example of the Cobb-Douglas production function that we discussed in Chapter 10. With this example we shall be able to carry out a complete analysis, and obtain some remarkable, and famous, results.

12.2 The Elasticity of Substitution

We now introduce the concept of the elasticity of substitution. Assume again the homogeneous, constant-returns, Cobb–Douglas function,

$$X = AL^\alpha K^{1-\alpha}. \tag{13}$$

To find the least-cost combination we proceed as on page 250 to maximise (13) subject to

$$C - wL - rK = 0. \tag{14}$$

We set equal to zero the partial derivatives of

$$V = AL^\alpha K^{1-\alpha} + \lambda(C - wL - rK) \tag{15}$$

obtaining

$$V_L = \alpha AL^{\alpha-1}K^{1-\alpha} - \lambda w = 0 \tag{16.1}$$

$$V_K = (1-\alpha)AL^\alpha K^{-\alpha} - \lambda r = 0 \tag{16.2}$$

$$V_\lambda = C - wL - rK = 0. \tag{16.3}$$

To solve these equations, we start in the usual way by eliminating λ. From (16.1),

$$\lambda = \frac{\alpha AL^{\alpha-1}K^{1-\alpha}}{w},$$

Substituting this into 16.2, we obtain

$$(1-\alpha)AL^{\alpha}K^{-\alpha} - \frac{r}{w}\alpha AL^{\alpha-1}K^{1-\alpha} = 0,$$

whence

$$L^{\alpha} = \frac{r}{w}\frac{\alpha AL^{\alpha-1}K^{1-\alpha}}{(1-\alpha)AK^{-\alpha}}.$$

Cancelling terms on the R.H.S., we get

$$L^{\alpha} = \frac{r}{w}\frac{\alpha}{(1-\alpha)}L^{\alpha-1}K.$$

Dividing through by $L^{\alpha-1}$, this gives

$$L = \frac{r}{w}\frac{\alpha}{(1-\alpha)}K. \qquad (17.1)$$

A simple rearrangement of (17.1) gives

$$\frac{L}{K} = \frac{r}{w}\frac{\alpha}{(1-\alpha)}, \qquad (17.2)$$

the familiar result that the least-cost labour:capital ratio, L/K, depends on the factor price ratio, r/w, and the exponents α and $(1-\alpha)$, and is independent of the scale of production, since C does not occur in (17.2). This result is familiar from the last chapter. From (16) we can now complete our solution of the least-cost problem. We substitute (17.1), from which λ has been eliminated, into (16.3), to obtain

$$C - w\frac{r}{w}\frac{\alpha}{(1-\alpha)}K - rK = 0. \qquad (18)$$

Rearrangement gives

$$rK\left[1+\frac{\alpha}{(1-\alpha)}\right] = C$$

or

$$rK\left(\frac{1-\alpha+\alpha}{1-\alpha}\right) = C$$

or

$$K = C\frac{(1-\alpha)}{r}. \qquad (19.1)$$

(19.1) says that the optimal amount of capital depends on its exponent $(1-\alpha)$, and its price, r, with outlay, C, as a multiplicative factor only. Finally, substitute this back into (16.3) to find L:

$$C - wL - rC\frac{(1-\alpha)}{r} = 0,$$

whence

$$wL = C[1-(1-\alpha)],$$

or

$$L = C\frac{\alpha}{w} \tag{19.2}$$

which is analogous with (19.1). We now merely check that we do obtain the same expression for factor proportions from (19.1) and (19.2) that we had before. Clearly division of (19.2) by (19.1) gives (17.2).

We saw in Chapter 10 that, in the case of a Cobb-Douglas production function, factor shares (the proportion of total product paid to each factor) depend on the exponents only, and are constant so long as the exponents are unchanged, being independent of actual factor prices or the scale of production. For factor shares, wL/rK, to remain constant, it is necessary that the reduced amount of L, times increased w, exactly cancels increased K. To see that this is what happens, we introduce a new term, *the elasticity of substitution*, denoted by σ (read 'sigma'; we encountered capital sigma, $\sum$, earlier). This is defined as

$$\frac{\text{proportionate change in factor proportions}}{\text{proportionate change in relative factor prices}}$$

so

$$\sigma = \frac{\mathrm{d}\left(\frac{L}{K}\right)}{\frac{L}{K}} \bigg/ \frac{\mathrm{d}\left(\frac{r}{w}\right)}{\frac{r}{w}}$$

or, more conveniently,

$$\sigma = \frac{\mathrm{d}\left(\frac{L}{K}\right)\frac{r}{w}}{\mathrm{d}\left(\frac{r}{w}\right)\frac{L}{K}}. \tag{20}$$

It is very easy to evaluate this here. We already have (17.2):

$$\frac{L}{K} = \frac{r}{w}\frac{\alpha}{1-\alpha}$$

hence

$$\frac{d\left(\frac{L}{K}\right)}{d\left(\frac{r}{w}\right)} = \frac{\alpha}{1-\alpha}. \tag{21}$$

If we substitute (17.2) and (21) into (20), we obtain

$$\sigma = \frac{\alpha}{1-\alpha} \cdot \frac{\dfrac{r}{w}}{\dfrac{r}{w}\dfrac{\alpha}{1-\alpha}}$$

$$= 1. \tag{22}$$

Thus the elasticity of substitution is equal to unity, and, as relative factor prices alter, we have the exact offsetting effect that our intuitive argument led us to expect.

It may help to see what σ means in terms of the shape of the iso-quants. Let the budget line AB of Figure 12.1 change slope, and slide it round to preserve tangency with an iso-quant: we are asking what happens to factor proportions as the slope changes. But as we have tangency, we are really only asking about the shape of the iso-quant: if we move along it, changing its slope, how 'far' do we move in terms of K/L for a given change in slope? That is, we can replace r/w with the ratio of the marginal products (refer back, if necessary, to equation (6)), and write σ, if we choose, as

$$\sigma = \frac{d\left(\dfrac{L}{K}\right)}{d\left(\dfrac{MPK}{MPL}\right)} \frac{\dfrac{MPK}{MPL}}{\dfrac{L}{K}} \tag{23}$$

where MPL and MPK are the marginal physical products of labour and capital respectively. The expression $d(MPK/MPL)$ looks forbidding, but remember that it is only the change in the slope of the iso-quant. By assuming tangency, we have simply replaced it with the change in the slope of the constraint, $d(r/w)$, and found

$$\frac{d\left(\dfrac{L}{K}\right)}{d\left(\dfrac{r}{w}\right)} = \frac{d\left(\dfrac{L}{K}\right)}{d\left(\dfrac{MPK}{MPL}\right)}$$

which is the rate of change in factor proportions as one alters the slope of the iso-quant by sliding along it.

12.3   The Efficient Allocation of Resources

We can now take up some quite new topics in economics. They are new in the sense that we have not discussed them before, and also in the sense that they are not included in principles courses, or, indeed, in many second-year courses. Thus in terms of its economic content, this section is ambitious. Yet we make such an enormous gain in efficiency by using what is now routine mathematical technique that this section should not be found particularly difficult: it is possible to concentrate on the economic interpretation rather than on the technical difficulties.

We shall prove the famous propositions of welfare economics that, for an efficient allocation of resources, the marginal product of a factor must be the same in all uses, and its price the same to all users. This is one of the conditions for allocative efficiency first proved by Pareto. It may be proved piecemeal by the method of finite differences, or geometrically, or much more generally and powerfully by calculus methods. We shall start with the geometry. This is worthwhile because the construction required is frequently employed in the economic literature, and it is useful to be familiar with it; but we shall shortly see that it is remarkably long-winded and cumbersome compared with our calculus methods.

We assume that society is endowed with limited quantities of two resources, say capital and labour, which can be combined, with given production functions, to produce two goods, A and B. We assume constant returns in the production of both A and B, and that there are no external economies or diseconomies. Now we construct the famous 'box diagram'[1]. In Figure 12.2 we mark off the endowments OK of capital and ON of labour along the axes in the ordinary way. Now draw in the iso-quants for one of the goods, say A. (Figure 12.2 is drawn complete, but it is helpful to take paper and pencil and construct it step by step for yourself if you have never done it before.) Complete the box by constructing a horizontal line through K, a vertical one through N, and marking their intersection O_B (correspondingly relabel the south-west origin O_A). Now consider a point in the box such as Q. At Q, $O_A D$ of capital and $O_A F$ of labour are used in the production of A, hence DK of capital and FN of labour are available for the production of B. But $DK = O_B E$, and $FN = O_B G$. Thus measuring along the axes from

---

[1] Since the box diagram is thoroughly explained in most intermediate textbooks, the geometrical treatment here is very condensed. See, e.g., G. J. Stigler, *The Theory of Price*, The Macmillan Co., N.Y. (latest edition 1966), Chapter 4, or K. Boulding, *Economic Analysis*, Harper and Row, 4th edition, 1966, Vol. I, Chapter 28.

O_A we have factor use in the A-industry, and measuring from O_B we have factor use in the B-industry: everywhere in the box we have full employment of both factors. We can now draw the B-iso-quants with O_B as origin. Every point in the box now corresponds to a unique allocation of factors between the two industries, and a unique pair of outputs. Suppose now that Q lies on the iso-quant B_0. Q is then inefficient because by sliding round A_0, A-output constant, to S, one can reach a higher B-output. At S we have tangency. But the slope of an iso-quant is the ratio of the marginal products, so when the iso-quants are tangential the ratio of the marginal products must be equal. We will consider this further in a moment.

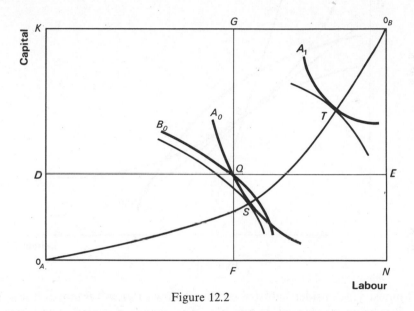

Figure 12.2

First, we notice that a point like S is efficient in the sense that it is impossible to reallocate resources in such a fashion as to increase the output of one good without reducing that of the other. Nothing is said about the relative valuations of the two goods, or what combination of the two society wants or 'should' want: an 'efficient point' is one that is *on the frontier*, and that is all. Second, we pick any other A-iso-quant, say A_1, and then search for a B-iso-quant that is tangent to it. Let the tangency occur at T. Then T is an efficient point in precisely the same sense as S. If we locate all such points of tangency and connect them up, we get the curve $O_A O_B$, *the locus of efficient allocations*. We shall meet a similar construction in 12.5 below under the title of 'contract curve'.

Figure 12.3 is merely the neighbourhood of S in Figure 12.2 blown up in scale for convenience. If firms in the A-industry are to be in equilibrium at S, the iso-quant must there be tangent to the price line, as we have drawn the price line PM. If industry B faces the same relative prices, it will be in equilibrium at S too, and not at an inefficient point such as Q. Suppose, on the other hand, that the price of labour were higher to industry B, due to some market imperfection or tax. (It is a good exercise now to work out for yourself in which direction this will rotate the relative price line to the

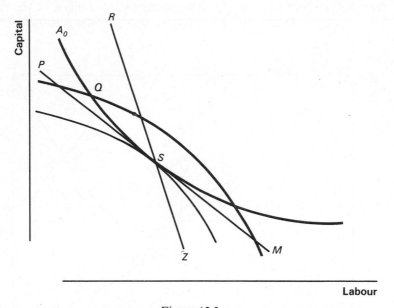

Figure 12.3

B-industry.) Consider industry B moving down PM. As B moves down, it is increasing its amount of capital – A is giving up capital – and losing labour. Thus a movement to the North West in the box corresponds to a gain of labour to B and loss of capital. Hence a steeper line such as RZ indicates that for a given gain in labour B must give up more capital. But if B's price line is RZ, B will certainly not be in equilibrium at S, so an efficient allocation cannot be achieved. On the full employment assumption, however, both industries must be at the same point in the box. The situation will therefore be one like V in Figure 12.4, where the A-iso-quant is tangent to PM and the B-iso-quant to RZ.

To achieve an efficient point if firms in each industry adjust to least-cost factor combinations therefore requires that the factor price ratio be the same for each industry: otherwise the ratios of marginal products will be unequal. But we already know that equilibrium for the firm requires that marginal products be equal to real factor prices or wages; hence we not only have equality of ratios but of the absolute marginal products themselves as a condition for efficiency. We have something else, too. The marginal-product-equals-real-wage condition, or money-wage-equals-marginal-value-product, holds only in perfect competition: we have in fact assumed that A and B are produced in condition of perfect competition.

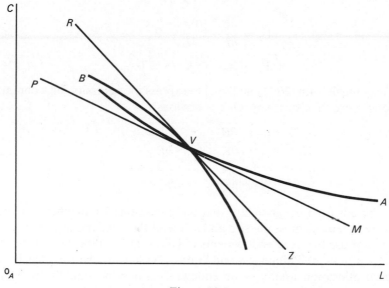

Figure 12.4

Hence it does not follow that the Selective Employment Tax *necessarily* leads to less efficient allocation if non-perfect competition already characterises the British economy.[1]

The mathematics of efficient allocation are now familiar and easy. We have two constant-returns production functions, which we write

$$A = f^a(K, L) \tag{24a}$$

and

$$B = f^b(K, L). \tag{24b}$$

---

[1] Since the tax differs between broad sectors of the economy, however, it is presumably assumed that some sectors are generally less competitive than others. It is good exercise to think out on what assumptions the tax is a movement *towards* a more efficient allocation, and what facts you would require to test these assumptions.

We pick a value of A, say A_0, and look for the conditions which maximise B subject to $A = A_0$. The problem is therefore to maximise $B = f^b(K, L)$ subject to $A_0 - f^a(K, L) = 0$. So we write

$$V = f^b(K, L) + \lambda(A_0 - f^a(K, L)) \tag{25}$$

and equate the partial derivatives to zero:

$$V_K = \frac{\partial B}{\partial K} - \lambda \frac{\partial A}{\partial K} = 0 \tag{26.1}$$

$$V_L = \frac{\partial B}{\partial L} - \lambda \frac{\partial A}{\partial L} = 0 \tag{26.2}$$

$$V_\lambda = A_0 - f^a(K, L) = 0. \tag{26.3}$$

We may juggle with (26.1) and (26.2) to express the necessity for a common ratio in more than one way. One is obviously

$$\frac{\dfrac{\partial B}{\partial K}}{\dfrac{\partial A}{\partial K}} = \lambda = \frac{\dfrac{\partial B}{\partial L}}{\dfrac{\partial A}{\partial L}}. \tag{27}$$

It is obvious from the geometry that our conditions for an efficient allocation are independent of the size and shape of the box, and in deriving (27) we do not use the fixed endowments of labour and capital for constraints. This is just as well since the conditions (27) have to be satisfied for an efficient allocation *whatever* the endowments may be, equally in a large country or a small one, one with much labour and little capital, or one with abundant capital and expensive labour. As far as the conditions for efficiency are concerned, the absolute size of Figure 12.2 is irrelevant, and so is the capital: labour ratio. An efficient allocation, however, obviously dictates the capital: labour ratio in each industry, and it is clear from inspection of Figure 12.2 that the ratios will neither be the same for each industry nor the same at different points on the contract curve $O_A O_B$.

12.4   Utility Maximisation

Now that we have dealt with production, the case of the individual consumer is straightforward and very similar. We assume two goods, x and y, and assume that the consumer can *rank* or *order* all combinations of them. If we also assume continuity, then we have an objective function

$$U = U(x, y). \tag{28}$$

We now need to consider very carefully just what properties we must assume (28) to possess. First of all, we assume that more of either good is better than less, so U is monotonic increasing in both x and y, or

$$U_x > 0, U_y > 0. \tag{29}$$

If we allow for the possibility of some satiety level, after which further increments of the goods afford no additional satisfaction, we may replace (29) with the '*weak* inequalities'

$$U_x \geqslant 0, U_y \geqslant 0. \tag{30}$$

(30) excludes disutility: it says that the marginal utilities must be positive or zero, i.e., non-negative. We shall make the simpler and stronger assumption (29), and add the assumption of diminishing marginal utilities,

$$U_{xx} < 0, U_{yy} < 0 \tag{31}$$

which appeals to the intuition. What we really want, however, is that the iso-U, or indifference, curves be convex to the origin, and, as we saw in the last chapter, (31) is neither necessary nor sufficient for this. The slope of an indifference curve is the marginal rate of substitution, given by

$$r = -\frac{U_x}{U_y}. \tag{32}$$

Since U_x and U_y are both positive by assumption, this is negative as required. Convexity means that the slope gets absolutely smaller as x increases. But as the slope is negative, this means that its rate of change must be positive, so our convexity condition is

$$\frac{dr}{dx} > 0. \tag{33}$$

As on page 246 above, we require the total differential,

$$\frac{dr}{dx} = \frac{\partial}{\partial x}\left(-\frac{U_x}{U_y}\right) + \frac{\partial}{\partial y}\left(-\frac{U_x}{U_y}\right)\frac{dy}{dx}.$$

Evaluating this, we obtain

$$\frac{dr}{dx} = -\frac{U_y^2 U_{xx} - 2U_x U_y U_{xy} + U_x^2 U_{yy}}{U_y^3}. \tag{34}$$

Since the denominator is positive, (34) is positive if

$$U_y^2 U_{xx} - 2U_x U_y U_{xy} + U_x^2 U_{yy} < 0. \tag{35}$$

Evidently the assumptions that $U_x > 0$, $U_y > 0$ and $U_{xx} < 0$, $U_{yy} < 0$ are not sufficient because the expression contains the cross-partial U_{xy}. So we must make the explicit assumption that (35) is true. This is the assumption of Diminishing Marginal Substitutability.

Our assumptions about utility may be briefly summarised. In (28), we assume the existence of a continuous and differentiable objective function, assume that it is monotonically increasing in both goods, (29), but at a decreasing rate (31), and we additionally assume convexity (35). Thus we have effectively assumed a well-behaved objective function, but nothing more. This much we have to do to obtain a model of consistently purposeful action. Whether it is empirically justified is, of course, an entirely separate question. We may, for example, be able to conceive a world in which consumers' tastes fluctuate so much that no one objective function can help us to derive a good model. Tastes, too, may be closely related to experience, in which case several of our assumptions will be inappropriate:

(i) if experience matters, today's purchases depend on yesterday's, and we require a dynamic instead of a static treatment;

(ii) possible experience depends on the budget constraint: if experience matters, tastes will not be independent of past and present budgets and prices.

It is also, of course, possible that there is a large random component in consumer behaviour. We may speculate on this matter, and speculation certainly helps us to see just what we are assuming; but our assumptions cannot be justified *a priori*: we require some testable predictions. The first step is of course to find equilibrium conditions.

We seek to maximise the objective function (28) subject to a budget constraint

$$B - p_x x - p_y y = 0. \tag{36}$$

Procedure is routine. Write

$$V = U(x, y) + \lambda(B - p_x x - p_y y) \tag{37}$$

and set the first-order partial derivatives equal to zero:

$$V_x = U_x - \lambda p_x = 0 \tag{38.1}$$

$$V_y = U_y - \lambda p_y = 0 \tag{38.2}$$

$$V_\lambda = B - p_x - p_y = 0. \tag{38.3}$$

Rearrangement of equations (38) gives us the famous equilibrium conditions. We find

$$\frac{U_x}{p_x} = \lambda = \frac{U_y}{p_y} \tag{39}$$

which says that the ratio of the marginal utility of each good to its price must be equal to the common ratio, λ, or, what comes to the same thing, that marginal utility per penny of expenditure must be the same in every line of expenditure. Notice particularly that (39) is formally identical with the least-cost production conditions derived from equations (5) in 12.1 above.

We now come to the familiar obstacle: to do comparative statics, and obtain signs, if we can, for dx/dp_x, dy/dp_y, etc., we require the formal second-order conditions for maximising (37). We shall therefore have to be content with a rather rough, intuitive treatment. Imagine that prices alter so that the budget line changes slope, but that it is slid in or out to preserve tangency with the indifference curve on which the initial equilibrium is located. We in fact conducted a similar experiment with the Cobb-Douglas production function. In the case of the consumer, the sliding in or out of the budget line to preserve constant utility after a price change is referred to as 'income compensation'. Now, from the assumption of convexity alone we know how demand alters in the case of compensated price changes. Thus suppose that x becomes relatively cheaper: the budget line becomes flatter. Thanks to convexity, a flatter portion of the indifference curve is reached by increasing x. Hence a compensated demand curve has a negative slope: this is the result of the 'substitution effect'. That is clear and is, in fact, as much as we could prove with the full armoury of second-order conditions. The reason why it is not sufficient to tell us that all demand curves slope down may be found in any 'principles' text: when we do not compensate, but leave the intercept of the budget line unchanged when its slope alters, there is an income effect as well as a substitution effect. To see that there is an income effect, imagine a two-step procedure. First, by compensating, we discover the chosen point at the new price ratio on the old indifference curve: this allows us to isolate the substitution effect. Next we 'uncompensate': we slide the compensated budget line, slope unaltered, until its intercept coincides with that of the old budget line. The whole line in fact now coincides with the new budget line; but the change in the demand for x induced by this parallel shift is the income effect on demand. If the income effect is positive (normal good), all is well, and we predict a downward-sloping demand curve. If the income effect is negative (inferior good), it and the substitution effect pull in opposite directions, and we can derive no general *qualitative* prediction.

This may be a little disappointing: we do not seem to get much out of consumer theory. We demonstrate that the substitution effect has the 'right sign', which we might indicate by

$$\left. \frac{\partial x}{\partial p_x} \right|_{U \text{ constant}} < 0,$$

and that is all. We shall see in the next section, however, that we can derive some rather remarkable and interesting results about economic 'efficiency', in a very carefully defined sense, with the help of utility functions. First, we may just notice how very easily our algebraic treatment can be extended to the case of many goods, to which geometry will not extend. We simply replace the objective function (28) with

$$U = U(x_1, x_2, \ldots, x_n) \tag{40}$$

where $x_1, x_2, \ldots, x_n$ are the goods consumed. Now employing the summation notation, we can write the budget constraint as

$$B - \sum_i x_i p_i = 0. \tag{41}$$

$\sum_i x_i p_i$ is the sum of the expenditures on each good, quantity of x_1 times its price, plus quantity of x_2 times its price, etc. Now we write

$$V = U(x_1, x_2, \ldots, x_n) + \lambda\left(B - \sum_i p_i x_i\right) \tag{42}$$

and obtain $n+1$ derivatives – one each for the x's, plus λ. This, as we saw in the last chapter, can be written conveniently and compactly as

$$V_{x_i} = U_{x_i} - \lambda p_i = 0 \qquad i = 1, \ldots, n \tag{43.1}$$

and

$$V_\lambda = B - \sum_i p_i x_i = 0. \tag{43.2}$$

(43.1) says that we have n equations identical in form, one for each x. If we pick out another, say the jth,

$$U_{x_j} - \lambda p_j = 0 \tag{44}$$

we can derive the conditions

$$\frac{U_{x_i}}{p_i} = \lambda = \frac{U_{x_j}}{p_j} \tag{45}$$

for *any* pair x_i and x_j. What this demonstrates is the enormous power and convenience of really good notation. We have derived (45) for *any* pair i and j, and we simply do not care about the value of n. Imagine the alternative: we should have to write out forty equations in the case of $n=40$, and if a cautious sceptic said 'What about the case of 41 goods? You haven't proved that yet' we should have to do it again. We have proved (45) once and for all for any n.

12.5 The Contract Curve

An important concept in economics is that of an *efficient* or *optimal* allocation. We have already worked out some conditions for an efficient allocation of factors in production (12.3 above). We can do something very similar for consumers, but we need to be particularly careful about what it means if we are not going to make unwarranted policy inferences. We know, of course, that the conditions for optimal allocations are those given by solution of the appropriate constrained maximum problem. They are therefore optimal from the point of view of the particular objective function chosen, and there is no occasion to interpret optimality in any wider ethical or political sense. The conclusion is the creature of the objective function chosen. If, however, we can work with a fairly general function, our results may be of considerable scope.

In our discussion of the box diagram, we found a locus of efficient points in the sense that, when off the locus, more of one good could be produced without sacrifice of the other, while, when on it, more of one good could be had only at the cost of the other. We can similarly draw a box for two consumers trading with each other, putting the two goods on the axes, measuring the amounts enjoyed by consumer A from one origin and the amount enjoyed by consumer B from the diagonally opposite origin. If we draw in their indifference maps, we shall find a locus of tangencies known as the 'contract curve'. This is a locus of efficient points in the sense that, once on it, one consumer can only be made better off at the expense of the other, while if off it, one can be made better off *without* making the other worse off. We shall show that if two consumers are faced by different price ratios, they will be off the contract curve: the welfare of one of them could be increased without loss to the other.

The geometry of the box is identical to that in the case of production. We laboured through the construction there, and then saw how much more quickly we could proceed by using calculus methods. Construction of the box for two consumers is left to you. What we shall do is derive the contract curve directly for the case of *three* goods, where the geometry would be impossibly cumbersome. Following the discussion at the end of the last section, you may be able to generalise this to the case of n goods for yourself and it would be worth while attempting the exercise. We assume two individuals, A and B, and three goods, x, y, z. We also have two utility functions,

$$U(A) = f(x, y, z) \tag{46}$$
$$U(B) = g(x, y, z). \tag{47}$$

The problem is what to take as an objective function and what as a constraint. The trick is to hold one individual's utility constant at some arbitrary level, and to maximise the other's: this gives one point on the contract curve. Suppose that we choose $U(B)=U_b$, a constant, and maximise for A. Then our familiar equation takes the form

$$V = f(x, y, z)+\lambda(U_b-g(x, y, z)). \tag{48}$$

We put all partial derivatives equal to zero, thus

$$V_x = f_x-\lambda g_x = 0 \tag{49.1}$$

$$V_y = f_y-\lambda g_y = 0 \tag{49.2}$$

$$V_z = f_z-\lambda g_z = 0 \tag{49.3}$$

$$V_\lambda = U_b-g(x, y, z) = 0. \tag{49.4}$$

From the pairs (49.1) and (49.2), (49.2) and (49.3), (49.1) and (49.3) we may obtain the conditions of equality of marginal rates of substitution:

$$\frac{f_x}{f_y} = \frac{g_x}{g_y}; \quad \frac{f_y}{f_z} = \frac{g_y}{g_z}; \quad \frac{f_x}{f_z} = \frac{g_x}{g_z}; \tag{50}$$

or

$$\frac{f_x}{g_x} = \frac{f_y}{g_y} = \frac{f_z}{g_z} = \lambda. \tag{51}$$

(50) and (51) hold at the point on the contract curve given by $U(B)=U_b$, but since U_b was arbitrarily chosen, they hold anywhere on the contract curve. We already know, however, that each individual, facing given prices, will maximise his utility by choosing that combination of goods that makes the ratios of the marginal utilities, or marginal rates of substitution, equal to the price ratios (equation (39) above). Hence if the two individuals are to have the same marginal rates of substitution, which by (50) is a condition for their being on the contract curve, they must face a common price ratio.[1] The analogy with the theory of production is very close. You are asked in Exercise 2 to extend the analysis a little for both cases.

Our analysis makes it very easy to settle a question that much perturbed our ancestors. They believed that a good must have some definite, inherent value; and they accordingly argued that, if one party to a transaction gains, the other must lose: one party must receive more, or less, than the good is really worth if either is to gain. Probably no one really believes this now save a few flat-earthers, but it was an important idea: it lay behind

---

[1] This is the reason for the economists' traditional dislike of price discrimination. But see R. G. Lipsey, *Introduction to Positive Economics*, 2nd edition, Chapter 24, especially page 333, for an example in which discrimination is 'good'. There is a *prima facie* contradiction between these two results; and its resolution is an important exercise in economics, left to the reader.

many schemes for non-commercial utopian communities, and its over-throw, the belief that *both* parties gain from exchange, was important to the development of the law of free contract. Once we give up the idea of goods having 'inherent value', instead of merely utility and relative scarcity, the problem is scarcely likely to bother us; but we can easily demonstrate the gains from trade with our box diagram. In Figure 12.5 we draw a box, and we give each individual an initial arbitrary allocation of the two goods. Suppose that they start at Q where A has $O_A E$ of x and $O_A D$ of y, and B has the remainder. If by trading they move to any

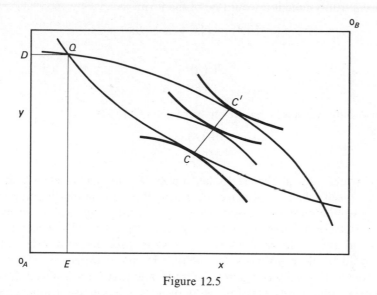

Figure 12.5

point outside the area enclosed by the two indifference curves through Q, someone is worse off than with his initial allocation: these two indifference curves enclose the area of mutually advantageous bargains. Thus there are trades, or swaps, which will benefit both parties. Bargains such that one party can make a further gain only at the expense of the other are those that take the parties to the contract curve CC'. Thus it is *possible* for both parties to gain from trade, and the old worry that one man's gain *must* be another's loss is dispelled.

If the two individuals' marginal rates of substitution had happened to be equal at their initial endowment, there would have been no possibility of gain from trade, and no motive for trade. Equality of the marginal rates of substitution, of course, means tangency of the indifference curves. Thus equality of the MRS's at the initial endowment would mean that Q happened to lie on the contract curve. Hence we can look on the possibility of mutual gain from trade as arising from the non-equality of MRS's, and as being exhausted once a bargain has been made that equalises the MRS's. Once the contract curve is reached, there is no further room for mutual benefit, but only for redistribution.[1]

This is a good moment to emphasise one assumption that we have made throughout this section: that the two utility functions are independent. In the real world, this may well not be the case. Thus suppose that A is jealous of B's opulence, and that an increase in B's well-being makes A less happy. Then A's utility function would be of the form

$$U(A) = f\{x, y, z, U(B)\} \tag{52}$$

with

$$\frac{\partial U(A)}{\partial U(B)} < 0. \tag{53}$$

Alternatively, we might have (52), but instead of (53)

$$\frac{\partial U(A)}{\partial U(B)} > 0, \tag{54}$$

which would suggest that A looked upon B with benevolence, and felt better himself when B's welfare increased. We may similarly complicate matters to allow for B's attitude to A, and a little imagination suggests a wide variety of attitudes of individuals towards others that occur in the real world and might be allowed for. In what cases the no-discrimination rule would break down has yet to be thoroughly investigated. All we can say is that both parties *can* gain from trade, and that there is a well-defined locus of efficient points *if* the utilities of the two individuals are independent of each other.

12.6 Profit Maximisation

It would be easy to set up the problem of profit maximisation for the firm as a constrained maximum problem, taking $\Pi = R - C$ as the objective function, and the market demand curve, $p - f(x) = 0$, as the constraint. Substitution from $p = f(x)$, however, so easily turns this into a single-variable problem that Lagrangean techniques are seldom employed. It is perhaps worth doing for yourself as an exercise. Two points may, however, be

[1] A fascinating account of the benefit from trade, arising from non-equality of individuals' MRS's at an initial arbitrary endowment, is given in R. A. Radford, 'The Economic Organisation of a P.o.W. Camp', *Economica*, 1945. This is an example of purely literary economics which may be read with great profit now that the underlying analysis has been mastered.

noticed. The first is technical. We can always substitute, and reduce the number of variables if we wish. Thus if the objective function is $f(x, y)$, and the constraint is $F(x, y) = B - rx - sy = 0$, we can express y by $y = (B - rx)/s$ and substitute into the objective function so that we only have to maximise $f\{x, [(B - rx)/s]\}$ with respect to x. In general, if $F(x, y) = 0$, we expect there to be a corresponding explicit relationship $y = g(x)$, *if* we can discover it by suitable manipulations of F, in which case we can maximise $f\{x, g(x)\}$ using the chain rule. So whether we substitute or use our Lagrangean method is a matter of convenience. The second point is that, if we can handle objective functions of two or more variables, we are equipped to handle other hypotheses about the behaviour of firms besides simple profit maximisation. A good deal of literature on this topic is now accessible to you.[1] We shall not pursue the matter here, but take up some other topics.

12.7 The Ubiquity of Constrained Maximum Problems

The Lagrangean method is now routine, although some complicated ex- pressions quickly occur. There are also analytical difficulties requiring a good deal of sophistication if the attack is to be complete, with second-order conditions and a full comparative-static analysis. The important point is that a choice problem is a constrained maximum problem. If an alleged choice problem does not appear to be a constrained maximum problem, either the problem has not been correctly formulated, or it is not in fact a choice problem! Where skill, indeed perhaps real insight, may be required is in sorting out what is really the objective function and what the constraint, and in finding out just what the constraint looks like. All politi- cal, social, and economic policy is subject to the constraints set by the actual behaviour of society, and we might define the task of social science as the discovery and elucidation of those constraints. We shall shortly consider some problems of economic policy, but first let us demonstrate the ubiquity of constrained maximum problems.

Imagine a politician who wishes conscientiously to support a policy which he believes will harm him electorally. His objective function has as arguments expediency and morality, while he is constrained by the be- haviour of his constituents. He may make his support more or less vocal and active, and may lose correspondingly many or few votes. Thus a 'dose' of support has an opportunity cost in terms of votes. There is, however, one

[1] See, for example, T. Scitovsky, 'A Note on Profit Maximisation and its Implications', re- printed in *Readings in Price Theory*, Blakiston Series, W. J. Baumol 'On the Theory of Oligopoly', *Economica*, N.S. XXV No. 99, 1958, and M. H. Peston, 'On the Sales Maximisa- tion Hypothesis', *Economica*, N.S. XXVI, No. 102, 1959.

awkward and important discontinuity: there is some critical number of votes that he must retain to secure re-election.

The Ministry of Defence has a constrained maximum problem, as is obvious from the fact that at any one time it has a limited budget, and all items of military equipment have price-tags. It also has a highly complicated objective function. It wishes to preserve some nuclear 'deterrent'; it must attach some value to nuclear defence; it must be prepared to cope with situations of the Malaysian kind, and must keep troops in Germany; it wants more weapons of the current model, and simultaneously it wants to improve the model; and, above all, it deals with a basically uncertain or probabilistic world. It is no accident that when McNamara became US Secretary of Defence he took some economists to the Pentagon. To specify with any degree of comprehensiveness and accuracy the constraints and the objective function would alone be a colossal task. That the rationality of the Ministry of Defence, in the sense of action *consistently* chosen to attain the desired goals given the possibilities, would be improved by their proper specification cannot be doubted. And notice that the Ministry will face a constrained maximum problem of this sort whatever its objective function: even if it happened to be yours, the formal nature of the problem would not be altered.

Consideration of the Defence problem prompts some further thoughts, of an extremely diverse character. The first is political. A policy-choice, made by any government, is some sort of attempted solution to some sort of constrained maximum problem. Now, the constraints are objectively given, by the nature of the world. If we disagree about them, we disagree about a positive, scientific question, one which is ultimately to be settled as a matter of fact. Disagreement over the objective function, however, is an ethical matter, one of judgement about values. If we are to judge our rulers fairly and adequately, it is important to understand *their* decisions, and to be able to distinguish their objective function. Thus suppose that less resources are devoted to building hospitals (or any other virtuous activity) than we judge desirable. We conclude that the responsible authorities are hard-hearted vote-catchers, indifferent to the sufferings of the unfortunate minority. If we knew the opportunity cost of hospitals in terms of some other goal, say, economic growth, we might have to agree, however grudgingly, with the decision – or we might conclude that hospitals had a rating so low in our rulers' objective function as to prove them the monsters we had thought. Unless we know the facts, it is hard to judge. In this context, let us consider economic planning.

An economic plan is a projected solution to a constrained maximum problem. The motive for planning is the belief that one can get nearer the optimum allocation, judged by some objective function, than the free market would get. For many objective functions to which many citizens would adhere, we assert that this may be true. But consider the planning process, and the manner in which the plan is revealed to society. We may distinguish two extremes, following our simple hospital example. On the one hand, after certain officially interested parties have been admitted to the conclave, some agreed 'targets' may be announced, without any confession of what was desired and what thought possible. On the other hand, the choices open to society may be revealed, and the particular choice of the authorities identified. This, of course, involves disclosing the costs of the chosen course, and permitting the populace to make an informed judgement.

If we wish to pursue the matter a little further, we may consider the recent British 'National Plan'[1], which is about economic growth. Now, growth has costs – current consumption forgone, to say nothing of collective goods and services and institutional changes. If we knew the trade-off rates, we might opt for 2% growth – or 6%. What then are we to make of a plan which contributes nothing to our knowledge of the constraints, and does not reveal anything of the planners' objective function, because it simply announces a unique target growth rate, and then goes on to a discussion of ways and means? The democrat who understood the nature of choice might conclude that this type of 'planning' is Stalinist in approach. Similar thoughts about democracy and choice are prompted by consideration of the fashionable and supposedly successful methods of contemporary French planning.

Consideration of the Defence problem suggests something else not yet discussed: decisions are commonly taken in a state of less than certainty about the nature of the world. It will be clear by now that by maximisation under constraints we mean nothing more than 'making the best of a bad job', which is the common human problem. The contribution of mathematical technique is, on the one hand, to help one to handle hypotheses about how people behave, and, on the other hand, to provide methods for finding 'better bests'. One fascinating technical innovation is the theory of decision taking under uncertainty, or 'how to gamble if you must'. In fact, in an uncertain world, we cannot help gambling, as we acknowledge when we hold 'precautionary balances', take out some insurance, buy shares or National Saving Certificates, or opt for a monthly or a yearly tenancy on a flat, but the theory of 'statistical decision making' is a recent innovation, in spite of the long history of insurance, and even longer history of gambling. Naturally, one needs some acquaintance with probability theory to follow the theory of decision taking, or optimising, under uncertainty, and we can do no more here than recommend it as extremely rewarding.

[1] *The National Plan*, Cmnd. 2764, Sept., 1965.

The Defence problem also suggests some thoughts on the nature and role of mathematical economics. In previous chapters, we have stressed its use in formulating a hypothesis accurately and discovering its implications in order that they may be exposed to test. In this chapter, we have encountered another use for mathematical technique, namely, helping to find the optimal solution when, due to the complexity of the problem, it is not immediately obvious to inspection and intuition. The whole modern development of 'operations research', and the technique of linear programming, is aimed at one thing – 'better' decision-taking, in a sense which will now be familiar. There are still, of course, those who oppose the development of mathematical economics on the grounds that it 'oversimplifies problems', or is 'too mechanical'. The Defence problem, like many others, has, of course, been 'solved' throughout human history by art, intuition, or guess-work, call it what one will. It seems purely obscurantist to oppose the development of systematic methods for dealing with it; and, what is ironic, the more one analyses such a problem the more difficult and complex it seems, and thus the more unlikely to yield to 'art'. It is the difficult problem that requires the powerful technique, and it seems extraordinary that people should object to the use of mathematical techniques on the grounds that the problems are too complicated! They may well be too complicated for our present techniques – but that should be an incentive to master more.

12.8 Macro-Policy

After that digression, it may be a relief to return to V, λ, and some practical problems of economic policy.

In Chapter 4 we introduced our two basic linear models, of a competitive market and of income determination. As the technique at our command has grown, we have dealt with increasingly demanding questions about the behaviour of these two models. We cleared up the comparative statics of the models in Chapter 6, and some questions of maximising tax yield in Chapter 8. In Chapter 4B, however, we found some relationships in the macro-model that constituted frontiers for the decision-taker. It will now be clear that the frontiers are constraints, and that the analysis would be completed by adding an objective function, and solving the constrained maximum problem. We do not, however, know what the objective functions of real-world governments look like, and further analysis would therefore only be illustrative. Interesting illustrations are provided by constructing objective functions such that one's solutions seem to correspond to those adopted, or advocated, in the world, and then enquiring closely into the properties of the objective functions. We have, however, already illustrated our basic ideas fairly comprehensively, and instead of pursuing this line shall take up a new topic. (You may, however, find it of interest to turn back to Figures 4B.1 and 4B.2 and to draw in some illustrative indifference maps. You should, in particular, be able to illustrate the tastes, and preferred solutions, of a 'conservative banker' who puts the strength of sterling above everything, and of the 'expansionist' who is reluctant to accept any trade-off between the balance of payments and income or employment.)

We now consider the choice between unemployment and the rate of inflation. The rate of inflation introduces a new concept: *the rate of change of a variable with respect to time.* Suppose that the variable x has different values at different moments of time. Then we may define the function $x = f(t)$, as we did in Chapter 2, and we may do this *without saying anything about causation*: $x = f(t)$ is merely a description of the time-path of x, with which we are familiar in graphs. Thus consider the number of students in a new British university. It grows at a rate which depends on the policy of the government, the policy of the University Grants Committee in allocating the funds given to it by the government, the policy of the university, and the efficiency of its building contractors. Clearly, we would not say that the growth of student numbers was caused by the passage of time. Nevertheless, we could draw a graph with numbers, x, on one axis, and t on the other, and this would be a graph of the (observed) functional relationship between x and t. It might even have a shape that we could approximate with a fairly manageable algebraic function. Anyhow, it would *be* a function: it would have the property that, if we knew a t-value, we could read off the corresponding x-value.

Now consider a function $x = f(t)$, and let it possess a derivative, dx/dt or $f'(t)$. This is the rate of change of x with respect to t, the tangent slope of the time path. Derivatives with respect to time occur so frequently that a special notation is often introduced, and dx/dt is written $\dot{x}$ (read 'x dot'). Further, d^2x/dt^2 is written $\ddot{x}$, and so on. The rate of inflation, or rate of change of prices, is now defined as dp/dt or $\dot{p}$, where p is the general price level. $\dot{p} > 0$ means that inflation is taking place, $\dot{p} = 0$ means that the price level is constant, and $\dot{p} < 0$ means that deflation is taking place. $\ddot{p} > 0$ means that inflation is speeding up, or deflation slowing down, and so on. We have, of course, to measure p here as an index number, and make $\dot{p}$ a *proportional rate of change*. All this means is that we define $\dot{p} = (1/p)(\Delta p/\Delta t)$ where p is the index base (100 for convenience). We choose the time increment Δt as unity for convenience. Then measured $\dot{p}$ approximates $(1/p)(dp/dt)$.

So much for definitions: we now introduce a hypothesis, that $\dot{p}$ itself depends on the level of unemployment, $\dot{p} = g(U)$ where U is the percentage level of unemployment. This is a *dynamic hypothesis*, derived from consideration of the *adjustment process* in a market in disequilibrium. We do not yet have the technique to derive such a hypothesis for ourselves – the necessary technique will be developed in the following chapters – and shall have to take it on trust for the moment. Nonetheless, it seems intuitively plausible if we add $g'(U) < 0$. This says that, the lower is the level of unemployment, the faster is inflation, a 'pressure of demand' argument. And we can go a bit further. It is widely believed that prices are 'sticky downwards'. We may interpret this as meaning that, even at high levels of U, deflation will not be very fast. There may therefore be some sort of 'floor' to $\dot{p}$. On the other hand, however high the pressure of demand may be, it is virtually impossible to drive U below some 'frictional floor' of 1% or so, and we expect big changes in demand in this neighbourhood to do relatively little to unemployment but a great deal to $\dot{p}$. These considerations suggest that we want $g''(U) > 0$, i.e., we want $\dot{p} = g(U)$ to be a curve that falls very steeply at first, and flattens off at the 'deflationary floor' value of (negative) $\dot{p}$. They suggest something else, too: that $\dot{p} = g(U)$ is no more 'caused' than $p = f(t)$ since we keep appealing to the 'pressure of demand' to justify the shape of the function g. Let the 'pressure of demand' be denoted by D. We are really arguing that $\dot{p} = P(D)$ and that $U = U(D)$. But, if this is the case, there is clearly a relation, which we have denoted by the function g, between $\dot{p}$ and U, at which we may look directly. In many ways, this is a superficial analysis: we want to know about $P(D)$ and $U(D)$, or how the economy works. But if $\dot{p}$ and U are arguments of the objective function, and if no one cares about D *for itself* (and why should they?), then it is indeed at the function g that we should look in determining policy.

Our function $\dot{p} = g(U)$ is illustrated in Figure 12.6. Its shape, which we have discussed above, is based on a relationship between the rate of change of money wage rates and percentage unemployment discovered by Professor A.W. Phillips,[1] which we shall look into later on. The required sort of shape is given by

$$\dot{p} = a + bU^{-1}. \tag{55}$$

Thus the first derivative is

$$\frac{d\dot{p}}{dU} = -bU^{-2}, \tag{56}$$

which is negative, as required, if we put $b > 0$. Then the second derivative is

$$\frac{d^2\dot{p}}{dU^2} = 2bU^{-3}, \tag{57}$$

---

[1] See A.W. Phillips, 'The Relation between Unemployment and the Rate of Change of Money Wage Rates in the United Kingdom, 1861–1957', *Economica*, November 1958, and R.G. Lipsey, 'The Relation...: A Further Analysis', *Economica*, February 1960.

which will be positive. As U gets large, b/U gets small, and $\dot{p}$ approaches more closely to the 'deflationary floor', which means that we require $a<0$.

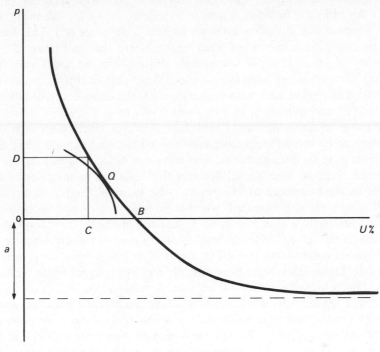

Figure 12.6

The function crosses the axis in Figure 12.6 at $U=OB$, so we have, for stable prices,

$$\dot{p} = 0 = a+\frac{b}{OB}$$

or

$$b = -a.OB.$$

Thus if the 'deflationary floor', $\dot{p}=a$, is, say, $\dot{p}=-3$ (per cent), and if price stability occurs at $3\% \ U$, say, we put $b=-(-3)(3)=9$. Finally, notice that we do get the required steepness at low U: try substituting $U=\frac{3}{4}$ and $U=1$ into (55), (56), and (57). If we insist upon inserting $U=0$, of course, we get $\dot{p}=a+(b/0)$. Division by zero is undefined, so we do not obtain a finite value for $\dot{p}$ here; but as $U=0$ does not seem possible, this seems appropriate.

We could easily construct another plausible objective function and go through our V, λ routine. But this is now so familiar that it does not seem worth the repetition. What we may do instead is consider the illustration of an indifference map in Figure 12.6, and the implications of certain policy views. An objective function is now to be written as $f(\dot{p}, U)$. We may, however, suppose that disutility attaches to *both* arguments of f. This means that (i) utility diminishes the further to the North East in Figure 12.6 the economy is located; (ii) if we assume diminishing marginal substitutability, the curves are concave to the origin. One indifference curve is illustrated in Figure 12.6, with tangency at Q: the chosen rate of inflation and level of unemployment may be read off. We have, of course, assumed a continuous objective function. People may, however, attach such emotional significance to the difference between $\dot{p} = +\frac{1}{2}\%$ and $\dot{p} = -\frac{1}{2}\%$ that their functions may be discontinuous; and there are other possibilities worthy of notice. Suppose that a man declares that inflation is an absolute evil, not to be countenanced at any price – 'the value of the pound must be maintained'. He is committed, whether he knows it or not, to choosing $U \geqslant OB$. Similarly, a man who believes that any unemployment level above OC, say, is an unforgivable offence by society against the unfortunate unemployed is committing himself to a rate of inflation equal to or greater than OD. These individuals have difficult and intransigent objective functions: they admit of no trade-off between possible objectives. (You will be asked in Exercise 6 to work out what their indifference maps may look like.) The individual who insists that it is the duty of the government to reduce unemployment to OC, say, while maintaining price stability, is asking for the impossible. If he persisted after he had been made aware of the position of the constraint, we might judge him to be either irrational or irresponsible. It is, however, perfectly sensible to say 'This constraint is very tough; the "best" attainable position is simply not good enough; I wish the constraint were closer to the origin'. It is then natural to ask 'how can it be moved?', and this question, about how to change the structure of society in a desired way, is the concern of the economist. The government itself, of course, usually accompanies a policy measure, which will slide us along the frontier, with speeches of exhortation intended to persuade people to change their behaviour. If the exhortation were effective, the structure would of course change in the desired fashion. The discovery of effective means of changing the structure is one of the aims of economics. We are, of course, again encountering the potential contribution of positive economics to the determination of social policy. If we are interested in social science for basically humanitarian reasons, because we wish to improve society, there is no reason to think that we have abandoned our obligations, or failed, because we are engaged in scientific discovery rather than moral exhortation.

We first encountered questions about moving frontiers in Chapter 4B, where we dealt with simple linear models of income determination. They were answered after acquiring the technique of derivation, by evaluating such things as dk/dt. But now we have a dynamic relationship, involving aggregate demand, unemployment, and the rate of inflation, and it will take a good deal of preparation before we can start to supply answers.[1]

Exercises

1 Assume that production is given by

$$X = 10L^{3/5}K^{2/5}$$

where X is output, L labour and K capital. Suppose that labour costs 3 per unit and capital 2. Find the least-cost capital: labour ratio.

2 In the discussion of the box diagram in 12.3 and the contract curve in 12.5, nothing was said about second-order conditions. In Chapter 11 we argued geometrically that, if the constraint is linear and the objective function convex, the first order conditions are sufficient. Can you extend the geometric and intuitive argument to the case of tangency between two iso-f curves?

3 Assume that an individual's utility function and budget constraint are given by

$$U = xy$$

and

$$100 - x - y = 0.$$

(i) Find the consumption of x and y.

(ii) Now assume that rationing is imposed, and that the individual is not allowed more than 40 units of x, prices being unchanged. Find, by geometrical or other methods, consumption of x and y. Do you expect calculus methods to work here? If not, why not?

4 Suppose the objective function is

$$f(x, y, z) = xyz^2$$

and that these three variables are associated by the following relations:

(i) $x = \frac{1}{2}y$

(ii) $y = B - az$.

Find the best attainable set of x, y, z. (*Hint:* By substituting from one of the relations, you can reduce this to a problem in two variables. Do not choose

---

[1] For a more detailed study of a policy-maker's objective function with a Phillips curve as a constraint see R. G. Lipsey, 'Structural and Deficient-Demand Unemployment' in *Employment Policy and the Labour Market*, A. M. Ross (ed.), University of California Press (1965).

(i) or (ii) at random: consider what has been said about choice, and the ways in which goods may be associated.)

5 Consider Figure 12.6, where the optimal level of unemployment depends on the decision taker's objective function. Can you define 'full employment'? Is it worth trying?

6 Draw the indifference maps in Figure 12.6 for the two individuals discussed in the text, he who will not trade any inflation to reduce unemployment, and he who will not trade unemployment over OC to reduce inflation. What do you find their marginal rates of substitution between $\dot{p}$ and U to be? What is your solution?

7 Paragraphs 69 and 70 of the Radcliffe Report, Cmnd. 827, 1959, discuss the objectives of monetary policy. Does it appear that the authors understood the nature of constrained maximum problems? Can you deduce any of the properties they attributed to the constraints or the objective function, and write them down symbolically?

8 Which of the above questions could be reduced by substitution to problems in one variable which could be solved without the Lagrangean technique?

CHAPTER 13

AN INTRODUCTION TO DYNAMICS

13.1 Statics and Dynamics

We have confined ourselves so far to the determination of positions of static equilibrium and to a comparison of two positions of equilibrium before and after a parameter shift. This is the method of comparative statics. In using this method we ignore the question of the time path that our variables may follow as they move from one equilibrium position to another, and the possibly even more fundamental question of whether or not a system that starts out of equilibrium (because, say, of some parameter shift) will ever move back into equilibrium. We now wish to begin a study of these two questions: (1) the time path of our variables as they move from one position of equilibrium to another, and (2) the stability of adjustment processes.

Dynamic analysis is not to be regarded as just a sophisticated frill added to a fully satisfactory static model. We live in a world in which many magnitudes are changing continually. Productivity, and hence real income, is growing continually, and, as a result, demand and supply curves are shifting continually, and at different rates for different commodities. The process of economic growth thus forces a process of continuous resource reallocation on the economy. We become acutely aware of this problem whenever a particular region of the country is heavily committed to industries the demand for whose products is not expanding fast enough to keep their existing labour force employed, given the increase in productivity that is occurring. In this case people are being discharged from employment at, say, a constant *rate* through time. Economic incentives will then lead to some rate of outflow of the population from the region, and the central authorities may introduce measures designed to change the rate of outflow. If we wish to analyse this process we must have a dynamic model capable of handling functional relations in which some of our variables are stated in terms of rates of change, for example, the *rate* of out-migration as a function of the *level* of unemployment. If we try to use a static model to analyse the problem of regional unemployment we may get completely mistaken predictions from it. In many static models we shall find that a single disturbance which creates unemployment in one region will lead to a chain of adjustments that eventually eliminates the unemployment. It would be quite wrong to conclude from this that the price system will remove regional unemployment. Once the problem is set up as a continuous model incorporating the rates of decline in a region's employment and of out-migration, we are likely to find that the price system will lead to a constant level of regional unemployment, which may be quite a high one. Government policies that affect some of these critical rates may well lower the equilibrium level of unemployment, but, if we are to study the effects of such policies, we require a dynamic model.

Regional unemployment was chosen merely as an example of a problem that could not be studied without a dynamic model.[1] We shall see several others in the next three chapters. In this chapter we begin by considering the problem of stability of equilibrium in the model of the single competitive market whose static properties we have several times studied. We then go on in the rest of the chapter to introduce some basic concepts in dynamics. We could assume that your study of economics had made you familiar with the basic theoretical notions of statics. Dynamic theory, however, is rarely studied in a first year course. The reason is simple: you can do almost no dynamics without mathematics! For this reason we must devote a chapter to a discussion of some basic concepts and definitions. In Chapter 14 we introduce you to some of the mathematics required for dynamics while in Chapter 15 we apply these mathematical techniques to the study of four problems in dynamic economics. Dynamics is a vast subject and requires much mathematics well beyond the scope of this book. Nevertheless we hope in this brief three-chapter introduction to give you an idea of the importance of the subject and to show you how some very interesting problems can be handled even with the very limited amount of mathematics that we can cover in Chapter 14.

13.2   The Conditions for Negative Feedback in a Single Competitive Market

Consider the two markets illustrated in Figures 13.1 and 13.2. In Market 1 there is excess demand at prices below the equilibrium and excess supply at prices above the equilibrium. We now recall the hypothesis, about the behaviour of a competitive market, that *there is an upward pressure on prices when quantity demanded exceeds quantity supplied and a downward pressure on prices when quantity supplied exceeds quantity demanded.* We can now see that in Market 1 there will be a tendency for price to be pushed in the direction of equilibrium if we start from any disequilibrium position. Such a tendency for a system to be pushed back in the direction of its equilibrium value should it deviate from it is called *negative feedback*. It is

---

[1] A further discussion of regional problems can be found in the symposium in *Oxford Economic Papers*, March 1967.

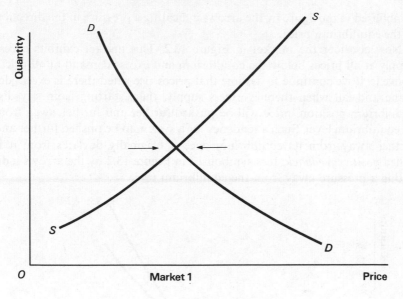

Figure 13.1

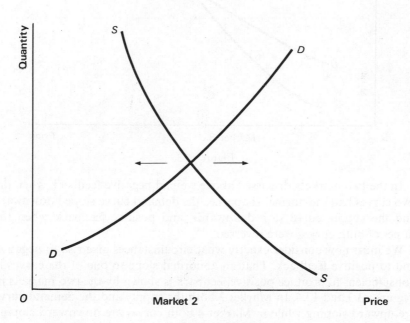

Figure 13.2

symbolised in the figure by the arrows indicating a pressure in the direction of the equilibrium price.

Now consider the market in Figure 13.2. This market exhibits excess supply at all prices below the equilibrium and excess demand at all prices above it. If we continue to assume that prices rise when there is excess demand and fall when there is excess supply, then, starting from any disequilibrium position, price will be pushed further and further away from its equilibrium level. Such a tendency for a system to be pushed further and further away from its equilibrium once it originally deviates from it is called *positive feedback*. It is symbolised in Figure 13.2 by the arrows indicating a pressure away from the equilibrium price.

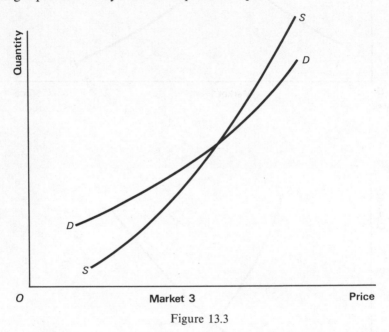

Figure 13.3

In the two markets discussed above we had negative feedback when the two curves had the normal shape, i.e., the demand curve sloped downward and the supply curve sloped upwards, and positive feedback when the slopes of both curves were reversed.

We must now consider exactly what circumstances give rise to negative and to positive feedback. That an abnormal slope to one of the curves is not sufficient to produce positive feedback is shown by the two markets in Figures 13.3 and 13.4. In Market 3 both the supply and the demand curve are upward sloping while in Market 4 both curves are downward sloping and yet both markets display negative feedback. In order to derive necessary and sufficient conditions for negative feedback we must define a new concept: *the excess demand function.*

By excess demand, E, we mean the difference between the quantity demanded and the quantity supplied: $E = q^d - q^s$. Note that excess demand can be positive $(q^d > q^s)$ or negative $(q^d < q^s)$. Negative excess demand is often called excess supply. Since q^d and q^s are both functions of price, it follows that E must be a function of price. We illustrate the excess demand *function*, $E = E(p)$ in Figure 13.5. Since equilibrium occurs where $E = 0$ and $p = \bar{p}$, it follows that any excess demand curve cuts the price axis at $\bar{p}$.

We shall now find that we can state the conditions for negative feedback

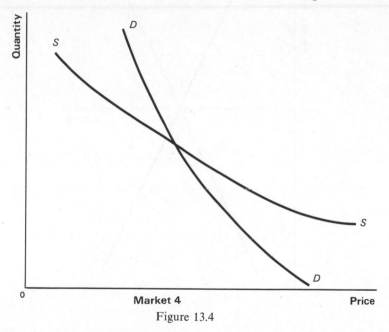

Figure 13.4

in terms of the slope of the excess demand function. If the market price is to move towards its equilibrium value $\bar{p}$ we require that price should rise when it is below equilibrium and fall when it is above equilibrium. The basic assumption about the behaviour of price in a competitive market is that price rises when $E > 0$ and falls when $E < 0$. This gives us the following requirements for negative feedback:

$$E > 0 \quad \text{when} \quad p < \bar{p}$$
and
$$E < 0 \quad \text{when} \quad p > \bar{p}.$$

Expressed graphically these requirements are that the excess demand function should slope downwards to the right as does curve (1) in Figure 13.5, and not upwards to the right as does curve (2) in Figure 13.5. In other words, we require that there should be positive excess demand at prices below the equilibrium and negative excess demand at prices above the equilibrium. A downward-sloping demand and an upward-sloping supply

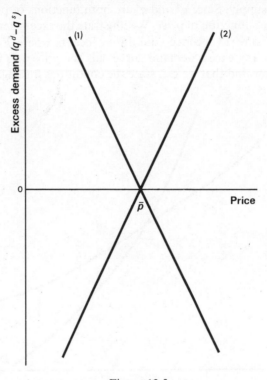

Figure 13.5

curve is sufficient to give the right slope to the excess demand function but is not necessary.

Now let us take the simple linear model that we have used several times before and consider the conditions for it to have negative feedback.

$$q^d = a + bp \qquad (1)$$

$$q^s = c + dp \qquad (2)$$

$$E = q^d - q^s \qquad (3)$$

$$= a + bp - c - dp$$

$$= a - c + (b - d)p. \qquad (4)$$

Equations (1) and (2) give the demand and supply curves while (4) gives excess demand as a function of price and the four parameters that determine the positions of the demand and supply curves. To discover how excess demand varies as price varies we merely take the derivative of E with respect to price:

$$\frac{dE}{dp} = b-d. \tag{5}$$

We have seen that for negative feedback we require that the excess demand curve be downward sloping, i.e., that $dE/dp < 0$. Equation (5) shows that the condition for this is merely that $b < d$. This condition gives rise to four possible cases distinguished by the signs of b and d. Let us consider each of them:[1]

(i)   if b<0, $d>0$, then $b<d$;
(ii) if $b>0$, $d<0$, then $b>$d;
(iii) if $b<0$, $d<0$, then $b<d$ if $|b| > |d|$;
(iv) if $b>0$, $d>0$, then $b<d$ if $|b| < |d|$.

We may state the following conclusions: negative feedback always occurs if the curves have the normal slope (case i); it never occurs if both curves have the 'wrong' slope (case ii); it occurs if both curves slope downwards as long as the demand curve is steeper than the supply curve (case iii); and it occurs if both curves slope upwards as long as the demand curve is flatter than the supply curve (case iv).[2] You should now illustrate graphically those cases that have not already been covered in Figures 13.1 to 13.4.

So far we have studied the conditions for the existence of positive or negative feedback in a competitive market. We now wish to consider *the stability* of the adjustment process in such markets. We say that a market adjustment process is *stable* if it restores equilibrium should the equilibrium be disturbed. We say that a market adjustment process is *unstable* if it does not restore equilibrium. We have seen from studying Market 2 above that positive feedback is sufficient to make a market unstable. Since positive feedback is a sufficient condition for instability, it follows that the absence of positive feedback, i.e., the presence of negative feedback, is a necessary condition for stability. The question now arises: is negative feedback a sufficient condition for stability? A counter example proving that negative feedback is not sufficient to produce a stable adjustment process is familiar to most students of elementary economics. This counter example is provided by the Cobweb Model in which markets with negative feedback

---

[1] Recall that $|x|$ is the absolute value of x. Thus, e.g., $|-2| > |+1|$ even though $-2 < +1$.

[2] 'Flatter' and 'steeper' refer to the curves when drawn, as we have throughout this book, with price on the x axis and quantity on the y axis.

may behave in a stable fashion or in an unstable one. When it was first developed the model was regarded by many as a theoretical curiosity, and not until much later was it generally appreciated that a serious omission had been discovered in the theoretical analysis of the behaviour of the price system.[1]

13.3   The Cobweb Model

In the cobweb model supply and demand depend on price, and the usual assumptions of a downward-sloping demand curve and an upward-sloping supply curve are adhered to. The model is distinguished from the ordinary model to which we have devoted much attention throughout this book by the single variation that supply is assumed to react to price with a *lag* of one time period. The common sense of this assumption is that supply decisions take time to implement. If price rises today firms may wish to increase their rate of production and sales from today, but they may not be able to do so for some time (more labour may have to be employed, more raw materials ordered *and* delivered, and more plant and equipment may even have to be installed). A simple case of a cobweb can, and often does, occur in agriculture. In the case of an annual crop, farmers will look at this year's price when planting crops which will not be harvested until next year, so that *this* year's harvest depends on last year's plantings, which were in turn influenced by last year's prices. The assumption made about demand is the normal one: current demand depends on current price. The market is assumed to be a competitive one in which the price is set so as to equate current demand with current supply.

We shall study a dynamic model of a market with linear demand and supply curves:

$$q_t^d = a + bp_t, \tag{6}$$

$$q_t^s = c + dp_{t-1}, \tag{7}$$

$$q_t^d = q_t^s. \tag{8}$$

Note the introduction of time subscripts, which have been made necessary by the introduction of time lags. A subscript t refers to any time 't' while $t-1$ refers to the time one period prior to 't'. Thus equation (6) states that quantity demanded at any time t is a linear function of the price ruling at

---

[1] One of the first writers to see and to state clearly that the cobweb model was not just a theoretical curiosity but showed that the stability analysis of the time was inadequate was N. Kaldor. See his 'Pigou on Employment and Equilibrium', *Economic Journal*, December 1941.

that time. Equation (7) states that quantity supplied at any time t is a linear function of the price ruling one period previously. Equation (8) states that the price will always be such as to equate current demand with current supply.

The first thing to do is to check that in equilibrium the model gives results that are consistent with those given by the linear model without time lags. When we are in equilibrium, the price must repeat itself period after period so that

$$p_{t-1} = p_t = p_{t+1} = \bar{p}. \tag{9}$$

We first substitute (6) and (7) into (8) to obtain an expression for price in period t in terms of price in the previous period:

$$a + bp_t = c + dp_{t-1}$$

whence
$$p_t = \frac{c-a}{b} + \frac{d}{b} p_{t-1}. \tag{10}$$

We now note from (9) that in equilibrium $p_{t-1} = p_t = \bar{p}$, and substituting this into (10) we get

$$\bar{p} = \frac{c-a}{b} + \frac{d}{b} \bar{p},$$

$$b\bar{p} = c - a + d\bar{p},$$

$$\bar{p}(b-d) = c - a,$$

$$\bar{p} = \frac{c-d}{b-d}. \tag{11}$$

This is, as we should expect, the static solution to the linear model that we first obtained in Chapter 4 and that we have used many times since. The equilibrium quantity is found from (11) and either (6) or (7) to be

$$\bar{q} = \frac{cb-ad}{b-d} \tag{12}$$

which agrees with the static solution first obtained in Chapter 4.

So far we have checked that our model does have a static solution and that it is the familiar equilibrium solution. We now wish to study the model's behaviour out of equilibrium. We have assumed that in each period price will be such as to clear the market by equating current demand with current supply. We can now substitute (6) and (7) into (8) to solve for current quantity in terms of prices now or one period ago:

$$q_t = a + bp_t = c + dp_{t-1}. \tag{13}$$

Now assume that an equilibrium has been established in which price repeats itself period after period: we may now substitute (9) into (13) to get an expression for the equilibrium quantity:

$$\bar{q} = a + b\bar{p} = c + d\bar{p}. \tag{14}$$

The difference between (14) and (13) is that, once equilibrium is established, the time lag on the supply equation ceases to influence the behaviour of the model because the price this period is equal to the price last period so that supply will be the same whether or not it is subject to a time lag.

We have an expression in (14) for the equilibrium quantity and in (13) for the quantity in any particular period (for which $p_t \neq p_{t-1}$). It is now convenient to deal in deviations of the actual values from their equilibrium ones. To obtain these deviations we subtract equation (13) from (14) to obtain:

$$\bar{q} - q_t = b(\bar{p} - p_t) = d(\bar{p} - p_{t-1}). \tag{15}$$

We now use a hat on the q's and p's to denote their deviations from their respective equilibrium values and rewrite (15) as:

$$\hat{q}_t = b\hat{p}_t = d(\hat{p}_{t-1}). \tag{16}$$

The last two terms in (16) allow us to express the deviation of price from equilibrium this period as a function of the deviation from equilibrium last period:

$$\hat{p}_t = \frac{d}{b}\hat{p}_{t-1}. \tag{17}$$

If we denote d/b by A we have

$$\hat{p}_t = A\hat{p}_{t-1}. \tag{18}$$

This is what is called a *first-order difference equation*, and it expresses this period's $\hat{p}$ as a function of last period's $\hat{p}$. It is called a difference equation because we are explaining differences; and it is a first-order equation because we are explaining the difference between price now and price only one period ago.

The solution to (18) is easily discovered. Start with the first period, t_0, and in order to get the cobweb process under way we assume some initial disequilibrium. The value of $\hat{p}$ at time zero, which we indicate as $\hat{p}_0$, is thus the initial deviation from equilibrium with which we start. Our task is to study how the market reacts to this disequilibrium situation. Once we have chosen a $\hat{p}_0$ (we shall see later how we can interpret it) equation (18) tells us how to find $\hat{p}_1$. Once we have $\hat{p}_1$ we again use (18) to find $\hat{p}_2$. Clearly we can continue the process to generate as many values of $\hat{p}$ as we wish. Let us follow out a few steps formally:

$$\hat{p}_1 = A\hat{p}_0$$

$$\hat{p}_2 = A(\hat{p}_1) = A(A\hat{p}_0) = A^2\hat{p}_0$$

$$\hat{p}_3 = A(\hat{p}_2) = A(A^2\hat{p}_0) = A^3\hat{p}_0$$

$$\hat{p}_4 = A(\hat{p}_3) = A(A^3\hat{p}_0) = A^4\hat{p}_0.$$

It is now obvious by inspection that the solution for $\hat{p}_5$ will contain A^5, that for $\hat{p}_6$ will contain A^6, and so on. We can now write the solution for $\hat{p}$ at any time, t, as

$$\hat{p}_t = A\hat{p}_{t-1} = A^t\hat{p}_0. \tag{19}$$

Equation (19) gives us the general solution for this linear cobweb model which allows us to find $\hat{p}_t$ at any time, given the initial disturbance (p_0) and the slopes of the demand and the supply curves $(A = d/b)$. If the demand curve slopes downward and the supply curve slopes upwards $b < 0$ and $d > 0$ so that A is negative. Thus A^t will alternate in sign, being negative in odd numbered periods and positive in even numbered periods. This proves that with normal shaped demand and supply curves the cobweb will always produce a two period oscillation with actual price being alternately above and below equilibrium price. It remains to see if these oscillations will converge onto or diverge from $\bar{p}$. If the demand and supply curves have their normal slopes there are still three cases to consider.

(1) The supply curve is steeper than the demand curve so that $|d| > |b|$ and $|A| > 1$. In this case the absolute value of A^t increases as A is raised to higher and higher powers. Thus *the oscillations are explosive*, and, unless they hit limits (as in practice they no doubt will), they get larger and larger indefinitely. The market displays an unstable adjustment process. (This is a good time to do question 2 on page 312.

(2) The demand curve is steeper than the supply curve so that $|d| < |b|$ and $|A| < 1$. In this case the absolute value of A^t diminishes as A is raised to higher and higher powers. *The oscillations are damped:* the market price converges on its equilibrium value of one. The market displays a stable adjustment process.

(3) The slopes of the two curves are equal so that $|d| = |b|$, $|A| = 1$ and $A = -1$. This is the limiting case in which the oscillations neither increase

nor decrease. The equation of the system is $\hat{p}_t = (-1)^t \hat{p}_0$ so that the original disequilibrium returns every other period. The system displays *regular oscillations* which are neither damped nor explosive.

This linear cobweb model displays negative feedback: whenever price is above equilibrium it falls in the next period, and whenever price is below equilibrium it rises in the next period; but the adjustment is *always* too much: the equilibrium price is *always* overshot. In the stable case the overshoot gets smaller and smaller so that the equilibrium price *is* approached. In the unstable case each overshoot is larger than the previous one so that the actual price diverges from equilibrium more and more as time passes.

Evidently, negative feedback, although a necessary condition for stability, is not a sufficient condition. This is one of the most important propositions in elementary dynamics. For hundreds of years economists concentrated on showing that most of the systems with which they were concerned displayed negative feedback, thinking that by doing so they had shown the systems to be stable. We now know that this is not sufficient, and that the behaviour of any adjustment mechanism depends critically on the time lags involved and on the magnitude of the adjustment once it occurs.

13.4 The Interpretation of the Initial Disturbance

When we considered the solution of the cobweb model we said we had to begin with some $\hat{p}_0 \neq 0$ in order to start the cobweb process working. This value of $\hat{p}_0$ is referred to as the *initial arbitrary disturbance*. The word arbitrary is meant to imply that $\hat{p}_0$ can take on any sign and magnitude that we like to give it. It is not meant to imply that this disturbance is created in any mysterious way. Indeed, the analysis is absolutely general with respect to this point, and it does not matter what caused the system to diverge from its equilibrium value.

Consider Figure 13.6. In part (a) of the figure we have shown the equilibrium price $\bar{p}$ and one initial 'arbitrary' disturbance $\hat{p}_0$. In parts (b) and (c) we illustrate the two possible ways in which the arbitrary disturbance could have occurred. In part (b) the disequilibrium is caused by some disturbance to price *other than* a change in demand or supply. The central authorities might have decreed for example, that price should be Op_0 at some time in the past, and then at time t_0 they might remove their price control leaving the price to be determined on a free market. In part (c) the initial disequilibrium is caused by a shift in one of the market curves. The original demand and supply curves in (c) are D_1 and S, and the equilibrium price is the same as the actual price p_0. The demand curve now shifts to D_2 and the equilibrium price shifts to $\bar{p}$. This leaves us with exactly the same discrepancy between p_0 and $\bar{p}$ as we had in (b). As far as the analysis of disequilibrium behaviour is concerned we can always start with some arbitrarily chosen discrepancy between actual and equilibrium values without concerning ourselves further with the cause of the discrepancy.

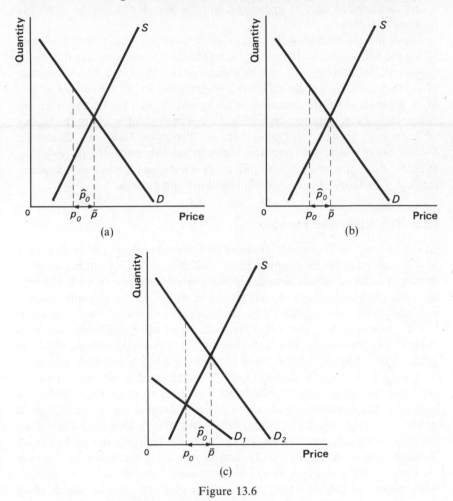

Figure 13.6

13.5   Time as a Discrete and as a Continuous Variable

We now have to make a fundamental decision about how we shall treat time: shall we divide it into discrete periods, as we did in the case of the cobweb, where discrete changes in price occurred only at the end of each period, or shall we assume time to be a continuous variable with continuous adjustments of price and quantity occurring through time? The choice is often dictated by the problem at hand. If supply suddenly changes when a new harvest appears, and then remains constant until the next harvest, as it did in the cobweb model, a discrete model is most appropriate. In other cases where supply may be varied daily, or even hourly, or where national income is growing continuously, a continuous model is more appropriate.

The approach selected will determine the mathematical techniques used to handle the model. In the case of discrete time periods we use difference equations, the simplest case of which occurred in (18) above, and in the case of continuous time we use differential equations. In the remainder of this book we shall adopt the continuous treatment of time. We do this both because it allows us to approach a wide class of important work on the theory of economic growth, and also because Professor Baumol's *Economic Dynamics* to which we have already referred (see page 16) provides an excellent do-it-yourself guide to difference equations together with applications to the theory of economic fluctuations and growth.

13.6 The Adjustment Function

In the cobweb model supply changed in a discrete jump once each period and it was possible to imagine price changing at the beginning of each period in order to adjust demand to the available supply. In such a model the price changes instantaneously from one short-run equilibrium position (where current demand equals current supply) to another short-run equilibrium position. No price other than the short-run equilibrium one ever rules in the market so that no sales ever take place at a disequilibrium price. Now, however, we are going to allow demand and supply and price to change continuously through time. This means that we must state the rule governing the speed at which price changes through time. So far we have contented ourselves with a qualitative statement about the change in price: price rises when $q^d > q^s$ and falls when $q^d < q^s$. This is enough if we are only doing comparative statics, but if we are to follow the path of price through time, as we must do in dynamics, we need to know *how fast price is changing at any moment of time*. This is measured by the derivative of price with respect to time, written dp/dt, which gives the rate at which price changes per unit of time. If, as in Figure 13.8, we draw a time-series graph showing the level of price at each point of time, dp/dt then measures the slope of the tangent to the curve at any point. We now make the basic assumption that *the speed with which price is changing depends on the magnitude of the disequilibrium*: the larger is the disequilibrium the faster will price be changing. If we write this assumption in functional form we obtain what is called a *reaction function*. In general, a reaction function states the rate of change of the dependent variable as a function of the magnitude of the disequilibrium. In the model of a single competitive market two possible reaction functions obviously are

$$\frac{dp}{dt} = f(q^d - q^s) \tag{20}$$

$$= f(E), \tag{21}$$

and

$$\frac{1}{p}\frac{dp}{dt} = g\left(\frac{q^d - q^s}{q^s}\right) \tag{22}$$

$$= g\left(\frac{E}{q^s}\right). \tag{23}$$

(Since E is $q^d - q^s$ we can write the functions in terms of either E or $(q^d - q^s)$.) Equations (20) and (21) give the absolute rate of change of price in terms of the absolute difference between quantity demanded and quantity supplied. Equations (22) and (23) state that the proportional change in price is a function of proportional excess demand. These represent different hypotheses about the way in which price reacts to market disequilibrium. We shall concentrate here on reaction functions in the form of (20–21), although in Chapter 15 we shall encounter one in proportional form.

In order to make the reaction function consistent with what we assume in static theory we must place two restrictions on it. First, since we assume in our static theory that price rises when $q^d > q^s$ and falls when $q^s < q^d$, we must choose our reaction function so that dp/dt and E vary directly with each other. Second, since we assume in static theory that price does not change when $q^d = q^s$, we want our reaction function to give $dp/dt = 0$ when $E = 0$. This means that the function must not contain an additive constant: the line relating dp/dt to E on a graph must pass through the origin.

We show some possible reaction functions in Figure 13.7 (page 308). Curve (1) illustrates a case in which dp/dt is simply proportional to excess demand, i.e., if you double excess demand you will double the speed at which price is changing. Curve (2) also illustrates a proportional relation, but one which is different for excess demand and for excess supply. Prices rise faster in response to a given amount of excess demand than they fall in response to the same amount of excess supply. In Curves (3) and (4) the relation is non-linear. In the case of (3) the reaction of price to excess demand or supply is greater the larger is the existing amount of excess demand (i.e., $d^2\dot{p}/dE^2 > 0$). Case (4) is the opposite of (3). In this case the rate of change of price approaches a maximum which it never exceeds no matter how great is the current discrepancy between q^s and q^d (i.e., $d^2\dot{p}/dE^2 < 0$).

It is very important to note that by specifying an adjustment function we have necessarily introduced a lag into the system. Whenever we allow the dependent variables of our system to react to the existence of disequilibrium with any speed less than infinity, we imply that some time must pass before a disequilibrium is removed. Of course, the reaction may be very fast so that the disequilibrium does not persist for long; but persist it must. Since the system necessarily takes a finite amount of time to move from one position of static equilibrium to another, states of disequilibrium must persist through time, and purchases and sales will take place at prices other than the equilibrium one.

We have seen that the reaction function necessarily introduces a lag into the system. There are other ways, however, in which lags can occur, and we must now consider more systematically the variety of possible lags in the model of a single competitive market.

13.7 Time Lags in the Competitive Model

Consider the dynamic version of the model of a single competitive market:

$$q^d = D(p),$$

$$q^s = S(p),$$

and
$$\frac{\mathrm{d}p}{\mathrm{d}t} = f(E).$$

There are three variables in this system, q^d, q^s, and p, and each of these can react to the other variables with a time lag. We now use τ (the Greek letter tau) to stand for an interval of time. Thus $t - \tau$ means the time t minus an interval of time, τ. If, for example, τ were two time periods, $t - \tau$ would refer to time two periods prior to t. We can now write the possible lags in the competitive model as follows:

$$q_t^d = D(p_{t-\tau_1}), \tag{24}$$

$$q_t^s = S(p_{t-\tau_2}), \tag{25}$$

$$\frac{\mathrm{d}p}{\mathrm{d}t} = f(E_{t-\tau_3}). \tag{26}$$

The first two equations are the familiar demand and supply equations, but they now allow for time lags in the adjustment of q^d and q^s to price: q^d responds now to the price that ruled τ_1 periods in the past, and q^s reacts to the price that ruled τ_2 periods in the past. Such lags arise because information only becomes available to decision takers with a time lag, because the decision process itself takes time, and because decisions, once taken, take time to implement. The third equation says that the speed at which price changes depends on the level of excess demand. We have already seen that the reaction function necessarily introduces a lag into the system. A further lag can be introduced through the reaction function if price reacts to the excess demand that existed at some time in the past. If $\tau_3 = 3$, for example, the price would be changing at any time t in response not to excess demand at time t but to the excess demand that existed 3 periods ago.[1]

Notice there are two sorts of lags in this model. The first sort occurs because people react to past value of the variables; the second sort occurs because, whatever values they react to, their rate of adjustment is less than instantaneous.

13.8 A Simple Dynamic Model of a Competitive Market

We now know that a competitive market can have a stable or an unstable adjustment mechanism. To discover how the adjustment mechanism works we must specify the dynamic model completely, and then study its behaviour when it starts from a position of disequilibrium. (We say the same thing in different words when we say that we study its behaviour in response to an arbitrary disturbance of equilibrium.) The various possible patterns of behaviour are illustrated in Figure 13.8 (page 309).

The figure is a time-series graph of various paths of price through time. The equilibrium price is initially Oc and we assume that at time t_0 there is a once-for-all discrete change in the equilibrium price from Oc to Od. This change in $\bar{p}$ could be due to a shift in either the demand or the supply curve. The change is often called a *step change*, for reasons that should be visually obvious from the figure. We now ask how the actual market price might respond to this step change in the equilibrium price. In curve (1) the market shows positive feedback. The price shoots off in the wrong direction from the outset. A market that behaves like this has an unstable adjustment mechanism. In all the remaining cases negative feedback exists because price begins by moving in the direction of equilibrium. In case (2) the price moves to its new equilibrium without oscillation. In case (3) the price overshoots and then goes back towards the equilibrium, overshooting again,

[1] It is difficult to think of reasons for τ_3 being significantly different from zero in a competitive market. In markets where the producers are the price setters such lags will occur whenever those setting prices do not have information regarding current sales. It could easily take a month or more to gather information on sales of a product marketed throughout the world. If this were so then when price setters met to consider price (or output) changes, they would be reacting to the state of sales as they existed one or more months prior to their meeting. One of the key problems of centrally controlled economies is that information lags can become very long, and the central administrators may sometimes find themselves reacting to situations that no longer exist.

but each time the swings diminish, and eventually the equilibrium price is reached. We say that price exhibits *damped oscillations*. In case (4), the oscillations get larger and larger so that the equilibrium is never reached. We say that price exhibits *explosive oscillations*. In (5) the first overshoot is also the last one: the price overshoots its equilibrium value and continues to rise indefinitely.

We now wish to see which of the paths will be followed by a model of a

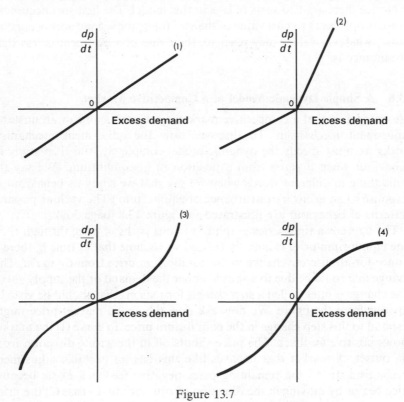

Figure 13.7

competitive market. The general type of model we need to analyse is set out in equations (24) to (26). In order to make a start we shall take a very simple case of this general dynamic model. We assume that there are no lagged values of the variables in any of the equations ($\tau_1 = \tau_2 = \tau_3 = 0$): the only lag in the system results from the fact that price adjusts to a state of excess demand with a speed of less than infinity. This allows us to concentrate on the effect of the reaction function on the behaviour of the model, and it paves the way for more complex models in which any one, or combination of, τ_1, τ_2, and τ_3 are non-zero.

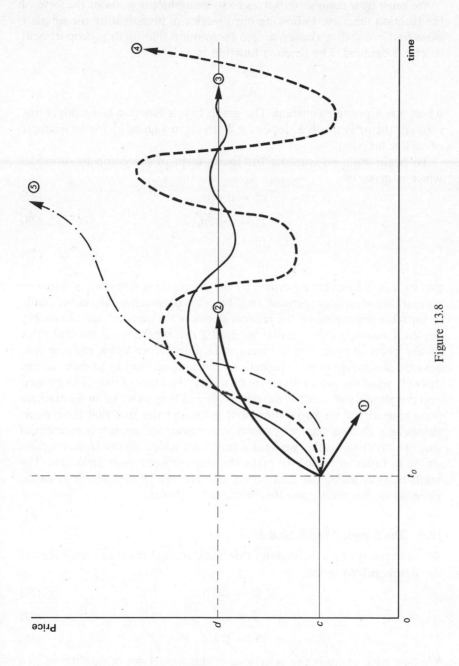

Figure 13.8

We must now commit ourselves to some assumption about the form of the reaction function. Following our practice of investigating the simplest cases first, we shall make the simple assumption that dp/dt is proportional to excess demand. The reaction function is

$$\frac{dp}{dt} = \alpha E$$

where α is a positive constant. The graph of this function is a straight line through the origin with a slope of α. Path (1) in Figure 13.7 is an example of such a function.

To begin with we consider the linear form of the competitive model which is given by

$$q_t^d = a + bp_t \tag{27}$$

$$q_t^s = c + dp_t \tag{28}$$

$$\frac{dp}{dt} = \alpha(q_t^d - q_t^s) \tag{29}$$

and we ask if a market described by these equations will show a stable or an unstable adjustment process, or if, like the cobweb, it will be either stable or unstable depending on the relative slopes of the demand and the supply curves. To answer this question we need a rule whereby we can find price at any point of time. Our problem is as follows: we know the rule that governs the change in price (equation (29)), and we want to know if we can discover what the actual price will be at each moment of time. The answer, and this should not surprise anyone, is 'yes, as long as we know from where price started': if we know the initial price and the rule that governs its subsequent change, then we can say where price will be at any moment of time. In order to do this we need a rule from which we can *deduce p from* dp/dt. In order to be able to make this step we need more technique. The mathematical technique that solves the problem posed above is called integration. We shall study this in the next chapter.

13.9   The Simple Macro-Model

We have many times throughout this book studied the static properties of the simple macro-model

$$C = C(Y) \tag{30}$$

$$I = \bar{I} \tag{31}$$

$$Y = C + I. \tag{32}$$

We now wish to study the behaviour of this model out of equilibrium. To do this we must give an adjustment function stating the speed with which income changes in response to a situation of disequilibrium. Before we can write down such a function we need to know how we can show a disequilibrium in the above model.

It is well known that it is possible to design an accounting system such that Y is necessarily the same as $C+I$ (this is done by adjusting the value of unsold production so as to make $Y \equiv C+I$). If, however, (30) to (32) is to be a genuine model of behaviour, (32) must be an equilibrium condition and not an identity. To make it an equilibrium condition we must interpret Y as the market value of current output (whether sold or not), and $C+I$ as the money value of current spending. If the two are unequal, inventories must be changing – rising if $Y > C+I$ and falling if $Y < C+I$. We now interpret (32) as an equilibrium condition that says that total output (Y) will be in equilibrium (i.e., not changing) when it is equal to the value of expenditure. We add a simple reaction function $dY/dt = \alpha[Y-(C+I)]$, which states that the rate of change of income is proportional to the discrepancy between the market value of current output and the value of current expenditure. Our dynamic version of a simple linear model of national income is

$$C_t = a + cY_t, \tag{33}$$

$$I_t = \bar{I}, \tag{34}$$

$$Y_t = C_t + I_t, \tag{35}$$

$$\frac{dY}{dt} = \alpha(Y - C - I). \tag{36}$$

This model is analogous to the one we developed in the previous section for the single competitive model. We wish to know how the model behaves out of equilibrium, and whether or not Y will return to its equilibrium value after a disturbance. To answer these questions we need a method of discovering where income is at any time t given its initial starting point and the rule whereby income changes (equation (36)). Again we require to know something of the technique of integration which is the subject of the next chapter.

Exercises

1 Consider the simple macro-model on page 311.
  (a) What is the sign of α in equation (36)?
  (b) Draw a graph of the reaction function relating dY/dt to the difference between output and expenditure.
  (c) Describe in words the condition for this model to have negative

feedback (i.e., we want Y to fall when it is above the equilibrium level and rise when it is below it).

(d) What restriction do we need on the sign of the parameters for there to be negative feedback in this model? (*Hint:* you require a relation analogous to equation (5) for the model of the competitive market.)

2 Consider the following two competitive markets.

Market 1: (i) $q_t^d = 1200 - 6p_t$
    (ii) $q_t^s = 2p_{t-1}$.
Market 2: (i) $q_t^d = 2700 - 4p_t$
    (ii) $q_t^s = 5p_{t-1}$.

(a) Discover the equilibrium price and quantity in both markets.

(b) Consider the stability of the adjustment to a disturbance in each market.

(c) Draw a time series graph for p in the first five periods following a disturbance that moves price 200 units above its equilibrium in Market 1, and 20 units below in Market 2.

(d) The explosive oscillations in one market cannot go on increasing indefinitely. What economic limits to the oscillation are finally reached? Illustrate graphically.

CHAPTER 14

INTEGRATION AND EXPONENTIAL FUNCTIONS

14.1 The Concept of Integration

In Chapter 5 we considered the problem of discovering, at any point on the function

$$y = f(x), \qquad (1)$$

the rate of change of y in response to a change in x. The expression which tells us this is called the derivative of y with respect to x and is denoted by

$$\frac{dy}{dx} = f'(x). \qquad (2)$$

In Chapter 13 we assumed that we knew the rule that determined *the rate of change* of price as a function of excess demand and we wondered if we could discover the rule for determining price itself. We also assumed that we had the rule determining the *rate of change* of national income as a function of the difference between income and expenditure, and we wondered if we could discover the rule for determining the *level* of national income. In general these problems amount to knowing (2) and trying to derive from it the function in (1). What we need to do, therefore, is to reverse the process of differentiating (1) to get (2). When we do this, we say that we *integrate* (2) in order to get (1).

In the case of simple power functions we can integrate by inspection. Consider two examples. First, we know that if $y = x^2$ then $dy/dx = 2x$. Thus if we are given $dy/dx = 2x$, we can immediately say that $y = x^2$. As a second example, assume that marginal revenue is given by

$$\frac{dR}{dq} = 100 - 10q. \qquad (3)$$

We seek to discover the total revenue function and the demand function. What we need is a function whose first derivative is $100 - 10q$, and, by inspection, $100q - 5q^2$ will do, so we may write

$$R = 100q - 5q^2, \qquad (4)$$

and to complete the problem we write

$$p = AR = \frac{R}{q} = 100 - 5q. \tag{5}$$

In general we can now say that if

$$\frac{dy}{dx} = f'(x) \tag{6}$$

or

$$dy = f'(x)\,dx \tag{6a}$$

then

$$y = \int f'(x)\,dx. \tag{7}$$

(7) reads 'y equals the *integral* of $f'(x)$ with respect to x'. $\int$ is the integral sign, an elongated S. (7) says that, if the derivative of y with respect to x is some function of x, then y is found by integrating this function with respect to x.

There is, however, one further problem in finding the integrals of the functions we have dealt with so far. Consider

$$\frac{dy}{dx} = 2x \tag{8}$$

and find

$$y = \int 2x\,dx. \tag{9}$$

$y = x^2$ is a function that satisfies (8), but so is $y = x^2 + 10$ or $y = x^2 - 200$. Indeed $y = x^2 + A$ satisfies (8), where A is any constant whatever. Since the constant disappears when we differentiate, all functions of the form $y = x^2 + A$ have the same derivative $dy/dx = 2x$. From this it follows that, when we reverse the process and integrate (8), we must add a constant. This shows that we cannot tell from a derivative alone what constant, if any, was contained in the function before it was differentiated.

An economic example is very familiar. Suppose that we have the marginal cost function

$$MC = \frac{dC}{dq} = 10 + 3q \tag{10}$$

and wish to find the total cost function. We write

$$C = \int MC\,dq = \int (10 + 3q)\,dq + A = 10q + 1 \cdot 5q^2 + A. \tag{11}$$

The constant A is, of course, fixed cost. It is that part of cost that does not vary with output. Every student knows that fixed cost has no influence on marginal cost, i.e., A disappears when we differentiate the total cost function, and the corollary of this is that we cannot tell how big A (fixed cost) is if we only have the marginal cost function.

This discussion suggests that, whenever we integrate a function, we must add an arbitrary constant to show that we cannot discover from the derivative of a function what constant, if any, was contained in the original function. This arbitrary constant is called the constant of integration. It is arbitrary in the sense that it could take on any value whatsoever, but not in the sense of being in any way mysterious: we know exactly why it arises.

14.2   The General Integral of a Power Function

We saw in Chapter 5 that if

$$y = ax^n \tag{12}$$

then

$$\frac{dy}{dx} = nax^{n-1}. \tag{13}$$

We may now reverse this and write:

if

$$\frac{dy}{dx} = ax^n \tag{14a}$$

or

$$dy = ax^n \, dx \tag{14b}$$

then

$$y = \int ax^n \, dx + C$$

$$= \frac{a}{n+1} x^{n+1} + C. \tag{15}$$

In any but the very simplest cases integration becomes a very tiresome and cumbersome business. There are many tricks of the trade to learn, but very few general principles. By and large, facility at integration is developed by learning a few techniques and then working through countless examples until you gain a sort of intuitive feel for the transformation of a function that will allow a particular technique to be applied to it. The student who goes further than this book will have to devote time to mastering the technique of integration. For the economics we wish to do here it is sufficient to know in an intuitive way what integration means, and to be able to integrate two sorts of functions, power functions, which we have just considered, and exponential functions, to which we must soon turn our attention.

Before we go on to exponential functions, however, there are a few elementary cases that we must consider. If we are told that dy/dx is the sum of two functions of x, how do we find y? For example we might have

$$\frac{dy}{dx} = 2x + 6x^2 \tag{16}$$

and wish to find y. We first rewrite this as a differential:

$$dy = 2x\, dx + 6x^2\, dx. \tag{17}$$

We can now integrate these two terms separately. We saw in Chapter 5 (see pages 110–11) that the derivative of the sum of two functions is the sum of their separate derivatives, and this allows us to write

$$y = \int (2x + 6x^2)\, dx + C \tag{18}$$

$$= \int 2x\, dx + \int 6x^2\, dx + C \tag{19}$$

$$= x^2 + 2x^3 + C. \tag{20}$$

You may demonstrate that this works by finding dy/dx from (20) and checking that it does equal the function in (16). Differences are easily dealt with in the same fashion as sums. Integration of products is, however, more difficult and we shall not here consider how to proceed when you encounter

$$\frac{dy}{dx} = f(x) \cdot g(x). \tag{21}$$

We must now consider the important case of the integral of the function

$$\frac{dy}{dx} = 1. \tag{22}$$

Taking differentials we have

$$dy = (1)(dx)$$

or $\qquad\qquad\qquad dy = dx \tag{23}$

which says that a small change in x will cause a change of exactly the same magnitude in y. We know from previous experience that if $y = x$ then $dy/dx = 1$, so we can now write for this function:

$$y = \int dx + C = x + C. \tag{24}$$

Thus we have the important result that $\int dx = x$, and of course $\int dy = y$ plus in each case, of course, arbitrary constants which when we integrate both sides of an equation can be collected up in the single constant C.

This leads us to the more general case of the integration of a constant. If we have

$$\frac{dy}{dx} = a$$

or

$$dy = a\,dx, \tag{25}$$

we can write

$$y = \int a\,dx + C$$

$$= ax + C \tag{26}$$

which we get just by recalling that $d(ax)/dx = a$. It is worth noticing that since an $x^0 (=1)$ is understood when we write $dy/dx = a$, i.e., $dy/dx = ax^0$, this result follows the general rule for the integration of power functions stated in (15). We have just seen that $\int dy = y$. Now consider again equation (14b). We can see that what we have in effect done is to integrate both sides. We have

$$dy = ax^n\,dx$$

whence

$$\int dy = \int ax^n\,dx + C$$

and

$$y = \frac{a}{n+1}x^{n+1} + C.$$

We are now able to integrate any polynomial

$$\frac{dy}{dx} = a + bx + cx^2 + dx^3 + \cdots + mx^n$$

to obtain

$$y = ax + \frac{b}{2}x^2 + \frac{c}{3}x^3 + \frac{d}{4}x^4 + \cdots + \frac{m}{n+1}x^{n+1} + C \tag{27}$$

where C is the constant of integration. Indeed, we can integrate any function made up of sums or differences of x's raised to fixed powers.

14.3   Integration as the Limit of a Process of Summation

So far we have relied merely on the idea of integration as being the reverse of differentiation. We can, however, give the process a little more intuitive appeal if we consider arriving at an integral through a process of summation. Consider, for example, the function

$$y = x^3 \tag{28}$$

for which

$$\frac{dy}{dx} = 3x^2. \tag{29}$$

For an arbitrarily small dx we have from (29)

$$dy = 3x^2\,dx. \tag{30}$$

(30) tells us how to estimate changes in y given arbitrarily small increments in x. The problem of integration is: if we are given only (30) can we reconstruct (28) from it? If we knew the change in y when x went from 0 to 1, and then the change in y when x went from 1 to 2, and also the change in y when x went from 2 to 3, we could sum these changes to find the value of y when x was 3. Indeed, if we knew the change in y for every increase in x from zero to some value of x we would merely sum these increments in y to get the value of y for any value of x in which we were interested. In fact equation (30) provides us with an estimate of what these changes are. Let us use (30) to do what we have suggested for the function in question. Since dx means a very small increment in x, and since we are going to begin our example by using rather large increments in x, we shall replace the 'd's' in (30) by Δ's, writing $\Delta y = 3x^2\,\Delta x$.

TABLE 14.1 $\Delta x = 1$

x (1)	$y=x^3$ (2)	$f'(x)=3x^2$ (3)	$\Delta y = f'(x)\,\Delta x$ (4)	$\sum \Delta y$ (5)
0	0	0	0	—
1	1	3	3	0
2	8	12	12	3
3	27	27	27	15

The relevant calculations are all given in Table 14.1. We let x increase by increments of 1 (i.e., $\Delta x = 1$) and the second column records the true values of y read from the function $y=x^3$. The next two columns give the calculation of Δy from equation (30). The first entry in column (3) is obtained by taking the value of $f'(x)$ when x is zero and the first entry in column (4) is found by multiplying the entry in column (3) by the change in x from 0 to 1. The second entries in columns (3) and (4) are obtained by taking the value of $f'(x)$ when x is one and multiplying it by the change in x from 1 to 2; and so on. Since in this case Δx is always unity, columns (3) and (4) are identical. Thus column (4) records the value of Δy as x increases *from* the value given in column (1). The final column estimates the value of y by summing the separate Δy's *up to* the value for x given in column (1). If we only had (30) and knew nothing about integration this would be all we could do to estimate y. A comparison of columns 2 and 5 shows, however, that by summing the successive increments in y as given by (30) we systematically underestimate the true value of y for any given x, as recorded in column 2. Our procedure in estimating y from (30) is illustrated geometrically in Figure 14.1. We have taken the value of dy/dx and multiplied it

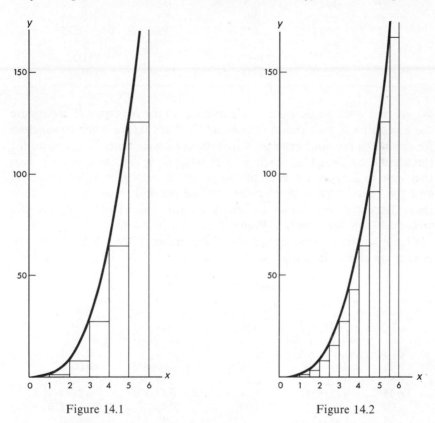

Figure 14.1   Figure 14.2

by the change in x, one unit in this case, to obtain the area of the rectangles shown in the figure. Clearly, when we sum the areas of these rectangles we underestimate the area under the curve by the areas of the little 'triangles'.[1]

Now let us try the same process again, this time taking smaller increments in x: we let $\Delta x = \frac{1}{2}$. The new set of calculations is shown in Table 14.2.

[1] We have purposely chosen a function in (28) which has no constant. If the function in (28) did contain a constant then our subsequent calculations would need to have the same constant added to them. Since there is no constant, the first row in Tables 14.1, 2 and 3 is zero.

TABLE 14.2 $\Delta x = \frac{1}{2}$

x	$y=x^3$	$f'(x)=3x^2$	$\Delta y=f'(x)$	$y=\sum \Delta y$
(1)	(2)	(3)	(4)	(5)
0	0	0	0	0
0·5	0·125	0·75	0·375	0
1·0	1·0	3·0	1·5	0·375
1·5	3·375	6·75	3·375	1·875
2·0	8·0	12·0	6·000	5·2
2·5	15·625	18·75	9·375	11·2
3·0	27·000	27·000	13·500	20·575

We see that when we estimate y by summing all the Δy's we still understate the true value of y as shown in column (2), but that we come closer than we did in the previous example when the Δx's were unity. The reason for this should be clear from Figure 14.2: by making our Δx's smaller than they were in the previous example we get more rectangles under the curve, and their total area is greater than in the previous case. We have now understated the area under the curve by the sum of the much smaller 'triangles' that are visible in Figure 14.2.

Finally we try one more example: this time we let $\Delta x = 0.25$. The calculations are shown in Table 14.3.

TABLE 14.3 $\Delta x = 0.25$

x	$y=x^3$	$f'(x)=3x^2$	$\Delta y=f'(x)\,\Delta x$	$y=\sum \Delta y$
(1)	(2)	(3)	(4)	(5)
0	0	0	0	0
0·25	0·015625	0·1875	0·046875	0·0000
0·50	0·125	0·75	0·1875	0·046875
0·75	0·421875	1·6875	0·421875	0·234375
1·00	1·00	3·000	0·75	0·656250
1·25	1·953125	4·6875	1·171875	1·406250
1·50	3·375	6·75	1·6875	2·578125
1·75	5·359375	9·1875	2·296875	4·265625
2·00	8·000	12·000	3·000	6·5625
2·25	11·390625	15·1875	3·796875	9·5625
2·50	15·625	18·75	4·6875	13·359375
2·75	20·796875	22·6875	5·671875	18·046875
3·00	27·000	27·000	6·75	24·796875

These calculations are illustrated geometrically in Figure 14.3. We now have twice as many rectangles under the curve as when we took $\Delta x = 0.5$

and four times as many as when we took $\Delta x = 1$. The total sum of the areas of the rectangles in Figure 14.3 is greater than the total sum of the areas in either 14.1 or 14.2, and the understatement of the total area under the curve is obviously less than when Δx was unity or 0·5.

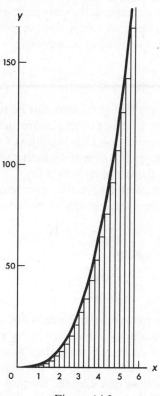

Figure 14.3

What we have done in these calculations may be expressed symbolically as

$$\text{estimated } y \text{ (at } x = \bar{x}) = \sum_{x=0}^{\bar{x}} f'(x)\,\Delta x. \qquad (31)$$

We began with Δx equal to unity and we then took progressively smaller Δx's for each of our subsequent sets of calculations. As we let Δx get very small we can write the increment of x as dx. It is visually clear that as dx approaches zero the rectangles under the curve with width dx approach a series of tightly packed vertical straight lines that will fill in the whole area under the curve. We have also seen that the value of $\sum f'(x)\,dx$ gets closer to the value of y as $dx \rightarrow 0$; indeed if the calculations were repeated for a very small dx (say $dx=0.001$), we would find that the sum $\sum f'(x)\,dx$ had come very close to the value of y. This has a strong intuitive appeal: if we take all the changes in y where there is no error in estimating Δy (and the error in estimating Δy from $f'(x)\,dx$ approaches zero as $dx\to 0$) then the sum of these should equal the value of y itself. Geometrically the graph of $f'(x)$ is a graph of a curve expressing the change in y in response to a change in x at each value of x; the area under the curve indicates the sum of all the changes in y. To express these ideas we write[1]

$$y = \lim_{dx\to 0} \left(\sum_{d} y = \sum f'(x)\,dx \right) = \int f'(x)\,dx + C. \qquad (32)$$

Now we see the sense in which the $\int$ sign can be regarded as indicating a summation process. The sign is nothing more than an elongated 'S'. It stands for a type of summation which is the limit of the value of the summation $\sum f'(x)\,dx$ as the change in x is made smaller and smaller. This limiting value is the area under the curve $dy/dx=f'(x)$.

We take the geometrical interpretation of integration a step further in Figure 14.4. The upper curve is a graph of the function

$$y = x^3 + 10 \qquad (33)$$

while the lower curve is a graph of

$$\frac{dy}{dx} = 3x^2. \qquad (34)$$

The area under the lower curve between zero and any value[2] of x is given by x^3 while the corresponding y value is given by x^3+10. Thus when $x=2$ the area under the lower curve is 8 while the value of y in the upper curve is 18. When $x=4$ the area under the lower curve is 64 while the value of y is 74. This shows us that if we can take the integral of the function $f'(x)$ and find its value for a particular x, we are finding the area under the graph of $f'(x)$ between zero and the value of x.[3]

[1] Although there was no constant in our numerical example we must recognise in (32) that y will be the area under the curve plus a constant which stands for that part of the value of y which cannot be accounted for by changes in x.

[2] Notice that if we let x approach infinity so do the values of both (33) and (34), which is to say that the value of the function and the area beneath it both go to infinity.

[3] Sometimes it is necessary to find the area under the curve $f'(x)$ between *two* non-zero limits. Figure 14.4 illustrates that the area under the curve $f'(x)=x^3$ between $x=2$ and $x=4$ is given by the area between $x=0$ and $x=4$ minus the area between $x=0$ and $x=2$. If we wish to find this we merely find the value of $\int f'(x)$ at $x=4$ and subtract the value of $\int f'(x)$ at $x=2$. This is called evaluating the *definite integral* between the limits of 2 and 4. A definite integral is written with the limits at the top and bottom of the integral sign. Thus $\int_2^4 3x^2$ means the area under the curve $f'(x)=3x^2$ between the limits $x=2$ and $x=4$.

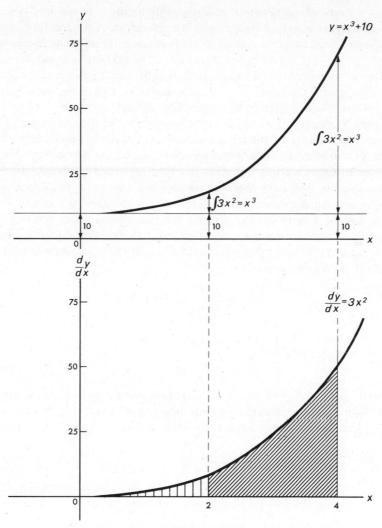

Figure 14.4

14.4 Differential Equations

A differential equation is an equation involving a derivative. The order of the equation is the order of the highest derivative that it contains. Thus the market adjustment equation (29) on page 310 of Chapter 13,

$$\frac{\mathrm{d}p}{\mathrm{d}t} = \alpha(q^d - q^s)$$

or

$$\mathrm{d}p = \alpha(q^d - q^s)\,\mathrm{d}t, \qquad (35)$$

11*

is called a *first-order differential equation*. Furthermore it is a first-order, *linear* differential equation with constant coefficients. A differential equation is linear if the variable and all its derivatives enter in linear combination (e.g., $dy = f'(x)f''(x)\,dx$ is not linear since the first and second derivatives appear as a product of each other). A differential equation has constant coefficients if the coefficients of the variable and all its derivatives are constants and do not contain the dependent variable in them.

Differential equations occur in any dynamic model that has time as a continuous variable (and difference equations occur in the remainder). The solution of a differential equation is an equation containing no derivatives of any order. Once such an equation has been obtained the whole model can be solved by ordinary algebraic methods. Differential equations are solved by integrating, and when we do this we are moving from an expression for the rate of change of y (or the rate of change of the rate of change of y if second derivatives are involved) to an expression for y. Thus suppose we are told that marginal cost is $10q + 20$ and we require the total cost function. We can write

$$MC = \frac{dTC}{dq} = 10q + 20 \qquad (36)$$

$$\int dTC = \int (10q + 20)\,dq + C$$

$$TC = 5q^2 + 20q + C. \qquad (37)$$

If, however, we were given an expression containing only a second derivative, we would have to integrate twice to obtain the 'solution'. Assume, for example, that we are only told that the second derivative of the cost function is

$$f''(q) = 10$$

and we wish to find the total cost function. We now proceed as follows:

$$f(q) = \int f''(q)\,dq + C_1 = \int 10\,dq + C_1 = 10q + C_1,$$

and again

$$f(q) = \int f'(q)\,dq + C_2$$

$$= \int (10q + C_1)\,dq + C_2$$

$$= 5q^2 + C_1 q + C_2 \qquad (38)$$

Having only $f''(x)$ does not give us sufficient information to put a numerical value on the parameter attached to q in the way we could when we had the marginal cost function given to us. We are nevertheless able to discover, by integrating the function $f''(q)$ twice, the general shape of the total cost function: in this case it is a quadratic.

14.5 Exponential Functions

So far in this book we have confined ourselves almost exclusively to power functions. In these functions, the variable x is raised to a fixed exponent, or power (which may of course be positive or negative, an integer or a fraction). A different class of functions is introduced if we consider putting the variable number x as an exponent to a fixed parameter a, thus

$$y = a^x. \tag{39}$$

This is called an exponential function, because the variable quantity, x, appears as the exponent of the fixed parameter, a. This is an important class of functions for economic dynamics. Indeed, we encountered a case of such a function in the cobweb model of the last chapter. The solution to the model (see page 301) was of the form

$$p_t = A^t$$

where the parameter A is the ratio of the slopes of the demand and the supply curves, while the two variables are price and time.

Exponential functions arise in virtually all dynamic problems, and we need to study their properties. Indeed, we have already seen one use of exponential functions which is to provide the basis of logarithms. If

$$y = a^x$$

we *define* the logarithm of y as

$$x = \log_a y.$$

In Chapter 3 we studied some of the uses of logarithms and, since we now intend to build on what was done in that chapter, anyone who then felt, or now feels, at all shaky on the subject of logarithms should re-read pages 56–63.

When we use logarithms as a short cut for accomplishing what would otherwise require laborious calculations (e.g., for finding $(8{\cdot}17)^{4/3}$) we usually use logs to the base 10. These are called *common logs* and they show the power to which 10 must be raised to get stated values. In theoretical work it is common to use logarithms to a base other than 10. This base is designated by the letter e. It has the value, correct to four decimal places, of $2 \cdot 7183$. Logarithms to the base e are called *natural logs*.[1] Indeed the number e is a most remarkable number which arises naturally in any growth problem. We must now sketch very briefly the derivation of e.

Consider the problem of the growth of a sum of money, say £P, invested at a rate of interest of $100r\%$ per year.[2] If the interest is paid once a year, the sum of money available to the investor at the end of the year, called V, will be

$$V = P(1+r). \tag{40}$$

Now consider what would happen if interest were paid every six months at the rate of $100r\%$ per annum. At the end of six months $r/2$ will have been earned and the sum available will be

$$V_1 = P\left(1+\frac{r}{2}\right). \tag{41}$$

But this whole sum V_1, which is more than P, will earn interest for the second six months, so, at the end of the year, the whole sum available will be

$$V_2 = V_1\left(1+\frac{r}{2}\right)$$

and if we substitute for V_1 from (41) we get

$$V_2 = P\left(1+\frac{r}{2}\right)\left(1+\frac{r}{2}\right)$$

$$= P\left(1+\frac{r}{2}\right)^2. \tag{42}$$

Reiteration of the same argument for the case in which $r/3$ is paid 3 times a year will show that the value of the sum available at the end of the year is

$$V = P\left(1+\frac{r}{3}\right)^3, \tag{43}$$

while if interest is paid four times a year (still at an annual rate of $100r\%$) it will be

$$V = P\left(1+\frac{r}{4}\right)^4. \tag{44}$$

---

[1] We have seen on page 62 how to move from one base to another merely by applying the rule

$$\log_b y = \log_a y \log_b a.$$

[2] If the rate of interest is 3%, for example, then $r=0 \cdot 03$, $100r\%=3\%$ and $1+r=1 \cdot 03$.

In general, then, the sum available at the end of the year when interest is paid n times a year at an annual rate of $100r\%$ on £P invested is

$$V = P\left(1+\frac{r}{n}\right)^n. \tag{45}$$

As interest is paid and reinvested (which is called compounding) more and more frequently, the sum available at the end of the year increases. This is because the interest paid during the early part of the year is added to the sum invested and is itself earning interest for the later part of the year. It seems obvious to ask what happens as interest is paid more and more frequently. Although V, the sum available at the end of the year, gets larger as interest is paid more and more frequently, it does not grow without limit. A particular limiting value is of great importance. Consider £1 invested at 100% per year, which gives $P=$£1 and $r=1$. The value of the sum available at the end of the year is then

$$V = \left(1+\frac{1}{n}\right)^n. \tag{46}$$

We may make a quick check on (46) by assuming that interest is paid only once a year. In this case $n=1$ and $V=2$ which checks with what we know: a sum of money invested at 100% interest payable at the end of the year will be doubled at the end of the year. If interest is compounded more and more frequently, however, n gets larger and larger, and, as $n\to\infty$, $[1+(1/n)]^n$ approaches a definite limiting value in the neighbourhood of $2\cdot7183$. This value, as we have already seen, is designated by the letter e. Thus

$$e = \lim_{n\to\infty}\left(1+\frac{1}{n}\right)^n \simeq 2\cdot7183. \tag{47}$$

Thus we may regard e as the value at the end of one year of £1 invested at an annual interest rate of 100% with continuous compounding ($n\to\infty$).

We now return to exponential and logarithmic functions and shall very soon find a most important use for the number e. Assume that we have the function

$$x = a^y \tag{48}$$

and we require its inverse. We have this quite simply by the definition of a logarithm:

$$y = \log_a x. \tag{49}$$

From this point we drop the sign for the base, since the argument refers to any base.

Let us consider first how to find the derivative of the logarithmic function (49). We proceed from first principles in the manner first introduced in Chapter 5 (see page 110):

$$\frac{dy}{dx}(y = \log x) = \lim_{h \to 0}\left[\frac{\log(x+h)-\log x}{h}\right]. \tag{50}$$

Now we need to perform a few manipulations on (50) in order to get it into a form from which the derivative is easily discovered. First we write

$$\frac{dy}{dx} = \lim_{h \to 0}\frac{1}{h}(\log(x+h)-\log x), \tag{51}$$

which merely separates the numerator from the denominator in (50). Next we note that subtracting logarithms corresponds to dividing natural numbers and this allows us to write

$$\frac{dy}{dx} = \lim_{h \to 0}\frac{1}{h}\log\left(\frac{x+h}{x}\right)$$

$$= \lim_{h \to 0}\frac{1}{h}\log\left(1+\frac{h}{x}\right). \tag{52}$$

We now wish to get this function into a slightly different form so that certain of its characteristics will become more apparent. We have the same problem that we have mentioned many times before: each step in our procedure may seem arbitrary but it is motivated by the desire to manipulate the expression into a form that will reveal something in which we are interested. In this case, we are going to do something analogous to multiplying and dividing by the same factor which leaves the value of the expression unchanged. To understand what we are going to do, we need a slight digression. Consider the function

$$C = \log r. \tag{53}$$

We now try to alter the power on r (as written, it is one) in such a way that the value of the function is unchanged. If we multiply the logarithm by a this has the effect of raising the original number, r, to the power a, thus:

$$aC = \log(r^a). \tag{54}$$

If we now divide by a, we get

$$C = \frac{1}{a}\log(r^a). \tag{55}$$

What (55) says is that if we raise r to the power a, take the logarithm of the result and divide by a, this will be the same value as the logarithm of r.

Using this result we can now raise the expression inside the brackets in (52) to any power as long as we divide the result by the same number. Let us raise it to the power x/h:

$$\frac{dy}{dx} = \lim_{h \to 0} \frac{h}{x} \frac{1}{h} \log \left(1 + \frac{h}{x}\right)^{x/h}$$

$$= \lim_{h \to 0} \frac{1}{x} \log \left(1 + \frac{h}{x}\right)^{x/h}. \qquad (56)$$

Now writing n instead of x/h, we have

$$\frac{dy}{dx} = \lim_{h \to 0} \frac{1}{x} \log \left(1 + \frac{1}{n}\right)^{n} \qquad (57)$$

and at last we are back to something familiar: compare (57) with (47), which defines e! Consider what happens as we let h, our arbitrary increment in x, approach zero. Since $n = x/h$ we have $n \to \infty$ as $h \to 0$. But we know from (47) that as $n \to \infty$ $(1 + 1/n)^{n} \to e$. Thus

$$\frac{dy}{dx} = \frac{1}{x} \log e. \qquad (58)$$

If we use e as our base (we are beginning to see more reasons for taking e as a base for logarithms) we have $\log_e e - 1$, so we may write[1]

$$\frac{dy}{dx} (y = \log_e x) = \frac{1}{x}. \qquad (59)$$

This is an extremely important result, and what it says is that as the value of x is changed, the value of the logarithm of x changes by $1/x$.

We have seen how to find the derivative of a logarithmic function, and we can use this to establish another result of fundamental importance. We want to find the derivative of the exponential function $y = e^x$. We can do this merely by reversing the process of logarithmic differentiation. We have seen that if

$$y = \log_e x \qquad (60)$$

then

$$x = e^y. \qquad (61)$$

We recall the inverse function rule (see pages 124–125).

$$\frac{dy}{dx} = \frac{1}{dx/dy}. \qquad (62)$$

---

[1] The expression $(y = \log x)$ has been understood after dy/dx in all the expressions since (49). In (59) we have to commit ourselves to the particular base e so that we can eliminate $\log e$ from (58).

From (59) we have

$$\frac{dy}{dx}(y = \log_e x) = \frac{1}{x}.$$

From (62) we know that the derivative of (61) is

$$\frac{dx}{dy} = x$$

but from (61) we have $x = e^y$ so we can write the derivative of (61) as

$$\frac{dx}{dy} = e^y. \tag{63}$$

This is a very interesting result. Evidently we have found a function whose derivative is itself. We should not regard this as particularly mysterious. Common sense suggests that there must be some function such that

$$f'(x) = f(x)$$

for all values of x, which is to say that *the slope tangent to the curve is at all points equal to the height of the curve.* What we have done is to find this particular function. We now know that if

$$y = e^x$$

then

$$\frac{dy}{dx} = e^x.$$

Now let us interpret the exponential and the logarithmic functions. Consider first the exponential function. The derivative of this function is the function itself, so the integral of the function must also be the function itself, but, as we have already seen, an arbitrary constant will appear when we integrate. Thus

$$\int e^x \, dx = e^x + C. \tag{64}$$

Now consider the logarithmic function whose derivative was given in (59). We obviously[1] have

$$\int \frac{1}{x} \, dx = \log x + C. \tag{65}$$

---

[1] This is a very important result. As you may quickly discover for yourself, x^{-1} cannot be integrated by the power function rule.

Since $1/x$ is the derivative of $\log x$ it follows that $\log x \, (+C)$ is the integral of $1/x$.

The function e^x is a most remarkable function. It always grows as x changes at a rate equal to its own value. This is of course the verbal translation of the fact that $\mathrm{d}(e^x)/\mathrm{d}x = e^x$. Having found a function that grows at a rate equal to its own value we must wonder if we can find a function that grows at a rate proportional to its own value. It might be true for example that national income is growing at a rate of 3 % per year. This means that the rate of change of national income is 0·03 times the current value of national income whatever the current value may be. To express this we require a function such that $\mathrm{d}y/\mathrm{d}x = 0 \cdot 03 y$ at all values of y where x is time measured in years. Indeed the function e^{rx} is the function we require. If r is any constant we shall find that the function e^{rx} is changing at a rate *proportional* to its own value and that the constant of proportionality is r. Let us check this by finding the derivative of the function $y = e^{rx}$. This is easily done using the function-of-a-function rule. With $z = rx$ we have

$$y = e^z$$

$$\frac{\mathrm{d}y}{\mathrm{d}z} = e^z$$

$$\frac{\mathrm{d}z}{\mathrm{d}x} = r$$

$$\frac{\mathrm{d}y}{\mathrm{d}x} = \frac{\mathrm{d}y}{\mathrm{d}z} \cdot \frac{\mathrm{d}z}{\mathrm{d}x} = e^z r$$

but since $z = rx$ we have

$$\frac{\mathrm{d}y}{\mathrm{d}x} = re^{rx}.$$

Thus
$$\frac{\mathrm{d}}{\mathrm{d}x}(e^{rx}) = re^{rx}. \tag{66}$$

If r is 0·03, for example, the rate of growth of this function is 3 % of the value of the function itself at all times. We have now found a function whose rate of growth is always proportional to its own value.

If we use this function for growth problems, it is more convenient to denote time by t than by x, whence we shall write e^{rt} where r is the rate of growth and t is time. The value of the function will grow at the rate of re^{rt} as time passes, and its proportional rate of growth will be $re^{rt}/e^{rt} = r$.

If we wish to express the assumption that national income is growing at a constant rate of $100r\%$ we write

$$Y_t = Y_0 e^{rt} \tag{67}$$

where Y_t is national income at time t, Y_0 is the national income at any 'base period' from which we begin our measurements, r is the constant rate of growth, and t is time. We assign the value zero to t at the base period and count the passage of time from there. At $t=0$ the right hand side becomes simply Y_0 as it should since $e^0 = 1$.

As a final example we consider a relationship that we shall require in the next chapter. Assume that the labour force is growing at a rate of $100r\%$ per year. We can now write

$$L_t = L_0 e^{rt} \tag{68}$$

where L_t is the labour force at time t, L_0 is the labour force in the base period, r is the constant rate of growth, and t is time.

We have now discovered the function, e^{rt}, whose rate of growth is proportional to its own value. In the next chapter we shall exploit this function in our study of some dynamic models.

14.6   Elasticity once again

Now that we know how to differentiate logarithmic functions, we can obtain a most convenient expression for elasticity. In Chapter 3 we introduced the log-linear function

$$y = ax^\beta. \tag{69}$$

In Chapter 5 we found that, if y denotes quantity and x price, then β is the elasticity of demand. We also took logs, and found that, since the function is linear in the logs,

$$\frac{d \log y}{d \log x} = \beta.$$

But now we know that $d \log y/dy = 1/y$ whence in differential form

$$d \log y = \frac{1}{y} \, dy.$$

Similarly

$$d \log x = \frac{1}{x} \, dx.$$

By the definition of the elasticity of any dependent variable with respect to an independent variable x,

$$\eta = \frac{dy}{dx} \cdot \frac{x}{y}$$

$$= \frac{1}{y} dy \cdot \frac{1}{dx} x$$

$$= \frac{d \log y}{d \log x}. \tag{70}$$

Now we know that for any function $y = f(x)$, the elasticity of y with respect to x is given by $d \log y / d \log x$. In the case of a function of two or more variables we may define a *partial elasticity*, the elasticity of the dependent variable with respect to any one of its arguments. Thus if $\eta_{y:x_i}$ stands for the elasticity of y with respect to its ith argument,

$$\eta_{y:x_i} = \frac{d \log y}{d \log x_i}. \tag{71}$$

Exercises

1 Solve the following differential equations:

(a) $\dfrac{dy}{dx} = 3x^2$.

(b) $\dfrac{dy}{dx} = \frac{1}{3}x^3$.

(c) $\dfrac{dy}{dx} = 6x^2 + 3x^3$.

(d) $\dfrac{dy}{dx} = \frac{1}{4}x^{1/2}$.

(e) $\dfrac{dy}{dx} = 3x^{-1/3}$.

(f) $\dfrac{dy}{dx} = x^2 - x$.

2 Marginal cost is given by

$$MC = 10 - 0.01x + 0.0009x^2$$

and fixed cost is 100. Find the total cost function.

3 Differentiate with respect to x
  (a) $3e^{0.03x}$.

  (b) $e^{-x/4}$.

4 Solve for y

  (a) $\dfrac{dy}{dx} = 0.1e^{0.1x}$.

  (b) $\dfrac{dy}{dx} = 6e^{2x}$.

5 (a) If y is growing at a constant proportional rate r, from an initial value $y = y_0$, find the equation for y as a function of time.
  (b) If $r = 0.01$ and $y_0 = 4$, what is y when $t = 10$?

6 Find the percentage change in quantity produced in response to a one percent change in (i) labour input and (ii) capital input if production is given by

$$q = L^{2/3}K^{1/3}.$$

7 A monopolist has the marginal revenue curve

$$MR = 100 - 10q.$$

  (a) Derive his total and average revenue curves.
  (b) Can you say what the value of the constant of integration must be in this case?
8 The elasticity of demand for a product is $-\frac{1}{4}$ at all prices. Derive the equation for the demand curve.
9 Consider an economy with a constant marginal propensity to import of $\cdot 2$ and a constant marginal propensity to spend on domestically produced commodities of $\cdot 7$.

  (a) Write the expression for dE/dY where E is expenditure and where the only two classes of expenditure that vary with income are imports and consumption of domestically produced goods.
  (b) Derive the equation for aggregate expenditure. What is the economic interpretation of the constant of integration?

CHAPTER 15

APPLICATIONS OF DYNAMICS

This is a long chapter. All economic problems have a dynamic aspect and we can thus take our examples from the whole of economics.

The restriction on our choice of examples is imposed purely by the technical tools at our disposal. It is evident that growth and fluctuations are inescapably dynamic topics: but, as we have seen, the analysis of the common problems of micro-economics, such as market behaviour, is left seriously incomplete if only the static equilibrium analysis is done. We shall restrict ourselves to the simplest continuous cases. Even so, there is a great deal here, and some of it is not easy, so that this chapter is probably best tackled piecemeal, an example at a time.

15.1 Dynamic Behaviour in a Competitive Market with Linear Supply and Demand Curves

Our first task is to complete some unfinished business left over from Chapter 13. In that chapter we took the familiar linear model of a single competitive price and specified in a reaction function the rule that the rate of change of market price was proportional to the amount of excess demand (see page 310):

$$q^d = a + bp \tag{1}$$

$$q^s = c + dp \tag{2}$$

$$\frac{dp}{dt} = \alpha(q^d - q^s)$$

$$= \alpha(a + bp - c - dp)$$

$$= \alpha[(a-c) + p(b-d)]. \tag{3}$$

We then posed the question of how price would behave if we began from a position of disequilibrium. The various possibilities for the behaviour of price were illustrated in Figure 13.8 on page 309 and we are particularly interested to see whether or not the actual price will converge on its equilibrium value. The necessary manipulations are not difficult but they will take a little time, particularly if we stop at every stage to check that what we have done makes economic sense.

First we check, as we have done previously, that the results obtainable from this model conform with those that we have obtained earlier. In particular we need to check the equilibrium value of p. In equilibrium, price is not changing so we have

$$\frac{\mathrm{d}p}{\mathrm{d}t} = 0 \tag{4}$$

which, substituting from (3), gives

$$\alpha[(a-c)+p(b-d)] = 0.$$

Manipulation now gives

$$p = \frac{c-a}{b-d} = \frac{a-c}{d-b} = \bar{p}. \tag{5}$$

This agrees with the result first obtained in Chapter 4 (see page 66). Note that we designate the equilibrium price by $\bar{p}$, while p stands for the price ruling at any time whether equal to $\bar{p}$ or not.

Now let us deal in divergences of price from the equilibrium value just as we did when we studied the cobweb. Thus we define

$$\hat{p}(t) = p(t)-\bar{p}. \tag{6}$$

Thus 'p-hat' is just the difference between the equilibrium price, 'p-bar' and the actual price, 'p'. We write 'p-hat' and 'p' as functions of time to emphasise that, once we have specified our demand and supply curves and the rule that governs the speed of change of price (equation (3)), both p and $\hat{p}$ will change in a definite way as time passes, i.e., they are functions of time.

Differentiating (6) with respect to time we have

$$\frac{\mathrm{d}\hat{p}(t)}{\mathrm{d}t} = \frac{\mathrm{d}p(t)}{\mathrm{d}t} - \frac{\mathrm{d}\bar{p}(t)}{\mathrm{d}t}. \tag{7}$$

The *equilibrium price* is, of course, determined solely by the demand and supply curves (see (5)) and does not change over time (assuming the curves to be given). Thus we have

$$\frac{\mathrm{d}\bar{p}(t)}{\mathrm{d}t} = 0 \tag{8}$$

so that (7) becomes

$$\frac{\mathrm{d}\hat{p}(t)}{\mathrm{d}t} = \frac{\mathrm{d}p(t)}{\mathrm{d}t}. \tag{9}$$

This says nothing more than that, since $\bar{p}$ is constant, the rate of change of $(p-\bar{p})$ is the same as the rate of change of p.

We can now take the expression for dp/dt from (3) and substitute it into equation (7) to obtain

$$\frac{d\hat{p}(t)}{dt} = \alpha[(a-c)+(b-d)p]-\alpha[(a-c)+(b-d)\bar{p}]. \tag{10}$$

Note that we have not only substituted in the expression for $dp(t)/dt$ into (7), but have also substituted in one for $d\bar{p}(t)/dt$ even though we know this expression has a value of zero.[1] We do this because some of the individual terms can be cancelled out with terms from $dp(t)/dt$ to obtain an expression cleared of irrelevant terms. Let us see how this happens:

$$\frac{d\hat{p}(t)}{dt} = \alpha[(a-c)+(b-d)p]-\alpha[(a-c)+(b-d)\bar{p}] \tag{10}$$

$$= \alpha(a-c)-\alpha(a-c)+\alpha p(b-d)-\alpha\bar{p}(b-d)$$

$$= \alpha(b-d)(p-\bar{p})$$

$$= \alpha(b-d)\hat{p}(t).$$

Now we have the rate of change of $\hat{p}$ expressed as a function of $\hat{p}$ and the difference between the slopes of the demand are the supply curves. The intercept terms, a and c, have disappeared. Finally let us designate $(b-d)$ by the Greek letter γ (pronounced gamma) so that we have

$$\frac{d\hat{p}(t)}{dt} = \alpha\gamma\hat{p}(t). \tag{11}$$

Next we divide through by $\hat{p}(t)$ to get all terms involving the dependent variable on the left-hand side of the expression:

$$\frac{1}{\hat{p}(t)}\cdot\frac{d\hat{p}(t)}{dt} = \alpha\gamma. \tag{12}$$

Finally to get it into the form of a differential equation we multiply through by dt to obtain

$$\frac{d\hat{p}(t)}{\hat{p}(t)} = \alpha\gamma\, dt. \tag{13}$$

Now at last we are getting somewhere. We have managed to derive a first

---

[1] You can easily check that the term for $d\bar{p}/dt$ in (10) is in fact zero if you substitute the solution for $\bar{p}$ from (5) into it. The term for $d\bar{p}/dt$ in (10) is $\alpha[(a-c)+(b-d)\bar{p}]$. Substituting from (5) for $\bar{p}$ we get $\alpha[(a-c)+(b-d)(c-a)/(b-d)]=0$.

order linear differential equation of the sort we studied in the last chapter. Fortunately we know how to solve it by integrating both sides:

$$\int \frac{1}{\hat{p}(t)}\, \mathrm{d}\hat{p}(t) = \int \alpha\gamma\, \mathrm{d}t + C. \tag{14}$$

In the previous chapter we saw that the integral of $(1/x)\, \mathrm{d}x$ was the log to the base e of x. This settles the left-hand side. The right-hand integration is even easier since we know that $\alpha\gamma t$ will give $\alpha\gamma$ when differentiated with respect to t so $\alpha\gamma t$ is what we require. Thus we have

$$\log_e \hat{p}(t) = \alpha\gamma t + C, \tag{15}$$

where C is the constant of integration. To find $\hat{p}(t)$ we now take antilogs to obtain

$$\hat{p}(t) = (e^{\alpha\gamma t}) \quad \text{(antilog of } C\text{)}. \tag{16}$$

If you were shaky on logarithms even after studying Chapter 14, you will have to think carefully how we got from (15) to (16). What we are trying to do is to find an expression for $\hat{p}(t)$ which is the divergence of the actual price from the market price given as a function of time. In (15) we are very close to this answer because the right-hand side is the log to the base e of what we want. If $\alpha\gamma t + C$ is the log of our answer then our answer is the number that corresponds to e raised to the power of $\alpha\gamma t$ (the antilog of $\alpha\gamma t$) multiplied by the antilog of C which is the number corresponding to e raised to the power C. We do not however write e^C as the antilog of C but instead merely designate this value by A. Now write[1]

$$\hat{p}(t) = Ae^{\alpha\gamma t}. \tag{17}$$

We have now solved our mathematical problem, and it remains only to inspect the solution in (17) to see what we can learn from it. First consider the constant A. This arose in the process of integration and, like all constants of integration, we cannot determine it without further extraneous information. It would be most unsatisfactory if the behaviour of our model turned out to depend critically on a constant whose value we could not

---

[1] If instead of writing A for the antilogarithm of C, we had written e^C, equation (17) would have become

$$p(t) = (e^{\alpha\gamma})e^C$$
$$= e^{\alpha\gamma t + C}. \tag{17a}$$

This is of course the same as (17), but the form in the text happens to be a more convenient one than is (17a).

determine. Fortunately, this is not the case: we can easily give the constant an economic interpretation by considering the value of (17) at the initial time period when the whole process is set in motion. The process begins at time t_0. In (17) we have $t=0$ at that time and thus $\alpha \gamma t = 0$ whatever the values of α and γ. We know that any number raised to the power zero is equal to unity so (17) reduces to

$$\hat{p}(t) = A \quad \text{(at time } t_0\text{)}. \tag{18}$$

Thus A is the initial value of the divergence of price from equilibrium.[1] This is our starting point; it is the divergence from equilibrium that is needed to put the whole process in motion. It is not surprising that we cannot tell what price will be at any time t unless we know the value from which it started.[2]

Next consider the coefficient $\alpha \gamma t$. t stands for time elapsed since t_0 and it is thus a variable which starts from zero and takes on larger and larger positive values thereafter. α is the adjustment coefficient and we have already seen (see page 310) that $\alpha > 0$. γ was substituted for $b - d$, the difference between the slopes of the demand and the supply curves. If the curves are of the normal slopes we have $b < 0$ and $d > 0$ so that $\gamma = b - d < 0$. Thus α and t are positive while γ is negative so that the sign of the coefficient on e is necessarily negative. (Note that this result is independent of the sign or magnitude of the constant A.) α and γ are constants and t is a variable, hence it follows that the absolute value of $\alpha \gamma t$ gets larger and larger as t gets larger and larger; in fact $\alpha \gamma t \rightarrow -\infty$ as $t \rightarrow +\infty$. It is easily seen by inspection that e^{-x} approaches zero as x gets larger and larger.[3] From this we conclude that $\hat{p}(t)$ gets steadily smaller and smaller as t increases.

Finally consider what would happen if the coefficient $\alpha \gamma t$ were positive (i.e., either both $\alpha, \gamma > 0$, or both $\alpha, \gamma < 0$ which means that one of α or γ must have the 'wrong' sign). e^x increases indefinitely as x increases as long as x is positive.[4] This means that $\hat{p}$ would increase steadily as t increased: the actual price would get further and further from the equilibrium price.

We have now reached a number of conclusions concerning our dynamic model of a competitive market. We may now describe the characteristics of the model of equations (1), (2), and (3).

---

[1] For any function of time, the constant of integration A gives the value of the function at t_0.

[2] See pages 302–3 for an analysis of the possible causes of the initial deviation from equilibrium.

[3] The expression e^{-x} is the same thing as $1/e^x$. As x gets larger and larger e^x gets larger and larger and thus its reciprocal gets smaller and smaller. Indeed it can be shown that as $x \rightarrow \infty$, $e^x \rightarrow \infty$ and from this it follows that as $x \rightarrow \infty$, $e^{-x} \rightarrow 0$.

[4] See note 3 above.

(1) Assuming that the adjustment coefficient has the correct sign, a necessary condition for stability in this market is the $\gamma = b - d < 0$ (all the possibilities were spelled out on page 297 of Chapter 13).

(2) Assuming that $\gamma < 0$, a necessary condition for stability is that $\alpha > 0$, i.e., that price falls when there is excess supply and rises when there is excess demand.

(3) There is a combination of two perverse reactions that will produce stable behaviour: $\alpha < 0$ and $\gamma < 0$, in which case there is excess supply above the equilibrium price and excess demand below it, but price falls when there is excess demand and rises when there is excess supply.

Now in the normal case in which $\alpha > 0$ and $\gamma < 0$ we have the following results.

(4) The adjustment process is stable in the sense that the actual price converges on the equilibrium one.

(5) The approach to equilibrium is a steady one and *not* one of progressively diminishing oscillations around the equilibrium; the path of price is similar to the one shown by curve (1) in Figure 13.8, on page 309.

(6) Conclusions (1) and (2) are independent of the size and direction of the initial disturbance.

(7) The actual shape of the time-path of price is determined by α, the strength of the response of price to excess demand, by γ, and by A which stands for the original disturbance. The statement, that the time-path depends on A, does not conflict with conclusion (3): the result that the approach to equilibrium is a steady one is independent of A, but the actual position of the path traced out must depend on A – the sign of A determines, for example, whether the approach is from above (initial price too high) or from below (initial price too low).

Result (3), although undoubtedly of little practical interest, does warn us that we must be careful how we define the necessary conditions for negative feedback. If we say that by negative feedback we mean

$$\frac{\mathrm{d}p}{\mathrm{d}t} > 0 \quad \text{when } p < \bar{p}$$

and

$$\frac{\mathrm{d}p}{\mathrm{d}t} < 0 \quad \text{when } p > \bar{p},$$

then the condition for negative feedback in the present model is that α and γ should have opposite signs.[1] It turns out that this condition is also *sufficient* to secure stability. It should be noted, however, that in slightly more complex models the conditions necessary to secure negative feedback will not be sufficient to guarantee stability of the adjustment process. We

[1] In Chapter 13 our discussion of negative feedback concentrated on the sign of γ because we had already introduced the prior assumption that $\alpha > 0$.

have not, for example, investigated any of the complex possibilities that arise if we take any one or combination of τ_1, τ_2, and τ_3 non-zero in equation (24) to (26) in Chapter 13.

The solution of the dynamic model of income determination set out at the end of Chapter 13 poses no new problems. The solution follows exactly the same steps as those used in the case of the single competitive market and it is left for the reader to do as an exercise. This would be a good time to do it.

15.2 A Simple Model of Economic Growth

A great deal of interest has developed in the last twenty years in the process of economic growth. Although the ability of governments to manipulate growth rates in free-market economics seems as far away as it was twenty years ago, a great deal of fundamental theoretical and empirical work has been done, and we may hope that this work will contribute towards our practical ability to manipulate growth rates in the not too distant future. The frontier of growth theory is a very long way off and a really large investment in technique is needed to get there. Nonetheless, we do have enough technique to study some elementary growth problems. If what we do here does interest you, you will find that an investment in technique on the scale of one chapter of this book will permit you to go quite a long way into the literature of economic growth.

When the formal theory of growth was still fairly new, Professors Harrod and Domar published independently two papers that laid out what has subsequently been called the Harrod–Domar model.[1] The authors tried in this model to analyse some long-term growth problems using a set of concepts – the multiplier, the accelerator, and the capital: labour coefficient – more usually applied to short-run problems. Their model had an equilibrium growth path along which the economy could grow at a steady rate while maintaining full employment of all resources. The equilibrium path in this model displayed, however, the startling property that, if the economy was moved even slightly off it, an explosive situation developed. The economy either blew up into perpetual inflation or collapsed into a state of ever-increasing unemployment, depending on the direction of the initial disturbance. Was this picture of a capitalist economy poised on a razor's edge between two alternative explosive paths one that would emerge from most reasonable models of growth, or was it the result of some special, and possibly quite unreal, characteristic of the Harrod–Domar model? The answer to this question was provided in 1956 by Robert Solow

[1] We will not lay out the Harrod–Domar model here since it is readily accessible to the student in most intermediate macro-tests.

in a famous article in the *Quarterly Journal of Economics*.[1] Briefly, Solow's answer to this question is that the instability in the Harrod–Domar model resulted from the assumption that capital and labour were used in a fixed proportion, and that, once the proportion in which factors were combined was allowed to vary in response to changes in relative prices, a model which was in other respects like that of Harrod and Domar would display a stable growth path in the sense that the economy would always move back towards it no matter how far it was pushed away by some temporary disturbance. Although the assumption of fixed factor proportions may not be an unreasonable one to make in the short run, we know that factor proportions can and do vary greatly in the long run. Thus Solow's answer was that the dynamic instability of the Harrod–Domar model was nothing more than a theoretical curiosity arising from a single assumption that is contradicted by a great deal of empirical evidence. Let us see how Solow arrived at his answer.

To study this problem we need to build a very simple model of a growing economy. There is a single commodity in the economy[2] and its annual rate of output is given by $Y(t)$. A fraction, s, of this output is saved and the rest, $1-s$, is consumed. The society's stock of capital, K, is merely the accumulated stock of the single commodity that has been saved in the past. This behavioural assumption ensures that what is saved is the same thing as what is invested. This allows us to say that current saving determines the rate of growth of society's capital. We write this as

$$\dot{K} = sY \qquad (19)$$

where $\dot{K}$ stands for dK/dt (see page 285 where this notation was first introduced). There are two factors of production, capital, K, and labour, L. Production is given by a production function

$$Y = F(K, L) \qquad (20)$$

that displays constant returns to scale.

We are now going to engage in some manipulations which, as we have so often observed before, may seem arbitrary at first sight. When you have some experience with growth theory you will begin to develop a feel for the tactics required to manipulate such models. In the meantime you will

---

[1] 'A Contribution to the Theory of Economic Growth', R. M. Solow, *Q.J.E.*, 1956, pages 65–94.

[2] This is a very 'primitive' growth model. It is complicated enough even with only one commodity. Many-commodity growth models exist but for the student, as for the developers of growth theory, the simplest problem must be solved before more complex ones can be tackled.

be able to follow what is done step by step even though the reason for taking a particular step may not be readily apparent until you have completed all the steps.

As a first step in these manipulations we substitute (20) into (19) and we obtain

$$\dot{K} = sF(K, L). \tag{21}$$

We now assume that the labour force is growing at a constant rate, n. Thus labour supply is a function of time, t, and we can write

$$L(t) = L_0 e^{nt} \tag{22}$$

where $L(t)$ is the labour force at time t, L_0 is the initial labour force at time t_0, and n is its rate of growth. We want to find out if the capital/labour ratio can always be such as to ensure full employment no matter how fast the labour force may be growing. We also wish to know if this ratio will approach some stable equilibrium level in all circumstances. In order to investigate this situation we *assume* that the labour force is fully employed and we investigate the consequences of this assumption. Given this assumption we can identify $L(t)$ with the amount of labour input in the production function. This allows us to substitute (22) into (21) to obtain

$$\dot{K} = sF(K, L_0 e^{nt}). \tag{23}$$

This equation tells us the time path that capital accumulation, $\dot{K}$, must follow if labour is to remain fully employed. If we were to solve this equation for K we would get the time path that the community's stock of capital $(K = \int \dot{K} \, dt)$ must follow if full employment is to be maintained.

We wish to know if there is always a time path for capital accumulation, $\dot{K}$, that will ensure full employment whatever the rate of growth of the labour force, n, might be. (23) tells us what $\dot{K}$ *must* be if full employment is to be maintained. It now helps to study the behaviour of the capital/labour ratio. To do this we introduce a new variable, r, to stand for the ratio of capital to labour. Thus $r = K/L$ or $K = rL$ and, substituting (22) into this expression, we have

$$K = rL_0 e^{nt}. \tag{24}$$

We now need to differentiate (24) with respect to time to get an equation for the rate of change of the capital stock (i.e., investment). Although this may look like a formidable task, it proves to be easily accomplished by a straightforward application of the product rule. There are two arguments that can vary with time and we set $r = v$ and $L_0 e^{nt} = u$. The product rule gives us

$$\frac{dK}{dt} = u \frac{dv}{dt} + v \frac{du}{dt}.$$

We know from page 332 that $(\mathrm{d}/\mathrm{d}t)\,(L_0 e^{nt}) = n L_0 e^{nt}$. Thus the time-derivative of (24) is given by

$$\dot{K} = \dot{r} L_0 e^{nt} + n r L_0 e^{nt}$$

$$= (\dot{r} + nr) L_0 e^{nt}. \tag{25}$$

(25) tells us what happens to the capital/labour ratio, r, as labour grows at its given rate n. We now take the crucial step of substituting (25) into (23) which tells us how capital is growing given that labour is fully employed and a fraction s of full employment output is saved each period. Thus we obtain

$$(\dot{r} + nr) L_0 e^{nt} = s F(K, L_0 e^{nt}). \tag{26}$$

To manipulate (26) into a more meaningful form we first make use of the assumption of constant returns to scale. This assumption means that the production function is linear and homogeneous and, as we saw in Chapter 10 (see pages 222–23), if we multiply all of the variables in such a function by λ we multiply the value of the function by λ. Thus we can *divide* all the *variables* by λ and *multiply* the whole *function* by λ and leave the whole unchanged. If, for example, we double both the inputs and divide the value of the whole function by 2 we must be back where we started. We now perform this operation, taking not 2 but $L_0 e^{nt}$ as our λ. This gives us

$$(\dot{r} + nr) L_0 e^{nt} = s L_0 e^{nt} F\left(\frac{K}{L_0 e^{nt}}, 1\right). \tag{27}$$

Next divide both sides of (27) by $L_0 e^{nt}$ to give

$$(\dot{r} + nr) = s F\left(\frac{K}{L_0 e^{nt}}, 1\right).$$

Now subtract nr from both sides

$$\dot{r} = s F\left(\frac{K}{L_0 e^{nt}}, 1\right) - nr.$$

Finally write r for the capital/labour ratio, $K/L_0 e^{nt}$, to give

$$\dot{r} = s F(r, 1) - nr. \tag{28}$$

This is a differential equation with the capital/labour ratio, r, as its only variable.

First consider the condition for the capital/labour ratio to be constant over time. This means that $\dot{r}=0$ and for this to be so capital must be growing at the same rate, n, as labour. In this situation we see from (28) that

$$nr = sF(r, 1). \tag{29}$$

Next consider the behaviour of the economy when the capital/labour ratio is changing, i.e., $nr \neq sF(r, 1)$. We first consider two limiting cases. If $s=0$ there is no capital accumulation and (28) reduces to $\dot{r} = -nr$ or

$$\frac{\dot{r}}{r} = -n. \tag{30a}$$

This says that the proportionate change in the capital/labour ratio is *minus* the proportionate rate of change in the labour force. If the labour force is growing at 3% per annum, for example, then the capital/labour ratio is declining at 3% per annum. To obtain the second limiting case assume that $n=0$, i.e., the labour force is constant over time. Now (28) reduces to $\dot{r}=sF(r, 1)$. This has more intuitive appeal if we express $\dot{r}$ in proportionate terms which requires some manipulation. First we divide both sides of $\dot{r}=sF(r, 1)$ by r:

$$\frac{\dot{r}}{r} = \frac{s}{r} F(1, r).$$

r is the capital/labour ratio and it is more convenient to replace r by K/L:

$$\frac{\dot{r}}{r} = s\frac{L}{K} F\left(1, \frac{K}{L}\right).$$

Finally we multiply both the inputs by L and divide the value of the function by the same amount (a procedure we justified in connection with (27)). This gives us

$$\frac{\dot{r}}{r} = \frac{sF(L, K)}{K}. \tag{30b}$$

(30b) says that the proportionate change in the capital/labour ratio is equal (in this case in which $n=0$) to the proportionate change in the capital stock (which is in turn equal to the amount of total production saved divided by the existing capital stock).

(30a) and (30b) show that $\dot{r}$ in (28) is the sum of two components, the first related to the change in labour, (30a), and the second related to the change in capital, (30b). The equation itself is difficult to interpret because it shows $\dot{r}$ instead of $\dot{r}/r$ as the dependent variable but, as we have seen, both terms on the right-hand side of the expression are easily interpreted when the dependent variable is made $\dot{r}/r$.

We are now able to see how the economy behaves when the capital/labour ratio is changing. In this case we have $\dot{r} \neq 0$ and (29) tells us that $nr \neq sF(r, 1)$. To see what happens in such cases we plot both nr and $sF(r, 1)$ in Figure 15.1 where r is plotted on the x-axis and $\dot{r}$ on the y-axis. This is an unusual diagram and we must explain carefully how the lines are obtained. To obtain the line nr we set $sF(r, 1)=0$ and plot the relation between $\dot{r}$ and r ignoring the negative sign. This line, which has a slope of n, tells us how fast the capital/output ratio would be declining for a given

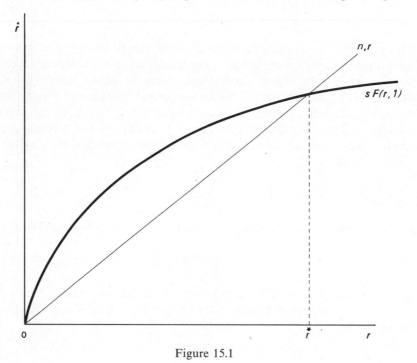

Figure 15.1

rate of growth of the labour force if savings were zero. To obtain the line $sF(r, 1)$ we let nr be zero and plot the relation between $\dot{r}$ and r given by $\dot{r} = sF(r, 1)$. This line tells us how fast the capital/output ratio would be growing as a result of capital accumulation if the labour force were not growing. If both s and n are non-zero then the actual value of $\dot{r}$ will be the *difference* between nr and $sF(r, 1)$. This difference is represented by the vertical distance between the two lines. When the line $sF(r, 1)$ is above nr the effect of capital accumulation outweighs that of population growth and $\dot{r}$ will be positive. When nr lies above $sF(r, 1)$ the reverse is true and $\dot{r}$ will be negative. Where the two curves intersect, the negative effect on r of population growth exactly balances the positive effect of capital accumulation and r will be constant at the value r^* with $\dot{r}=0$.

It remains to consider the shape of the curve $sF(r, 1)$. The expression $F(r, 1)$ may be interpreted as the total product curve with labour input held constant at one unit and capital as the variable factor. In this case r equals K, since $K/1 = K$. The whole term $sF(r, 1)$ shows the amount of this total output that is saved and invested per worker. The assumption of diminishing returns to one factor is sufficient to ensure that the slope of $F(r, 1)$ and therefore of $sF(r, 1)$ must be declining as r is increased. The curve drawn in Figure 15.1 is consistent with the Cobb–Douglas production function. We saw in Chapter 10 that with the Cobb–Douglas function diminishing returns occur over all ranges of r so that the slope of $sF(r, 1)$ must decline from the outset.

If the economy is at r^* in Figure 15.1 then $nr = sF(r, 1)$ and from (28) $\dot{r}=0$, which says that the capital/output ratio is not changing. This is an equilibrium growth situation in which capital and labour are growing at the same proportionate rate so that r remains constant. Because of the constant returns to scale assumption, the rate of growth of output is exactly equal to the rates of growth of capital and labour, and income per head will be constant.[1] Now consider what will happen if the economy is at a point where $r \neq r^*$. To the right of r^*, $r > r^*$, $nr > sF(r, 1)$ and from (28) we know that $\dot{r}<0$. Thus actual r will decrease towards r^*. To the left of r^*, $sF(r, 1)>nr$ and from (28) we know that $\dot{r}>0$. Actual r will increase towards r^*. Thus the equilibrium value of the capital/output ratio, r^*, is a stable one, and the economy will *always* move towards a position in which the rate of growth of capital is equal to the rate of growth of labour and there is full employment at a constant level of *per capita* output.

The stable equilibrium shown in Figure 15.1 is necessary in a Cobb–Douglas production function[2] where the slope of $sF(r, 1)$ is infinite at the

[1] Don't forget that there is no technical progress in this model, i.e., the function F is constant with respect to time.

[2] With Cobb–Douglas we have

$$\frac{\partial q}{\partial K} = \alpha K^{\alpha-1}L^{\beta}$$

$$= \frac{\alpha L^{\beta}}{K^{\alpha}}.$$

With labour held constant at unity this gives

$$\frac{\partial q}{\partial K} = \frac{\alpha}{K^{\alpha}}.$$

By inspection the value of this marginal productivity function approaches infinity as K approaches zero and approaches zero as K approaches infinity.

12

origin and falls steadily as r is increased. Other production functions can give different results, but the restriction usually placed on production functions, that the marginal product of capital eventually approaches zero as capital approaches infinity, labour held constant ($F_K \to 0$ as $K \to \infty$), is sufficient to guarantee that if $sF(r, 1)$ cuts nr at all it will eventually cut it from above and produce a stable equilibrium growth path.[1]

You are now in a position to refer to Solow's classic article to follow his analysis of other production functions and to appreciate, when you have done this, Solow's general conclusion that '... when production takes place under the usual neo-classical conditions of variable (factor) proportions and constant returns to scale ... there may not be – in fact in the Cobb–Douglas function there never can be – any knife edge. The system can adjust to any given rate of growth of the labour force, and eventually approach a state of steady proportional growth.'[2]

You can also study Solow's analysis of the Harrod–Domar model. He uses the technique developed above to display the working of this model, and to show why it produces an explosive situation rather than the stable situation of the neo-classical model studied above.

15.3   The Derivation of the Phillips Curve

We have many times considered a simple macro-model with only real variables. We have also had occasion to use a macro-relation between the level of unemployment and the rate of change of money wages. The empirical evidence for this relation was first put forward by A.W.Phillips[3] and later elaborated by Lipsey.[4] This relation is in fact a reaction function expressing the dynamic behaviour of wage rates (and with suitable amendments, earnings) to situations of excess demand for, and excess supply of, labour. Some such reaction function is a necessary part of any dynamic macro-model. Unfortunately we have not yet studied enough dynamics to allow us to develop a full macro-model with a real and a monetary sector and with the Phillips function embedded in it – although it was for this purpose

---

[1] If the function $sF(r, 1)$ has a slope less than nr at the origin and declines continuously as r increases there is no equilibrium at all. r will fall to zero and the economy will have no capital whatsoever. Although this is a possibility it is not one in which we are interested if we are concerned with economies of which we have empirical knowledge.

[2] Solow, *op. cit.*, p. 73.

[3] A.W.Phillips, 'The Relation Between Unemployment and the Rate of Change of Money Wage Rates in the United Kingdom 1861–1957', *Economica*, 1958.

[4] R.G.Lipsey, 'The Relation Between Unemployment and The Rate of Change of Money Wage Rates in the United Kingdom, 1862–1957: A Further Analysis', *Economica*, 1960. Reprinted in AEA *Readings in the Theory of Business Cycles*, 1966.

that Phillips originally developed this particular function. We can, however, study this function in a little more detail. It is given importance by the fact that, if we are to have a dynamic macro-model of the economy, we must have a reaction function relating wage changes to something else in the economy, and thus if we are to dispense with this function we must substitute another. In this section we will be doing mathematical economics even though much of the argument is carried on verbally. Notice how it is necessary to resort to mathematics at several critical points in the argument. If you are still in any doubt that this is mathematical economics try replacing the mathematical steps with verbal argument and see how unsatisfactory and inconclusive the whole argument then becomes.

First of all, we assume the simple linear reaction function, that the rate of change of money wages is proportional to excess demand for labour. Since we shall eventually have to use percentage unemployment as the independent variable it is useful to make the reaction of wages a function of proportional excess demand, $(q^d - q^s)/q^s$. Obviously if the labour force is constant, it makes no difference, since if q^s is constant, we can always find α' such that

$$\frac{dw}{dt} = \alpha(q^d - q^s) = \alpha' \frac{q^d - q^s}{q^s}: \qquad (31)$$

in fact, this only requires that $\alpha' = \alpha q^s$. But, over the period of nearly a century to which the Phillips curve has been applied, the labour force has certainly not been constant, so we are in fact making a definite hypothesis, that it is the *percentage* excess demand rather than the *absolute* excess demand for labour that determines the rate of change of the money wage rate. We are also committing ourselves to the hypothesis that the *reaction function* $\dot{w} = f[(q^d - q^s)/q^s]$ is linear; but there is not much in this: it is merely the simplest assumption that will lead to our observed results, and, vice versa, we have no means of telling, with the information we now have, whether the function is more complicated.

It is also convenient to take as the dependent variable the percentage rate of change in money wages. dw/dt is the rate of change of money wages; $(1/w)(dw/dt)$ is the proportional rate of change. Thus in what follows $\dot{w}$ will stand for $(1/w)(dw/dt)$. This is not merely a matter of notation but also of hypothesis. Just as we are assuming that it is proportional excess demand rather than its absolute amount that determines the rate of adjustment, so we are assuming that a given proportional excess demand leads to a given percentage rather than absolute change in wages. These assumptions are illustrated in Figure 15.2, where proportional excess demand is measured on the horizontal axis and $\dot{w}$ on the vertical, and the solid straight line is the function $\dot{w} = \alpha[(q^d - q^s)/q^s]$. We may illustrate some alternative assumptions.

It is possible, for example, that the response of wages, while linear in the magnitude of the disequilibrium, is faster upwards than downwards: this is illustrated by the broken line which is flatter in the south-west quadrant than in the north-east, and therefore kinked at the origin. Similar results would follow from a suitably chosen non-linear function such as the solid curve illustrated in Figure 15.2.

The striking feature of this analysis is that it appears to apply to the British labour market the assumptions and techniques we have developed

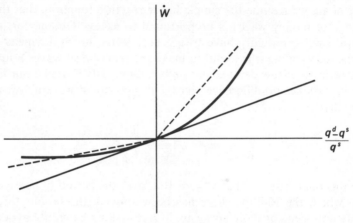

Figure 15.2

for a perfect market! Given the existence and importance of trade unions, the practice of wage negotiation between big unions and employers' organisations, the innumerable imperfections in the labour market such as apprenticeship rules, closed shops, redundancy agreements, and non-transferable pension rights, to say nothing of frequent government interference in the bargaining process, this may seem wildly unrealistic. Before we condemn it, however, we should stop to consider just how an efficient trade union would show up in terms of Figure 15.2. Suppose, first, that, in its absence, we should have the reaction function illustrated by the solid straight line. One possible result of an efficient union would be to obtain for its members quicker results in a situation in which there was excess demand for their services, and to slow down the wage cuts in a situation of excess supply. We might then have something like the kinked broken straight line. Thus if the effect of unions is solely on the speed of reaction of wages to situations of excess demand and excess supply they will change the values of the parameters of our system but will not affect its structure. (When we say that the structure is unchanged we mean that the equations of the system are unaltered, only the values of parameters change.) It is also possible, however, that unions could change the actual structure of the model so that, for example, wages reacted only to union strength and not at all to excess demand. In this case there *would be* a structural change in the model. The use of a Phillips curve in the simple form presented here does not, therefore, imply that unions are powerless but it does imply that union power, in so far as it does exist, does not introduce relations between wages and variables that would be absolute in a competitive world.

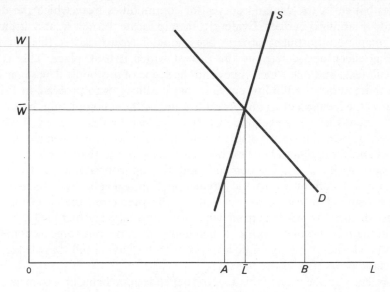

Figure 15.3

It is important to realise that, *if* the Phillips curve is observed to be a stable real-world relation, it is one that policy-makers have to live with since it gives a very important frontier, and that this is true *even if* we do not fully understand the structure that produces it. If we wish to move the frontier, we must understand the structure, and we are therefore provided with an agenda for research: we hope to learn, by further experimenting with the Phillips curve, how, e.g., unions do affect it, and how we may move it. To see that it is possible to locate the Phillips curve observationally, and understand its properties, without having mastered the structure behind it, we now consider the relationship between Figure 15.2 and an ordinary supply and demand diagram.

12*

Diagrams of aggregate demand for and supply of labour have rather gone out of fashion. Nevertheless, we present one in Figure 15.3, where equilibrium exists at $\bar{w}$ and $\bar{L}$. Now suppose that we have excess demand of AB. Our hypothesis is that wages rise, at a rate proportional to AB/OA, and, if neither curve shifted, we should continue with the analysis of section 15.1. An important characteristic of the aggregate or macro-labour market, however, is precisely the existence of interdependence between supply and demand that we assume away in micro-analysis. We can be certain that, as the wage rate rises towards $\bar{w}$ in Figure 15.3, $\bar{w}$ itself will move because one, at least, of the curves will move: the demand curve for labour will be shifted up because increased spending from the increased wages bill shifts the demand curves for commodities from which the demand for labour is derived. Evidently, then to locate the new $\bar{w}$, and discuss the complete adjustment process, we should have to master this curve-shifting effect, and determine the rate at which it took place. This is a difficult task, and one which is beyond the scope of this book. The remarkable thing about the Phillips curve is that it allows us to proceed, at least as far as the location of an important frontier, without completing this task. The reason is that $\dot{w}$ is explained by excess demand independently of what caused the excess, and thus of any feedback there may be between increased wages and the magnitude of excess demand. Suppose that in Figure 15.3 we start with AB excess demand and the appropriate $\dot{w} = \alpha(AB/OA)$. We are not committed to the prediction that when w has reached $\bar{w}$, excess demand will be zero, but only to the prediction that, so long as excess demand is AB/OA, from whatever cause, $\dot{w} = \alpha(AB/OA)$. Thus we are in the remarkable position of being able to carry out some extremely useful and interesting dynamic analysis without having full knowledge of the static properties of the system.

Evidently application of this analysis depends upon being able to measure excess demand: indeed, the whole approach is based on the notion that it is easier to measure excess demand than to locate the supply and demand curves themselves. A great deal of effort has been put into measuring the excess demand for labour and the National Institute of Economic and Social Research now publishes such an index. The excess demand for labour turns out to be very closely related to the percentage of the labour force unemployed and, although for sophisticated models it is preferable to use an index of excess demand for labour, for cruder work the figures for percentage unemployment can be substituted with little loss. So we now make the additional hypothesis that percentage unemployment will serve as a *proxy* for proportional excess demand. This means that we introduce a new function $U = U[(q^d - q^s)/q^s]$ where U is the percentage of the labour force unemployed. Since it is U that we can measure, it is actually more convenient to look at the inverse function $(q^d - q^s)/q^s = g(U)$. So our hypothesis is now

$$\dot{w} = \alpha \frac{q^d - q^s}{q^s} = \alpha g(U). \tag{32}$$

The question is, what shape will $g(U)$ be? Excess demand can, in principle, take on any value from $-\infty$ to $+\infty$, whereas U can only take on values in the range 0–100, so it is evident that the transformation cannot be linear. Consider first low levels of unemployment. Not only is there a limit – zero – below which U cannot fall, but, as it approaches some low positive value,

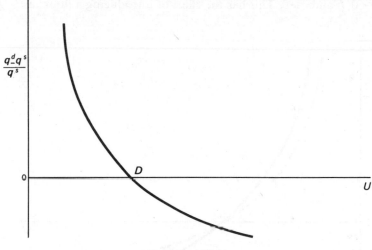

Figure 15.4

say 1%, it is going to be increasingly difficult to lower it further by further increases in aggregate demand since there must be some minimum level of frictional unemployment caused by people voluntarily changing jobs and so on. Thus it seems likely that increasing excess demand in this range can have little effect upon U, and that increases in excess demand sufficient to cause major inflations would have little effect upon U. This would cause the curve relating excess demand to U to be 'squashed up' against the axis for low U, and to become very steep indeed, perhaps asymptotic to the vertical, as it is illustrated in Figure 15.4. For high unemployment levels, on the other hand, there seems to be no reason why the relationship should not be linear: a fall in demand for labour (increase in excess supply) sufficient to raise unemployment by 1% from 10% might well raise it by 1% from 15% too. The relationship illustrated in Figure 15.4 is not in fact linear for high-U, although the curve approaches a straight line.   This is done to avoid the awkward discontinuity which would follow from trying to 'splice' a curve to a segment of a straight line.

We now have to graph equation (32), using Figure 15.4 for the relation $q^d - q^s/q^s = g(U)$. This is done in Figure 15.5, where the curve of $\dot{w}$ on U crosses the axis at OD, rises steeply at low U, and flattens out at higher U. If the basic reaction-function is linear, we should expect a straight line at high U: in fact, a continuous curve has been drawn again. The curve actually fitted to the data by Lipsey[1] is

$$\dot{w} = a + bU^{-1} + cU^{-2} \tag{33}$$

with $a < 0$, b and $c > 0$. This has the effect of introducing a floor: as U gets

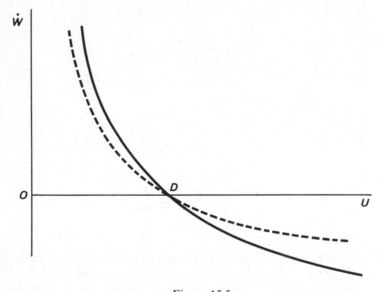

Figure 15.5

large, U^{-1} and U^{-2} get small, and the curve approaches the horizontal floor, a, rather than a negatively sloped straight line. This may raise doubt about our initial assumption of a linear reaction-function. But now compare equations (32) and (33). (33) is what we observe, and we cannot observe independently either α (or the more complicated relationship, if linearity is wrong) or the function $g(U)$. So nothing much is to be achieved by arguing about the precise form of the reaction function: equation (33), with some modifications, is all we have, and does not permit us to isolate

[1] R.G. Lipsey, *Unemployment and Money Wage Rates*, *op. cit.*

the reaction function. And that is why nothing is presupposed in this analysis about the effect of trade unions on the reaction function.

There are many interesting questions for further research raised by the Phillips curve, and many important questions are unsettled: what has been said here should be understood as explanatory, and carries no implication that the curve is a completely understood, stable, reliable, real-world constraint. Furthermore, we have not discussed the effect of rising prices upon wage rates, simply because this involves no new technical ideas that we want to discuss. Thus the treatment here is far from complete, and the original literature should be read.

We will conclude this section by showing how the curve of $\dot{p}$ as a function of U used in Chapter 12 was obtained. First, purely for illustrative simplicity, we dropped the term in U^{-2} from equation (33). We also needed some hypothesis about price formation and assumed that

$$\dot{p} = \dot{w} - \dot{m} \tag{34}$$

where $\dot{m}$ is the rate of growth of productivity, and is some exogenously determined constant. On this very simple assumption, (34) and the truncated (33) are combined to give the curve of Chapter 12, Figure 12.6.

It is now of some interest to see how equation (34) – or some alternative relationship between changes in wages, prices, and productivity – may be derived from a hypothesis about price formation. It can in fact be obtained in more than one way, that is, on more than one hypothesis about the mechanism of inflation and the determination of product prices. We shall derive it from one popular hypothesis about price determination, and discuss an alternative.

We make the following assumptions:

(1) products are priced 'administratively' (markets are not perfect) according to the rule of adding a constant mark-up to variable costs 'to cover overheads and allow for a profit';

(2) excess aggregate effective demand (excess demand for products) does not, by (1), of itself raise product prices, but it causes excess demand for labour at current prices, bidding up wages, and thus, by (1), causing product prices themselves to rise;

(3) average variable costs are constant (average and marginal products equal);

(4) since we aggregate over the whole economy, the only variable cost we need take into account is labour.

Assumption (4) is obviously wrong for an open economy which imports materials whose prices may change exogenously, but we will assume it for simplicity. Assumptions (1) and (3) may be expressed symbolically as

$$p = (1 + \mu)c \tag{35}$$

where μ is the mark-up (100μ is the percentage added to direct variable cost) and c variable cost. But by assumptions (3) and (4), and the relationship between marginal product and marginal cost (see Chapter 6), (35) may be rewritten

$$p = (1+\mu)\frac{w}{r} \qquad (36)$$

where w is the wage rate and r the marginal product of labour, constant with respect to output. But, by assumption (1), wages are exogenous from the point of view of price formation, and we are assuming that some increase in productivity is given exogenously. We require the total differential of (36) with respect to time. Using the quotient rule,

$$\frac{dp}{dt} = (1+\mu)\frac{d}{dt}\left(\frac{w}{r}\right)$$

$$= (1+\mu)\left[\frac{r\dfrac{dw}{dt}-w\dfrac{dr}{dt}}{r^2}\right]. \qquad (37)$$

This looks cumbersome, and without any obvious interpretation, but in fact it simplifies very nicely. First, separate the terms within the square brackets:

$$\frac{dp}{dt} = (1+\mu)\left[\frac{1}{r}\frac{dw}{dt}-\frac{w}{r^2}\frac{dr}{dt}\right]. \qquad (38)$$

Now factor out w/r. To do this, first multiply the first term inside the square brackets by w/w:

$$\frac{dp}{dt} = (1+\mu)\frac{w}{r}\left[\frac{1}{w}\frac{dw}{dt}-\frac{1}{r}\frac{dr}{dt}\right]. \qquad (39)$$

From (36), however, $(1+\mu)w/r=p$. Dividing both sides of (39) by p

$$\frac{1}{p}\frac{dp}{dt} = \frac{1}{w}\frac{dw}{dt}-\frac{1}{r}\frac{dr}{dt} \qquad (40)$$

which says that the proportional rate of change of prices equals the proportional rate of change of wages minus the proportional rate of change of productivity, which is the simple relation we assumed in (34).

There are a few points to notice here. The first is that the assumption that productivity is a constant with respect to changes in output saves considerable complication: we do not have to take account, in deriving (40), of the effect of changing output and employment as the firm adjusts to changing wages and prices. (If we assumed perfect competition and diminishing returns we should get an added term, the change in the marginal product of labour times the proportional change in employment.) The second point is that we have assumed that there are no lags in the firm's adjustment of its prices to changes in costs. Thus in (40) we have prices adjusting continuously as wages are altered by the disequilibrium in the labour market. The disequilibrium in the labour market is derived from disequilibrium in the product market. Thus the firm cannot have equilibrium output and employment. Once again we see how much the assumption of constant costs has simplified the analysis; but, more important, we see that a thorough analysis of the dynamics of inflation requires an analysis of the behaviour of firms in disequilibrium positions, and this we have not tackled. The third point is a comment on 'Cost–Push versus Demand–Pull': we have selected an illustration in which demand pulls up costs, and costs push up prices!

We conclude with a brief consideration of wages – or incomes – policy in a world described by the Phillips curve.

If one thinks only in static terms, then wages policy appears simply as an attempt to hold a price or wage below its equilibrium value. Any standard first year text will explain why this may prove to be both difficult and unsatisfactory. In dynamic terms, however, the picture becomes rather different. Suppose that the adjustment coefficient, α, is reduced, which is to say that the reaction function of Figure 15.2 is rotated in a clockwise direction. Then $\dot{w}$ will be smaller for any level of excess demand. This means that the rate of inflation associated with any level of unemployment is reduced. In terms of Figure 15.5 the solid curve is replaced by something like the broken curve. (You should satisfy yourself that it still passes through D.) But this is a movement of the frontier in a favourable direction. Thus if a wages policy has the effect of reducing α, it secures a desirable shift in the constraint faced by the policy makers, without shifting any of the static demand or supply curves. (Notice that the shift is not necessarily free. There may be allocative effects, interferences with the process of collective bargaining, difficulties between union membership and leadership. Assessment of the policy depends upon the individual's evaluation of these effects.) A wage 'freeze', however, is a different matter. Our model does not predict what happens if we force α to be zero for some time interval during which $(q^d - q^s)/q^s > 0$, and then release the control. This problem is left to you as a worthwhile subject for speculation.

15.4 The Stability of an Inflationary Process
In earlier sections (12.8, 15.3) we have discussed the frontier between unemployment and inflation, and the constrained choice that must be made

by the policy maker. We implied that it is possible to choose a package of some rates of inflation and unemployment. Some people, however, would argue that this is not possible because *any* rate of inflation other than zero is inherently unstable. The argument is that, as people become aware of the fact of continuous inflation, however slow, they will come to anticipate it, and that action based on the anticipation of inflation generates inflation : this is a case of 'self-justifying' destabilising expectations. We have here the familiar notion of 'flight from money': if a man anticipates a decline in the value of money, we expect him to reduce, if he can, the proportion of his wealth that he holds in the form of money; if he does this by endeavouring to buy goods he creates inflationary pressure; thus not only is there inflation, as he expected, but more than there would have been had he not expected it. But any continuous inflation will come to be expected, thus lead to flight from money, thus to faster inflation, and so on.

This is a very powerful intuitive argument that one cannot, in fact, settle for a package of, say, 2% unemployment and 2% annual price increase: the rate of inflation will, as soon as people 'catch on', accelerate, and force one to increase unemployment to contain the inflation. Thus the argument gives heavy backing to the conservative view that the target of price stability is necessary, and cannot be traded-off against other goals. This is so important, if true, that we cannot let it pass. We cannot pretend to determine the empirical truth of it here, but we can produce a counter-example, a model in which a 'flight from money' takes place that is *not necessarily* unstable. We can manage this easily with the mathematical technique we now have; but to keep the problem within the reach of that technique, we shall have to use some care in designing a simple model! This is not as limiting as it sounds: a counter-example is sufficient to upset the assertion that a flight from money necessarily causes any inflation to become explosive. If the theoretical verdict is that a flight from money may or may not be explosive depending on the precise values taken by various parameters, then the debate must become an empirical one about the existence in our world of certain quantitative magnitudes; there is no longer a qualitative theoretical prediction that inflations always are, or always are not, explosive.

We must now begin to construct our simple model of an inflation-induced flight from money. We assume a simple quantity-theory world in which demand for money is for transactions purposes only and no speculative balances are held, thus

$$M^d = kPX \tag{41}$$

where M^d is money demanded, k is a constant determined by the behaviour of money holders, P the price level, and X real income or output.[1] The money supply is assumed to be a parameter whose value is determined exogenously by the central authorities. Thus

$$M^s = M. \tag{42}$$

In equilibrium

$$M^s = M^d \tag{43}$$

so that by substituting into (43) and rearranging terms we have

$$P = \frac{M}{kX}. \tag{44}$$

If we were only interested in comparative statics, we would merely note the familiar quantity-theory results, which we may sum up in two important relations (each of which can be expressed in several alternative forms).

(1)
$$\frac{dP}{dM} = \frac{1}{kX} \tag{45}$$

or

$$dP = \frac{1}{kX} dM \tag{46}$$

or

$$\frac{1}{P}\frac{dP}{dM} = \frac{1}{kX}\frac{kX}{M} = \frac{1}{M} \tag{47}$$

or

$$\frac{dP}{dM} = \frac{P}{M}. \tag{48}$$

This says that, with output constant, the change in the price level is directly proportional to the change in the quantity of money (the constant multiple being $1/kX$). The final version (48) of the relation says that the ratio of any *change* in the price level to a *change* in the money supply is the same as the ratio of the price level itself to the total money supply.

To derive the second relation we now regard X as something that can vary as well as M and P and we write

(2)
$$dP = \frac{\partial P}{\partial M} dM + \frac{\partial P}{\partial X} dX \tag{49}$$

$$= \frac{1}{kX} dM - \frac{M}{kX^2} dX \tag{50}$$

---

[1] The behavioural theory on which the quantity equation is based requires that we put the gross value of all transactions, T, into (42). By writing X in place of T we are adding the implicit assumption that gross value of turnover, T, and the net value of output, X, stand in a constant ratio to each other.

or by the method of page 209,

$$\frac{\mathrm{d}P}{\mathrm{d}t} = \frac{1}{kX}\frac{\mathrm{d}M}{\mathrm{d}t} - \frac{M}{kX^2}\frac{\mathrm{d}X}{\mathrm{d}t} \tag{51}$$

or

$$\frac{1}{P}\frac{\mathrm{d}P}{\mathrm{d}t} = \frac{1}{M}\frac{\mathrm{d}M}{\mathrm{d}t} - \frac{1}{X}\frac{\mathrm{d}X}{\mathrm{d}t}. \tag{52}$$

This second main result states that the rate of change of prices is proportional to the rate of increase in the money supply minus the rate of increase in real income.

We are interested, however, in disequilibrium behaviour, the adjustment of the system when $M^d \neq M^s$. Before introducing 'flight from money', let us set up the simplest hypothesis about adjustment, assuming again that the rate of change of the equilibrating variable is proportional to excess demand. An inflationary situation, in this model is one in which there is an excess supply of money: this is the necessary and sufficient condition for inflation. The basic assumption, of course, is that an excess supply of money means an excess demand for goods: if people find themselves holding more money than they require, they spend it on goods. Notice that this is the adjustment mechanism without any 'flight': it is the spending out of excess money balances that drives the price level up until the balances are no longer found excessive: i.e., the price level satisfies equation (44) again. So we take excess demand for goods to be identical to excess supply of money (this is often called Walras' Law), and, on the assumption that the rate of change of prices is proportional to excess demand, we have

$$\frac{\mathrm{d}P(t)}{\mathrm{d}t} = \alpha(M^s - M^d) \tag{53}$$

$$= \alpha M^s - \alpha k X P(t) \tag{54}$$

where $P(t)$ denotes price at time t and we assume real income, X, to be constant. We now recall all the tricks of section 15.1. Define the discrepancy in the price level by

$$\hat{p} = P(t) - \bar{P} \tag{55}$$

where $\bar{P}$ is the equilibrium price level from equation (44). Following the procedure of section 15.1 again, we differentiate $\hat{p}$ with respect to time:

$$\frac{\mathrm{d}\hat{p}}{\mathrm{d}t} = \frac{\mathrm{d}P(t)}{\mathrm{d}t} - \frac{\mathrm{d}\bar{P}}{\mathrm{d}t}.$$

We note that $d\bar{P}/dt$ is zero and substitute for $dP(t)/dt$ from (54):

$$\frac{d\hat{p}}{dt} = \alpha M^s - \alpha k X P(t) - 0. \tag{56}$$

We want to express the right-hand side of (56) in terms of $\hat{p}$ again, so we exploit the fact that $M^s - kX\bar{P} = 0$, and so, therefore, does $\alpha M^s - \alpha k X\bar{P}$. Inserting this in (56) we have

$$\frac{d\hat{p}}{dt} = \alpha M^s - \alpha k X P(t) - \alpha M^s + \alpha k X\bar{P}$$

$$= -\alpha k X(P(t) - \bar{P})$$

$$= -\alpha k X\hat{p} \tag{57}$$

which is a differential equation that we know how to solve. We rearrange (57) to get

$$\frac{1}{\hat{p}}\, d\hat{p} = -\alpha k X\, dt, \tag{58}$$

and recall that the derivative of $\log_e x$ is $1/x$. We now integrate both sides of (58) to get

$$\log_e \hat{p} = -\alpha k X t + C$$

and, taking antilogs,

$$\hat{p} = Ae^{-\alpha k X t}. \tag{59}$$

We can continue by finding A so that $\hat{p} = 0$ when $P(t) = \bar{P}$ in the manner of 15.1, but this introduces nothing new. Equation (59) is what we are really interested in: the economy is stable if and only if $\hat{p}$ goes to zero as t goes to infinity, which requires that the exponent be negative. This it clearly is, since α, k, and X are all positive: there is no difficulty here.

We now want to introduce the idea of flight from money into this otherwise stable model. The idea is that experience of inflation causes people to expect inflation and therefore to hold less money – demand more goods – than they otherwise would, which in turn causes the inflation to be faster than it otherwise would be. We want the simplest possible case of this behaviour. Let us assume that the expected change in prices is simply proportional to the current rate of change,

$$\left(\frac{dP(t)}{dt}\right)_E = \beta\,\frac{dP(t)}{dt}, \tag{60}$$

where $(\mathrm{d}P(t)/\mathrm{d}t)_E$ is the expected change in the price level and β is a constant relating expected changes to observed changes in the price level. If $\beta > 0$, the observation of inflation leads people to expect further inflation; if $\beta = 1$, people expect inflation to continue at whatever rate is currently observed; if $\beta > 1$ people expect the rate of inflation to accelerate. This last case must be the most unfavourable case for stability, but we shall find that even this is not sufficient to produce instability.

To proceed we now need a new demand for money equation to take account of the effects on the demand for money of expectations about the future course of prices. A simple one is:

$$M^d = kP(t)X - \gamma \left(\frac{\mathrm{d}P(t)}{\mathrm{d}t} \right)_E. \tag{61}$$

The first term in (61) gives the 'static' demand for money which is the complete demand if the expected change in the price level is zero. In this case the demand for money is simply a fraction, k, of the money value of national income. When prices are expected to rise, however, people hold less money than they would if prices were expected to remain stable.[1] The coefficient γ determines the amount by which a given expected inflation reduces the demand for money. There are some implications of (61) to which we shall refer shortly. First, let us substitute (60) into (61);

$$M^d = kP(t)X - \gamma\beta \frac{\mathrm{d}P(t)}{\mathrm{d}t}. \tag{62}$$

It would be hard to tell γ, the demand coefficient, from β, the expectations coefficient, from any empirical observations, so we combine them into one *reaction coefficient*,

$$\delta = \beta\gamma \tag{63}$$

for simplicity. We interpret δ as follows: it tells us the amount by which

---

[1] An expected inflation raises the opportunity cost of holding money. If the price level is expected to remain constant the opportunity cost of holding money is given by the interest rate. If the interest rate is 5 % per year the opportunity cost of holding £100 for one year is £5 or 5 %. If the price level is also expected to rise by 5 % the opportunity cost of holding £100 cash, rather than an *equity* that will earn £5 and whose capital value will be £105 at the end of the year is 10 % because the holder ends up with £100 instead of £110. Thus an expected inflation has the same effect on the opportunity cost of holding cash as has a rise in the rate of interest. Just as we expect a rise in interest rates to cause the demand for money to fall, but not to zero, so we expect an expected rate of inflation to cause the demand for money to fall, but not to zero.

the demand for money is less than it otherwise would be at any given absolute price level because of the observed rate of change of the price level.[1]

We retain the assumption that the rate of change of prices is proportional to the excess supply of money, $M^s - M^d$. We substitute (63) into (62) to replace $\gamma\beta$ by δ and then substitute (62) into our dynamic adjustment equation (53) to obtain:

$$\frac{dP(t)}{dt} = \alpha M^s - \alpha\left(kP(t)X - \delta\frac{dP(t)}{dt}\right). \tag{64}$$

We retain the same definition of $\hat{p}$, equation (55), and again use the trick that $aM^s - \alpha k\bar{P}X = 0$, so

$$\frac{d\hat{p}}{dt} = \alpha M^s - \alpha kP(t)X + \alpha\delta\frac{d\hat{p}}{dt} - \alpha M^s + \alpha k\bar{P}X$$

$$= -\alpha kX[P(t) - \bar{P}] + \alpha\delta\frac{d\hat{p}}{dt}. \tag{65}$$

One additional trick has been employed here: since $d\hat{p}/dt = (dP(t)/dt) - 0$, $d\hat{p}/dt$ has been substituted for $dP(t)/dt$ in the 'flight from money' term in M^d.

We proceed with (65) in the usual way, but taking the $d\hat{p}/dt$ term to the left-hand side:

$$\frac{d\hat{p}}{dt}(1 - \alpha\delta) = -\alpha kX\hat{p}$$

so

$$\frac{1}{\hat{p}}\,d\hat{p} = -\frac{\alpha kX}{1 - \alpha\delta}\,dt. \tag{66}$$

[1] We might wish to ask in what circumstances, if any, demand for money can fall to zero. Put

$$kP(t)X - \delta\frac{dP(t)}{dt} = 0$$

and we have a set of pairs of values of $P(t)$ and $dP(t)/dt$, positively associated: the higher the price level the larger must $dP(t)/dt$ be to reduce desired money holdings to zero. In fact, the relationship is homogeneous: from the above equation we have

$$\frac{1}{P(t)}\frac{dP(t)}{dt} = \frac{kX}{\delta}$$

which defines the proportional rate of inflation at which $M^d = 0$. Evidently the larger the reaction coefficient δ, the lower this will be. But observe that it can occur at finite positive price levels, i.e., 'inside' the values 0 and ∞.

We can now integrate both sides of (66) and write down the solution straight away as a routine matter:

$$P(t) = Ae^{\frac{-\alpha kXt}{1-\alpha\delta}}.\tag{67}$$

As before, we are not particularly interested in finding the value of A to conform with the equilibrium condition $\hat{p}=0$; we are interested only in stability, or convergence of actual $P(t)$ on equilibrium $\bar{P}$. This depends on the sign of the exponent in (67). Since α, k, and X are still positive this is *negative* if and only if

$$\left.\begin{array}{c} 1-\alpha\delta > 0 \\[2mm] \alpha\delta < 1 \\[2mm] \alpha\beta\gamma < 1 \end{array}\right\}\tag{68}$$

or

or

So the system is stable if the *product* of α, the goods-market reaction coefficient, β, the expectations coefficient, and γ, the 'flight' coefficient, is less than one. Evidently 'flight' is *not* sufficient to make the system explosive. Even if the expectations coefficient, β, exceeds unity, it may be 'damped' by a weak market coefficient, and/or a weak flight coefficient; similarly, a large flight coefficient may be outweighed by small values of the other coefficients.[1]

This is as far as we shall carry the analysis: after all, a single counter-example is logically sufficient to refute a general assertion. Our analysis shows that the simple argument that continuous inflation, even if initially slow, will *always* accelerate into hyper-inflation is invalid. To go further, we should have to develop alternative models, and compare them with the evidence. In the case of very rapid inflation, we should not expect our simple model to fit well at all: the assumption of a linear system, with constant coefficients, may provide a useful approximation, but over a limited range only (compare our discussion in Chapter 4.3). If inflation is

---

[1] We have conducted the analysis in absolute rather than proportional terms (e.g., we have $dp/dt = f(M^d - M^s)$ rather than $(dp/dt)(1/p) = (M^d - M^s)/M^s$) for reasons of mathematical simplicity. When the analysis is conducted in these terms we cannot give any simple interpretation to the coefficients α and γ. If we did deal in relations such as

$$\frac{dp}{dt}\cdot\frac{1}{p} = \alpha\left(\frac{M^d - M^s}{M^s}\right)$$

we could give a simple interpretation to α and could have some idea of the likelihood of α being greater than or less than unity. Our present model is not the best one to use for more sophisticated attacks on the basic problem (because it is hard to interpret α and γ) but it is quite enough to show that there is no general theoretical presumption that any flight from money necessarily causes inflation to be explosive.

very rapid, our 'flight' turns to panic, and *something* is likely to change drastically: there is, after all, no way of stopping people from actively trying to swap for goods any money balances they believe it folly to hold. Thus a sophisticated model that provided an analysis of hyper-inflation would have to take account of changing behaviour and institutions.

In fact, even our constant-coefficients linear model could be made a little more sophisticated. We have only dealt with the stability of the system when a (static) equilibrium is disturbed by a single event, whereas the original argument was really about the stability or otherwise of an inflationary *path*. Thus we should really have investigated a situation set up as follows. Let real income and the money supply both be increasing, but the latter faster than the former, so that

$$\frac{1}{P}\frac{dP}{dt} = \frac{1}{M}\frac{dM}{dt} - \frac{1}{X}\frac{dX}{dt} > 0 \tag{69}$$

(from equation (52)). Now, this describes the equilibrium rate of change: we should have to add our assumption about the adjustment in the goods market to the continuous disequilibrium (as excess money supply continually poured into the system) to find the path of $P(t)$. It is not hard to guess, however, that, once the system has 'settled down' to continually adjusting to a continual disequilibrium given by a *constant* excess of rate of money creation over rate of real income growth, the path of the actual price level, $P(t)$, will follow exactly the path of the equilibrium price level, which we could now call $\bar{P}(t)$; this amounts to guessing that, if the system is stable for a 'one-shot' change, it is stable for continuous change. The guess is a good one; we cannot substantiate it here, but $P(t)$ will in fact follow the path of $\bar{P}(t)$, and how far behind it will be will depend on the speed of reaction of prices to excess demand, which is, of course, given by our coefficient α. We should have a 'continuous inflation' model and could enquire into its 'dynamic stability': if, due to 'error', $P(t)$ was displaced from the path of $\bar{P}(t)$, would it return to it? We may guess that, with suitable coefficient values, it would. Then we should have to add the 'flight hypothesis' and ask two questions: (i) would this be sufficient to stop $P(t)$ 'shadowing' $\bar{P}(t)$ at all, i.e., to make the system 'blow up'? (ii) if the answer to (i) is no, in the event of error, would this be sufficient to stop $P(t)$ from returning to its path? Once again, we may guess that, with suitable coefficient values, the answers will be no, or, in general, 'not necessarily'. But we cannot go further without a substantial investment in technique, in this case differential equations which, except for the simple ones we have dealt with, are beyond the scope of this book. They obviously 'come next', and the reward for a personal investment – in human capital –

is the ability to tackle the fascinating economic problems of continual change.

Exercises

1 Consider the macro-model on page 311 of Chapter 13. Investigate the stability of the adjustment process using the same technique as was used in the text of Chapter 15 to handle the model of the single competitive market. (This is an important question and it will be worth your while to spend quite a lot of time in working it out.)

2 Consider a Cobb–Douglas production function in which technical progress is introduced by making A a function of time rather than a constant. Make the simple assumption that technical progress occurs at a constant rate so that

$$A(t) = A_0 e^{rt}$$

and production at time t is given by

$$q(t) = A_0 e^{rt} L_{(t)}^{\alpha} C_{(t)}^{1-\alpha}$$

where α is not changed by technical progress.

(a) How do the marginal products of labour and capital change over time if the inputs are constant?

(b) How does the marginal rate of substitution change over time?

(c) How are relative shares affected by the passage of time?

(d) What is the rate of growth of output if labour and capital are constant?

(e) Write the total differential of the function.

(f) Find the rate of growth of output if capital grows at the rate n and labour at the rate m.

3 National income in two economies is growing at the constant rates n in economy 1 and r in economy 2, where $n > r$. In year zero national income was A in economy 1 and B in economy 2.

(a) If $B > A$ at what time will economy 1 overtake economy 2?

(b) Show that if $r > n$ (and with $B > A$) the ratio of the 2 economies' incomes diverges constantly over time.

(c) If $n = r$ but $A > B$ show the relations between (i) the % rates of growth in 1 and 2, (ii) the ratios of income in 1 and 2, and show (iii) what happens to the absolute difference between the incomes of countries 1 and 2.

ANSWERS TO EXERCISES

Chapter 2

1
$$AVC = \frac{TVC}{Q}$$

$$TVC = Xw$$

where X is the quantity of the variable factor used, w is its price per unit, and Q is the quantity of output

$$Q = AP.X$$

$$AVC = \frac{Xw}{AP.X}$$

$$= \frac{w}{AP}$$

2
$$MC_n = TC_n - TC_{n-1}.$$

Let * indicate post-tax magnitudes and t the tax rate.

$$TC_n^* = TC_n + Nt$$

$$TC_{n-1}^* = TC_{n-1} + t(N-1)$$

$$MC_n^* = TC_n^* - TC_{n-1}^*$$

$$= TC_n + tN - TC_{n-1} - tN + t$$

$$= TC_n - TC_{n-1} + t$$

$$= MC_n + t.$$

3 Follow the same procedure as in (2) but use $\bar{Z}$ for the tax rather than tN and show that $MC_n = MC_n^*$.

4 (i) Insert the two specific values of Y and C, labelled Y_1, Y_2, C_1, and C_2 into the function, subtract the two resulting equations one from the other to form an expression in $\Delta Y \,(= Y_2 - Y_1)$ and $\Delta C \,(= C_2 - C_1)$ and manipulate to get $\Delta Y / \Delta C = a$.

(ii) and (iii)

$$C = aY + b$$

$$APC = \frac{C}{Y} = \frac{aY + b}{Y}$$

$$= a + \frac{b}{Y} > a.$$

5 a and b must refer to exactly the same thing or set of things ($a \equiv b$).

6 (1) Necessary but not sufficient (either (2) or (3) must also be present).
(2) Neither (not necessary because (3) will do instead, not sufficient because (1) must be present).
(3) Neither (for reasons analogous to (2)).
(1) and (2) Sufficient (not necessary because (1) and (3) will do just as well).
(1) and (3) Sufficient (not necessary for the same reasons as (1) and (2).
(2) and (3) Neither necessary nor sufficient (not sufficient because (1) is needed; not necessary because *either* (2) *or* (3) will do).
(1), (2), and (3) Sufficient but not necessary (it is not necessary to have (1), (2), and (3) because (1) and (3) or (1) and (2) will do; moral: if any subset of conditions is sufficient, the full set cannot be necessary).

7 (1) Necessary (but not sufficient).
(2) Necessary (but not sufficient).
(3) Necessary (but not sufficient).
(1) and (2) Necessary (but not sufficient).
(1) and (3) Necessary (but not sufficient).
(2) and (3) Necessary (but not sufficient).
(1), (2), and (3) Necessary and sufficient.

Chapter 3A

1 (i) $f(x) = 0$ where $x = 0$; $f(x) = 0$ is solved by $x = 0$ or $x = -3$; hence the curve goes through the origin, and has a minimum point at $x = -\frac{3}{2}$.
(ii) $f(x) = -2$ where $x = 0$; $f(x) = 0$ is solved by $x = -2$ or $x = 1$; minimum at $x = -\frac{1}{2}$.

2 We are told that the function is linear, so $q = a + b$ and $\Delta q / \Delta p = b$. When p goes from 10 to 12, $\Delta p = 2$ and $\Delta q = -10$, whence $b = -5$. q will fall to zero when $p = 22$ since each unit change in p reduces q by 5, and $q = 60$ at $p = 10$. So $0 = (-5)(22) + a$, whence $a = 110$.

3 (i) Yes. The mapping rule is simply 'for any x, $y = c$'. This may sound like a fiddle, but it is consistent with our geometry: we can draw a

horizontal straight line at height c above the x-axis. Consider the case of the demand curve to the individual firm in perfect competition.

(ii) Yes: given x we can read-off y. We cannot express the mapping rule in convenient symbolic form, but have to write it out extensively; but it still exists.

4 (i) Function; arguments: x and z.
(ii) Ambiguous; may be a function with argument the ratio w/v, or a coefficient, depending on context.
(iii) Constant; the function has been written out in full.
(iv) Ambiguous; may be a function, with argument $(x+z)$, or a coefficient, depending on context.

5 (i) Consumption is equal to a constant times income.
(ii) Consumption is a function of income.

6 (i) Choice of lettering is arbitrary, but the argument goes like this:
$D = D_1(R)$ (1) where D is the divorce rate and R measures religious belief; decreasing function;
$A = A(t)$ (2) where A is attendance at church, and t time; decreasing function;
$R = R_1(A)$ (3) religious belief can be measured by church attendance, an essential step in the argument; increasing function;
$R = R_2(t)$ (4) an inference from (2) and (3); decreasing function;
$D = D_2(t)$ (5) observed; increasing function.
Hence 1 is true.
(ii) Only (2) and (5) refer to observation.
(iii) Both attributable to common cause itself an increasing function of time; compare the increase in purchases of motor cars and gramophone records.
(iv) The argument is certainly not inconsistent with observation, which is the best that can ever be said. But (1) would be more firmly supported if (3) were based on observation. It would not be a bad plan to enquire into the divorce rates of church-going and non-church-going married couples.

Chapter 3B

1 (i) $9 = 3^2$ whence $\log 9 = 2 \log 3 = 0.9542$
        $27 = 3^3$ whence $\log 27 = 3 \log 3 = 1.4313$
  (ii) $4 = 16^{1/2}$ whence $\log 4 = \frac{1}{2} \log 16 = 0.6020$
        $2 = 4^{1/2}$ whence $\log 2 = \frac{1}{2} \log 4 = 0.3010$
  (iii) $6 = 3.2$ whence $\log 6 = \log 3 + \log 2 = 0.7781$.

2
$$2x+3 > 4$$
$$\underline{-3 \quad -3}$$
$$2x \quad > 1$$

multiplying both sides by $\frac{1}{2}$,

$$x \quad > \tfrac{1}{2} > 0.$$

3 (i) $\log y = \log 7 + \frac{1}{3} \log x$.

(ii) No. There is no operation in logarithms to correspond to adding natural numbers.

(iii) No, if x is a positive number: there are no logarithms of negative numbers, because raising a number to a power can never produce a negative number. This suggests that our trick of logarithmic transforms must be confined to cases in which the independent variable is always positive.

4 The form is $\log y = \log a + b \log x$. From the incremental ratio, $b = 3$. The intercept, $\log y = 1$, gives $\log a$. Hence

$$y = (\text{antilog } 1)(x^3)$$

$$= 10x^3.$$

Chapter 4A

1 Substitute $p = (a-c)/(d-b)$ into $q^s = c + dp$. Only rearrangement is required to find $q = (ad-bc)/(d-b)$.

If we find p by assuming that $q^d = q^s$ we must find the price such that we are simultaneously on both the demand and the supply curves. Hence we may read off the corresponding equilibrium quantity from either curve and must get the same answer.

2 Substituting (17) into (1),

$$q = a + b\left[\frac{a-c}{d-b} + \frac{d}{d-b}\,t\right]$$

$$= \frac{ad-bc}{d-b} + \frac{db}{d-b}\,t.$$

The intercept parameters do not appear in the coefficient of t. Compare this result with equation (12).

3 $p = 250$ instead of 200 and $q = 700$ instead of 800. The easiest way of obtaining this answer is to substitute directly into (17) to find p; then subtract 75 and substitute into (5) to find q.

4 (i) Yes; (ii) no (notice that, if the demand curve is above the supply curve, consumers are willing to purchase at a higher price than suppliers

require – the trouble is that they cannot discover an equilibrium – whereas if the supply curve is everywhere above the demand curve, the answer must be that nothing is produced); (iii) the two curves coincide.

6 By perfectly inelastic demand, we mean that a given quantity, $\bar{q}$, is demanded, irrespective of price.

Hence in place of (1) we have $q^d = \bar{q}$. Together with (15), $q^s = c + dp - dt$, we have $p = [(\bar{q} - c)/d] + t$. This says that price goes up by the full amount of the tax, which is the standard result.

By a perfectly elastic demand curve, we mean a vertical one: consumers will take anything they are offered at some given price $\bar{p}$. Proof that the tax falls entirely upon suppliers should now be routine. Consider $q^s = c + d(\bar{p} - t)$, where $\bar{p}$ is a constant.

Chapter 4B

1 (a) The increase in government spending leads to increased income; this increases tax yield; hence the deficit cannot rise by the full amount of the increase in government spending.
(b) $1/[1 - c(1-1)] = 1$: income increases by exactly the increase in government expenditure, but so does tax yield, so $\Delta D = 0$.
(c) Obvious error: it is assumed that taxable income is independent of the tax-rate. In our judgement, British Budget speeches usually leave the basis of the Treasury's calculations obscure.

2 It is necessary to show that $k/(1 - tk) > k$ or that $1/(1 - tk) > 1$. From (14) and (15) we know that $1 - tk < 1$.

3 The slope is k.

4 Starting at S, on the full-employment frontier, an increase in the provision of collective goods requires a transfer of resources from households to the government. This means increased taxation, which is unpopular. If society is inside its production frontier, private consumption and government expenditure are complementary instead of competitive.

5 (a) Evaluating the multiplier of equation (20), we find $k = \frac{25}{13}$. The sum of autonomous expenditures is 299, whence $Y = 575$.
(b) Balance requires $G = T$. $T = tY = tk(I + G + X)$. Hence the answer is provided by solving for G the equation

$$G = tk(I + G + X)$$
$$= tkG + tk(I + X)$$

whence

$$G - tkG = G(1 - tk) = tk(I + X)$$

13

and

$$G = \frac{tk}{1-tk}(I+X)$$

$$tk = \tfrac{1}{5} \cdot \tfrac{25}{13} = \tfrac{5}{13}; \quad 1-tk = \tfrac{8}{13};$$

hence

$$G = \frac{5}{13} \cdot \frac{13}{8} \cdot 200 = 125.$$

(c) Balance requires $M = X$.

$$M = mY(1-t) = m(1-t)k(I+G+X).$$

Hence the answer is provided by solving for G the equation

$$X = m(1-t)k(I+G+X).$$

Rearrangement gives

$$m(1-t)kG = X - m(1-t)kX - m(1-t)kI$$

whence

$$G = \frac{1-m(1-t)k}{m(1-t)k} X - I.$$

Substituting in numerical values of m, t, k, x, and I, required $G=60$. Notice that by transferring I to the left-hand side of the last equation, we have the solution for the level of total home injections that lead to balance of payments equilibrium for a given X.

(d) Merely solve for G

$$700 = kG + kI + kX$$

to find $G = 320$.

(e) $M = mY(1-t) = 160$ in this case, so the deficit is 80.

(f) (i) $\dfrac{\Delta D}{\Delta Y} = \dfrac{tk}{k} = \dfrac{1}{5}$: rather obviously the tax rate.

    (ii) $\dfrac{\Delta D}{\Delta M} = \dfrac{tk}{m(1-t)k} = \dfrac{5}{4}$.

    (iii) $\dfrac{\Delta Y}{\Delta M} = \dfrac{1}{m(1-t)} = \dfrac{4}{25}$ directly.

(g) $S+T+M=(1-c)Y(1-t)+tY+mY(1-t)=229$ if $G=99$ as in (a). $I+G=219$ and $S+T=225$, so home investment is entirely home financed, and capital is being exported: there is a balance of payments surplus of 6 as may be verified. It is sometimes said that the export of capital takes place 'at the expense' of home investment. Here, at least, this is impossible since I is fixed. An increase in G will lead to balance of payments deficit, i.e., capital imports!

(h) Deficit–financed expenditure is required to reach full-employment, at which there is a large balance of payments deficit. Consider devaluation; any other measures for reducing the balance of payments deficit; and measures to increase domestic investment.

Chapter 5

1 (a)
$$\frac{dq}{dp} = \frac{-1200}{p^2}$$

$$\eta = \frac{dq}{dp} \cdot \frac{p}{q} = \frac{-1200}{p^2} \cdot \frac{p}{q}$$

$$= -\frac{1200}{pq}$$

$$= -\frac{1200}{1200}$$

$$= -1.$$

(b)
$$\frac{dq}{dp} = -Cp^{-2}$$

$$\frac{dq}{dp} \cdot \frac{p}{q} = -\frac{C}{p^2} \cdot \frac{p}{q}$$

$$= -\frac{C}{pq}$$

$$= -\frac{C}{C}$$

$$= -1.$$

2
$$q = Cp^{-\alpha}$$

$$\frac{dq}{dp} = -\alpha Cp^{-\alpha-1}$$

$$= -\frac{\alpha C}{p^{\alpha+1}}$$

$$\frac{dq}{dp} \cdot \frac{p}{q} = -\frac{\alpha C}{p^{\alpha+1}} \cdot \frac{p}{q}$$

$$= -\frac{\alpha C}{p^{\alpha} q}$$

$$= -\frac{\alpha C}{C}$$

$$= -\alpha.$$

3 (i) Car 1   Speed $= \dfrac{dD}{dt} = 40$

Car 2   Speed $= 30 + t$

Car 3   Speed $= 50 + 20t^{-2}$

Car 4   Speed $= +20 - 2t.$

(ii) Car 1 is travelling at a constant speed of 40 m.p.h.

(iii) Car 2 is accelerating at a constant rate of 1 m.p.h.; i.e., every hour its speed is increasing by 1 m.p.h., i.e.,

$$\frac{d \text{ speed}}{dt} = \frac{d^2 D}{dt^2} = +1.$$

(iv) Car 3 is decelerating. To see this calculate

$$\frac{d \text{ speed}}{dt} = \frac{d^2 D}{dt^2} = -40t^{-3};$$

its speed is decreasing as time passes. Car 4 is more difficult. It is first decelerating, i.e., $d^2 D/dt^2 = -2$, but it then turns round and rushes towards Marble Arch at an ever-increasing speed.

(v) The speed of Car 3 approaches the limit of 50 m.p.h. because

$$\lim_{t \to \infty} (20t^{-2}) = 0.$$

(vi) Car 4 returns to London. To discover when, set $D = 0$ and solve for t to get $t = -10$ or $+30$. We are not interested in negative times so we conclude that Car 4 arrives back at London 30 hours after it sets out. If all cars were heading north we can regard distances south of London as negative ones and Car 4's path is then defined as speeding south of London at an ever faster rate as time passes.

4

$$\frac{dy}{dx} = 3 + 15x^2 + 35x^4$$

$$\frac{d^2y}{dx^2} = 30x + 140x^3$$

$$\frac{d^3y}{dx^3} = 30 + 420x^2$$

$$\frac{d^4y}{dx^4} = 840x$$

$$\frac{d^5y}{dx^5} = 840.$$

5 (a)
$$TR = 1000p - 3p^2$$
$$MR = 1000 - 6p.$$

(b)
$$p = AR = a - bq$$
$$TR = pq = aq - bq^2$$
$$MR = a - 2bq.$$

(c)
$$p = f(q)$$
$$TR = qp = qf(q)$$
$$MR = \frac{dTR}{dq} = f(q) + qf'(q).$$

6
$$\frac{dq^d}{dp} = -5 - 0{\cdot}3p^2$$

$$\frac{dp}{dt} = 3t^{1/2}$$

$$\frac{dq^d}{dt} = (-5 - 0{\cdot}3p^2)3t^{1/2}$$

$$= -15t^{1/2} - 0{\cdot}9p^2t^{1/2}$$

but
$$p = 2t^{3/2}$$
so
$$p^2 = 4t^3.$$

Substituting to remove p^2 gives

$$\frac{dq^d}{dt} = -15t^{1/2} - 3{\cdot}6t^{7/2}.$$

Substituting directly into the expression for q^d gives

$$q^d = 1000 - 10t^{3/2} - 0.8t^{9/2}$$

$$\frac{dq^d}{dt} = -15t^{1/2} - 3.6t^{7/2}.$$

7 (a) (i)
$$\frac{dy}{dx} = 2$$

(ii)
$$\frac{dy}{dx} = 2x$$

(iii)
$$\frac{dy}{dx} = 3x^2.$$

(b) (i)
$$\frac{dx}{dy} = \frac{1}{2}$$

(ii)
$$\frac{dx}{dy} = \frac{1}{2x}$$

(iii)
$$\frac{dx}{dy} = \frac{1}{3x^2}.$$

(c) (i)
$$x = \frac{y}{2} - 5$$

(ii)
$$x = y^{1/2}$$

(iii)
$$x = y^{1/3}.$$

(d) (i)
$$\frac{dx}{dy} = \frac{1}{2}$$

(ii)
$$\frac{dx}{dy} = \frac{1}{2y^{1/2}}$$

but
$$y = x^2.$$

so
$$\frac{dx}{dy} = \frac{1}{2(x^2)^{1/2}}$$

$$= \frac{1}{2x}.$$

(iii)
$$\frac{dx}{dy} = \frac{1}{3y^{2/3}}$$

but
$$y = x^3$$

so
$$\frac{dx}{dy} = \frac{1}{3x^2}$$

Chapter 6

1 (a) $MC = 1000 - 1000q + 2q^2$.

(b) $\dfrac{d^2C}{dq^2} = 4q - 1000$.

(c) $\dfrac{C}{q} = 5000q^{-1} + 1000 - 500q + \frac{2}{3}q^2$.

(d) $q=0$ or $q=375$ by solving for q the equation
$$1000 - 1000q + 2q^2 = 1000 - 500q + \tfrac{2}{3}q^2.$$

2 (a) No, because $MC = 1\cdot32 - 0\cdot0004q$ is a decreasing function of q: faced with a constant price, the firm would expand output indefinitely.
(b) No, by (a) and the result of 6.3 above, that diminishing marginal product is *necessary* as well as sufficient for increasing marginal cost given a constant factor price.

3 (a) $MR = \dfrac{d}{dq}(100q - 2q^2) = 100 - 4q$.

(b) MR falls twice as fast as AR ($4q$ to $2q$).
(c) 50, by putting $100 - 4q = 0$, whence $q=25$ and $p=100-50$. Note that this occurs at the half-way point between zero and the intercept of 100.

4 (a) $\dfrac{d(pq)}{dq} = \dfrac{d(aq^{\beta+1})}{dq} = a(\beta+1)q^\beta$.

(b) $\eta = \dfrac{dq}{dp}\cdot\dfrac{p}{q} = \dfrac{1}{\beta aq^{\beta-1}}\cdot\dfrac{aq^\beta}{q} = \dfrac{1}{\beta}$.

Notice that we have written the function in the Marshallian way. The function $q=ap^b$ has an elasticity of b.

(c) If price is to be positive, a must be positive. But a downward-sloping demand curve requires $\beta aq^{\beta-1}$ negative, hence β must be negative.

5 (a) $\dfrac{dq}{dl} = 3al^2 + 2bl + c.$

(b) $AP = al^2 + bl + c + dl^{-1}.$

6 To use (18), notice that

$$g(l) = cl + dl^2$$

$$g'(l) = c + 2dl$$

$$f'(q) = b$$

and, to eliminate q, we have

$$f[g(l)] = a + b(cl + dl^2).$$

Thus substitution into (18) gives

$$\frac{dR}{dl} = (cl + dl^2)b(c + 2dl) + (c + 2dl)\{a + b(cl + dl^2)\}$$

and only routine simplification is now required.

7 (a) From (22)

$$\frac{dV}{dq} = \frac{w}{g'(l)} = \frac{10}{(0\cdot2)(100) - (0\cdot0015)(100^2)} = 2.$$

(b) $d^2q/dl^2 = 0\cdot2 - 0\cdot003l$. This becomes negative (diminishing returns set in) when l exceeds $66\frac{2}{3}$, hence with constant wages marginal cost starts to increase (see 6.3).

8 $-ck^2 = \dfrac{-75}{16}$: see equation (32).

9 (a) $-ck^2 = \dfrac{-4}{5}\left(\dfrac{25}{13}\right)^2 = \dfrac{-500}{169}.$

(b) From (38),

$$\frac{k^2(1-c)}{(1-tk)^2} = \frac{\left(\dfrac{25}{13}\right)^2 \cdot \dfrac{1}{5}}{\left(1 - \dfrac{5}{13}\right)^2} = \frac{125}{169} \cdot \frac{169}{64} = \frac{125}{64}.$$

(c) From (42),

$$\frac{1}{m(1-t)^2} = \frac{1}{\frac{1}{5}\left(\frac{4}{5}\right)^2} = \frac{125}{15}.$$

10 (a)

$$\frac{\Delta Y}{\Delta B} = \frac{\Delta Y}{\Delta M} = \frac{\Delta Y}{\Delta G} \cdot \frac{\Delta G}{\Delta M}$$

and

$$\frac{\Delta Y}{\Delta G} = k(1-g)$$

hence

$$\frac{\Delta Y}{\Delta B} = \frac{k(1-g)}{g + m(1-t)k(1-g)}.$$

(b) We may apply the quotient rule to (a), or the product rule to take

$$\frac{\mathrm{d}}{\mathrm{d}t}\left(\frac{\Delta Y}{\Delta G} \cdot \frac{\Delta G}{\Delta M}\right) = \frac{\Delta Y}{\Delta G}\frac{\mathrm{d}}{\mathrm{d}t}\left(\frac{\Delta G}{\Delta M}\right) + \frac{\Delta G}{\Delta M}\frac{\mathrm{d}}{\mathrm{d}t}\left(\frac{\Delta Y}{\Delta G}\right)$$

$$= k(1-g)\frac{\mathrm{d}}{\mathrm{d}t}\{g + m(1-t)k(1-g)\} + \{g + m(1-t)k(1-g)\}\frac{\mathrm{d}}{\mathrm{d}t}\{k(1-g)\}.$$

Persistent application of the product rule, the use of $\mathrm{d}k/\mathrm{d}t = -ck^2$, and brute force would be required to take this much further: we should look for an easier way to proceed! We know from (42) that $(\mathrm{d}/\mathrm{d}t)(\Delta Y/\Delta B) > 0$ in the case in which there is no import-content in the *multiplicand*. If all the import coefficients in the multiplicand are, however, positive fractions, it is impossible that the *direction* of any effect be altered: only magnitudes are affected.

Chapter 7

1 The sign of x depends on the sign of $-b/2a$; to find the sign of y, substitute:

$$y = a\left(\frac{-b}{2a}\right)^2 + b\left(\frac{-b}{2a}\right) + c.$$

2 (i) $x = 25$;   maximum
  (ii) $x = 100$; minimum
  (iii) $x = 5$;   maximum
  (iv) $x = -5$;   minimum.

3 Maximum at $x = -2$, minimum at $x = 5$, non-stationary inflexional point at $x = \frac{3}{2}$.

13*

4 (i) Stationary inflexional point at $x=-1$ (the roots of $dy/dx=0$ are both equal to -1, and $d^2y/dx^2=0$ at $x=-1$); no extreme values.

(ii) Maximum at $x=-1$, minimum at $x=1$, non-stationary inflexional point at $x=0$ (the roots of dy/dx are $x=\pm1$, and $d^2y/dx^2=0$ at $x=0$).

(iii) Minimum at $x=-\frac{3}{2}$; no other extreme or inflexional values ($(x+1)$ is a factor of the numerator, so that the function proves to be a quadratic. If the quotient rule is applied directly, the resulting numerator is divisible by $(x+1)^2$).

(iv) Minima at $x=\pm1$, maximum at $x=0$, points of inflexion at $x=\pm\sqrt{\frac{1}{3}}$ (to find the first derivative, use the substitution $z=x^2-1$. Solution of $dy/dx=0$ gives $x=0$ *or* $x=\pm1$; solution of $d^2y/dx^2=0$ gives $x^2=\frac{1}{3}$; by inspection, $y=0$ when $x=\pm1$, and increases monotonically for values of $x>1$ or $x<-1$).

(v) Maximum at $x=-2$ (the quotient rule may be applied directly; but it is much easier to divide out, obtaining $y=x^{-2}+x^{-1}$).

(vi) Minimum at $x=1$, maximum at $x=-2\frac{1}{3}$, point of inflexion at $x=-\frac{2}{3}$ (the required factors are $(3x+7)$, $(x-1)$).

Chapter 8

1 Let $C=c(q)$, $AC=c(q)/q$, and $MC=c'(q)$. If there is a value of q that satisfies $dAC/dq=qc'(q)-c(q)=0$, i.e., if the average cost curve is U-shaped (it could, after all, be monotonically increasing), then $AC=MC$ at that value: $c'(q)=c(q)/q$.

2 With zero MC, Π is maximised by maximising $TR=pq$. Using the product rule, set

$$p+q\frac{dp}{dq}=0$$

whence

$$\frac{dp}{dq}\cdot\frac{q}{p}=-1.$$

But this is the elasticity of demand by definition.

3 (i) Choose w to maximise wl subject to being on the demand curve, i.e., to $l=100-2w$. Thus set

$$\frac{d(wl)}{dw}=\frac{d}{dw}(100w-2w^2)=100-4w=0,$$

hence put $w=25$. Since $w=25$ maximises wl, it follows that no larger sum can be extracted from employers consistent with their being in equilibrium. To generalise, follow the Cournot case: maximise $w.f(w)$, where $f(w)$ is the employers' demand, by setting $d[w.f(w)]/dw=w.f'(w)+f(w)=0$. It follows that the wages bill is maximised at the wage at which the elasticity of employers' demand is unity. This follows from maximising $x.f(x)$, not from linearity.

(ii) To maximise $(0.9\bar{w})l$ where $l=100-2\bar{w}$ set $d/d\bar{w}[0.9\bar{w}(100-2\bar{w})]=d/d\bar{w}[90\bar{w}-1.8\bar{w}^2]=90-3.6\bar{w}=0$, whence $\bar{w}=25$, but take-home pay is $(0.9)(25)l$, i.e., has been reduced by 10%: the workers bear the whole tax. There is nothing freakish about this: it is better to pay tax on the maximum than on anything less! To check, set $(d/dw)[\alpha w.f(w)]=0$ where α is the proportion of after-tax wage to gross wage ($\alpha=0.9$ here). If $\alpha\neq0$ then $w.f'(w)+f(w)=0$ as before.

4 Substituting directly into (10), 8.2,

$$t = \frac{(-2)(0)-(1200)(4)}{(2)(-2)(4)} = \frac{-4800}{-16} = 300.$$

5 (i) $AVC=(1/q)(\frac{1}{3}q^3-5q^2+30q)$ which is minimised by $q=7\frac{1}{2}$: with $p=6$, is pays better to shut down.

6 (i) Quite straightforward: $q = \dfrac{a-c}{2(b+d)}$ and $p = a-\dfrac{b(a-c)}{2(b+d)}$.

If cost is to be a monotonic increasing function of output, d must be positive.

(ii) Now $\Pi = -(b+d)q^2-(c-a+t)q$. Setting the first derivative equal to zero, we find

$$\bar{q} = \frac{a-c}{2(b+d)} - \frac{t}{2(b+d)}$$

whence obviously

$$\frac{d\bar{q}}{dt} = -\frac{1}{2(b+d)} \quad \text{and} \quad \frac{d\bar{p}}{dt} = \frac{b}{2(b+d)}.$$

7 (i) Adding $3q$ to profit (instead of subtracting tq),

$$\Pi = -7.5q^2+150q-100$$

which is maximised by $q=10$, whence $p=145$.

(ii) $AVC = 3 + 7q$: in the short run, it pays to produce at any price above 3. From the demand curve, it is obvious that this can be done without a subsidy. At what price it pays to stay in business, i.e., at what price the fixed cost of 100 is covered, is another question.

(iii) $\Pi = -7 \cdot 5q^2 + 147q - 100 + sq$. First-order conditions give

$$q = \frac{147}{15} + \frac{s}{15}$$

whence, writing s for the subsidy per unit,

$$\frac{d\bar{q}}{ds} = \frac{1}{15} \quad \text{and} \quad \frac{dp}{dq}\frac{d\bar{q}}{ds} = (-0 \cdot 5)\frac{1}{15} = -\frac{1}{30}.$$

Chapter 9

1 (i)
$$f_x = 6x + 4y$$
$$f_y = 4x + 2y$$
$$f_{xx} = 6$$
$$f_{yy} = 2$$
$$f_{xy} = f_{yx} = 4.$$

(ii)
$$f_x = 3x^2 + 2xy + 2y^2$$
$$f_y = x^2 + 4xy + 6y^2$$
$$f_{xx} = 6x + 2y$$
$$f_{yy} = 4x + 12y$$
$$f_{xy} = f_{yx} = 2x + 4y.$$

(iii)
$$f_x = ay^{-2}$$
$$f_y = -2axy^{-3}$$
$$f_{xx} = 0$$
$$f_{yy} = +6axy^{-4}$$
$$f_{xy} = f_{yx} = -2ay^{-3}$$

(iv)
$$f_x = -x^{-2}y^{-1}$$
$$f_y = -x^{-1}y^{-2}$$
$$f_{xx} = +2x^{-3}y^{-1}$$
$$f_{yy} = +2x^{-1}y^{-3}$$
$$f_{xy} = f_{yx} = x^{-2}y^{-2}.$$

2
$$\frac{dx}{dy} = -\frac{f_y}{f_x} = -\frac{-x^{-1}y^{-2}}{-x^{-2}y^{-1}}$$

$$= -\frac{x}{y}.$$

Of course $dy/dx = -(y/x)$. The slope in either case depends only on the ratio of x to y and not on their absolute values.

3
$$\frac{dx}{dt} = 3, \qquad \frac{dy}{dt} = 6t.$$

Now substitute into $dz/dt = f_x\, dx/dt + f_y\, dy/dt$ to obtain

(i) $\dfrac{dz}{dt} = 18x + 12y + 24xt + 12yt.$

(ii) $9x^2 + 6xy + 6y^2 + 6x^2t + 24xyt + 36y^2t.$

(iii) $3ay^{-2} - 12axy^{-3}t.$

(iv) $-3x^{-2}y^{-1} - 6x^{-1}y^{-2}t.$

4 $f_c = (t-1)k^2$
$f_m = (1-t)k^2$
$f_t = (c-m)k^2$
$f_{cc} = 2(t-1)^2k^3$
$f_{mm} = 2(1-t)^2k^3$
$f_{tt} = 2(c-m)^2k^3.$

5 (i) Marginal utility of $x = \dfrac{\partial U}{\partial x} = \alpha x^{\alpha-1}y^\beta.$

Marginal utility of $y = \dfrac{\partial U}{\partial y} = \beta x^\alpha y^{\beta-1}.$

Since $\alpha, \beta < 1$ it follows that $\partial U/\partial x$ diminishes as x increases and $\partial U/\partial y$ diminishes as y increases. This is obvious from inspection but you can also take f_{xx} and f_{yy} and show that these necessarily have a negative sign.
(ii) Holding U constant we have $x^\alpha = \overline{U}/y^\beta$ or $x = \overline{U}^{1/\alpha}/y^\beta$. These are convex indifference curves asymptotic to the x- and y-axes.

$$\frac{dx}{dy} = -\frac{f_y}{f_x} = -\frac{\beta x^\alpha y^{\beta-1}}{\alpha x^{\alpha-1}y^\beta} = -\frac{\beta x}{\alpha y} = -\frac{\beta}{\alpha}\cdot\frac{x}{y}.$$

This is the general case of which 1(iv) was an example in which $\alpha = \beta = -1$. Inspection shows the slope to have the correct sign.

(iv) $$f_{xy} = \alpha\beta x^{\alpha-1} y^{\beta-1}$$

as y increases the marginal utility of x decreases.

(v) No, as you will see by calculating f_{yx} just as a check.

(vi) Set $f_x = 0$ to get

$$\alpha x^{\alpha-1} y^{\beta} = 0.$$

This is only true for $x = 0$ or $y = 0$. The household attaches no utility to consuming one product on its own; if $y = 0$, $f_x = 0$ for all x! If y is held constant at some positive amount, $f_x > 0$ for all positive finite x. As $x \to \infty$, however, $f_x \to 0$, showing that marginal utility gets very small as x gets very large although it is always positive for any finite value of x.

Chapter 10

1
$$f_x = 2xz^{-1}$$
$$f_z = -x^2 z^{-2}.$$

According to Euler's theorem

$$y = f_x x + f_z z.$$

Thus $$y = (2xz^{-1})x + (-x^2 z^{-2})z$$

with $x = 2$, $z = 4$ this gives $y = 1$.

Now substitute into $y = x^2 z^{-1}$ to get $y = 1$ also.

2 (i) Decreasing returns to labour:

$$\frac{\partial q}{\partial L} = \frac{2C^{2/3}}{3L^{1/3}}, \qquad \frac{\partial^2 q}{\partial L^2} = -\frac{2C^{2/3}}{9L^{4/3}}.$$

Similarly for capital.

(ii) Increasing returns to scale: $q\lambda^{4/3} = (\lambda C)^{2/3} (\lambda L)^{2/3}$.

(iii) $\frac{2}{3}q$ to labour and $\frac{2}{3}q$ to capital making an (impossible) total of $\frac{4}{3}q$.

3 (i) $\dfrac{\partial q}{\partial L} = \alpha A C^{\alpha} L^{\alpha-1}$.

If marginal product of L is to be constant $\partial^2 q / \partial L^2$ must be zero for positive L and C and $\partial q / \partial L$ must be a constant. By inspection if $\alpha = 1$, $\partial q / \partial L = AC$, $\partial^2 q / \partial L^2 = 0$. Similarly for capital.

(ii) Increasing returns to scale are just strong enough so that the scale effects of raising output, even by raising only one input, just counterbalances the effect of changing factor proportions.

4 A simple substitution of $d\alpha=0$, $d\beta>0$ and $d\alpha=0$, $d\beta<0$ is sufficient to establish $dp=S_\beta\,d\beta/(D_p-S_p)$. Insertion of $d\beta$ appropriately positive or negative is all that is required.

5 Substitute $d\alpha>0$ and $d\beta=0$ into (70) and manipulate to obtain

$$\frac{dY}{d\alpha}=\frac{C_\alpha}{1-C_Y}>0.$$

6 (i) $P=MT^{-1}k^{-1}$.

(ii) $\dfrac{\partial P}{\partial M}=\dfrac{1}{Pk}>0$ (and the same at all levels of M)

$\dfrac{\partial P}{\partial T}=\dfrac{-M}{T^2k}<0$

$\dfrac{\partial P}{\partial k}=\dfrac{-M}{Tk^2}<0.$

Thus an increase in T or k lowers P but the relation between ΔP and ΔT and ΔP and Δk is not one of simple proportionality (as it is between ΔP and ΔM).

(iii) $dP=f_M\,dM+f_k\,dk+f_T\,dT$

$=\dfrac{dM}{Tk}-\dfrac{M\,dk}{Tk^2}-\dfrac{M\,dT}{T^2k}.$

Chapter 11

1 (i) $x=50$, $y=100$. Comparison with (16) shows that the equilibrium quantity of both goods is doubled. This suggests that the locus of equilibria for given prices and varying income is a ray through the origin. The objective function $2x^{1/2}y^{1/2}$ is homogeneous of degree one.
(ii) None. Replacing the multiplicative constant 2 by 10 only means that 'utility' is 5 times as large. This is an irrelevant assertion: equilibrium values are unchanged. So are they if a constant is added.
(iii) $f_{xx}=-\frac{1}{2}x^{-3/2}y^{1/2}$; $f_{yy}=-\frac{1}{2}x^{1/2}y^{-3/2}$; $f_{xy}=\frac{1}{2}x^{-1/2}y^{-1/2}$.

2 (i) $x = 75$; $y = 30$.

(ii) Substitute into (20), or use (21), taking advantage of the fact that the value of a positive multiplicative constant cannot affect the sign of the derivative.

3 (i) $x = 52$; $y = 25$.

(ii) Positive first derivatives,

$$f_x = (20)(25) - (2)(52) > 0$$
$$f_y = (20)(52) - (2)(25) > 0,$$

and negative second derivatives,

$$f_{xx} = f_{yy} = -2.$$

4 (i), (ii) Both functions linear. If the slope of $f(x, y)$ is not equal to that of $F(x, y)$, corner solution; if it is, anywhere on $F(x, y)$ is optimal.

(iii) Perfect substitutes; slope of iso-f curve $= -a/b$, a constant.

Chapter 12

1 One to one. The function is the form of (13), and the answer may be obtained by substitution into (17.2).

2 Maximising one objective function subject to a given value of another, we have a convex iso-f curve and a concave constraint. If a linear constraint is sufficient so, *a fortiori*, is a concave one.

3 (i) $x = y = 50$.

(ii) The rationing is effective: see points S and Q in Figure 11.5. With unchanged prices, only 40 can be spent on x, so consumption of y becomes 60. Calculus methods will not work: no tangency.

4 x and y are positively associated, y and z negatively. Hence (i) is not a constraint, (ii) is.

Substitute from (i) into f, and maximise

$$V = \tfrac{1}{2}y^2 z^2 + \lambda(B - az - y).$$

The usual manipulations yield $z = B/2a$, $y = \tfrac{1}{2}B$; substitution into (i) yields $x = \tfrac{1}{4}B$.

5 Discussion question.

6 Parallel horizontal lines, parallel vertical lines; slope undefined ($MRS = \infty$), slope zero ($MRS = 0$); discussion.

7 Discussion question.

8 Questions (1), (3(i)), and (4).

Chapter 13

1 (a) Macro-theory tells us that $\alpha < 0$: income falls when income (Y) exceeds expenditure $(C+I)$ and rises when $Y < C+I$.

(b) The graph will be a straight line through the origin with a slope of α. (dY/dt is on the Y-axis and $Y-C-I$ on the X-axis.)

(c) We require expenditure to exceed income for $Y > Y^*$ and expenditure to be less than income for $Y < Y^*$.

(d) At equilibrium income equals expenditure. $dY/dY = 1$ and thus we require for (c) that $dE/dY < 1$ (where E is expenditure and is the same thing as $C+I$). This is easily established:

$$E = C+I$$
$$= a+cY+\bar{I}$$

$$\frac{dE}{dY} = c \quad \text{(the marginal propensity to consume).}$$

Therefore we require $c < 1$, which is the familiar condition that the aggregate expenditure line should have a slope less than the 45° line.

2 (a) Market 1: $p = 150$
$\qquad\qquad\quad q = 300$
$\quad$ Market 2: $p = 300$
$\qquad\qquad\quad q = 1500$.

(b) Market 1 is stable since $A = -\frac{1}{3}$
$\quad$ Market 2 is unstable since $A = -\frac{5}{4}$.

	Market 1	Market 2
p_0	350	280
p_1	83·34	325
p_2	172·22	268·75
p_3	142·59	339·06
p_4	152·43	251·17
p_5	149·19	361·04

(d) Eventually the price falls to zero ($q^d > q^s$ at $p=0$). In the next period $q^s = 0$ and there can be no price in subsequent periods if nothing is produced. On this interpretation the oscillations cease as soon as p reaches zero. If we were not constrained to the positive quadrant the oscillations would grow indefinitely.

Chapter 14

1 (a) $y = x^3$.

  (b) $y = \frac{1}{12}x^4$.

  (c) $y = 2x^3 + \frac{3}{4}x^4$.

  (d) $y = \frac{1}{6}x^{3/2}$.

  (e) $y = \frac{9}{2}x^{2/3}$.

  (f) $y = \frac{1}{3}x^3 - \frac{1}{2}x^2$.

2 $TC = 100 + 10x - 0.005x^2 + 0.0003x^3$.

The constant of integration is fixed cost, here equal to 100.

3 (a) $0.09e^{0.03x}$.

  (b) $-\frac{1}{4}e^{-x/4}$.

(Notice that $e^{-x/4} = e^{(-1/4)x}$, and the rule $(d/dx)e^{ax} = ae^{ax}$ may be applied at once.)

4 (a) $e^{0.1x}$.

  (b) $3e^{2x}$.

5 (a) $y = y_0 e^{rt} : \dfrac{dy}{dt} = ry_0 e^{rt}$ and

$$\frac{1}{y}\frac{dy}{dt} = \frac{ry_0 e^{rt}}{y_0 e^{rt}} = r.$$

  (b) $y = 4e^1 = 10.853$.

6 (i) $\frac{2}{3}$ of one percent (ii) $\frac{1}{3}$.

'Percentage response' is elasticity, by definition, and $\eta_{y:x} = d \log y/d \log x$. Thus the exponents in the Cobb–Douglas function are the elasticities of output with respect to the inputs.

7 (a) $TR = 100q - 10q^2 + C$

$$AR = 100 - 10q + \frac{C}{q}.$$

  (b) When nothing is sold nothing can be earned, hence the total revenue function must pass through the origin: C is zero.

8

$$\frac{d \log q}{d \log p} = -\frac{1}{4}$$

$$d \log q = -\tfrac{1}{4} d \log p$$

$$\int d \log q = \int -\tfrac{1}{4} d \log p$$

$$q = p^{-1/4}.$$

9 (a)
$$\frac{dE}{dY} = m+c = 0{\cdot}2+0{\cdot}7 = 0{\cdot}9$$

(b)
$$E = a+0{\cdot}9Y.$$

The constant a stands for all forms of expenditure that do not vary with income.

Chapter 15

1 You should answer the question in the following steps.
  (a) Calculate the equilibrium level of income Y^*.
  (b) Derive an expression for the deviation of actual income Y from its equilibrium level Y^*. Call this $\hat{Y}$.
  (c) Substitute into the adjustment function to obtain an expression for dY/dt.
  (d) Integrate this expression to get Y.
  (e) Inspect the solution to show that an arbitrary disturbance $\hat{Y}_0$ gets progressively smaller as time passes.

2 (a) $\dfrac{\partial q}{\partial L} = \alpha A_0 e^{rt} L^{\alpha-1} C^{1-\alpha}$

$$\frac{\partial^2 q}{\partial L\, \partial t} = \alpha r A_0 e^{rt} L^{\alpha-1} C^{1-\alpha}.$$

and, for the proportionate rate of change,
$$\frac{1}{\partial q/\partial L} \cdot \frac{\partial^2 q}{\partial L\, \partial t} = r$$

and similarly for capital.
  (b) It doesn't, since α is unaffected, so both marginal products grow at the same rate. Thus the shapes of the iso-quants are unaffected: they simply move towards the origin. Technical progress which does not alter the MRS may be called neutral.

  (c) They aren't, since they depend only on α.

  (d) $\dfrac{1}{q}\dfrac{dq}{dt} = r.$

  (e) $dq = \dfrac{\partial q}{\partial t}\, dt + \dfrac{\partial q}{\partial L}\, dL + \dfrac{\partial q}{\partial C}\, dC$

  or

  $$\frac{dq}{dt} = \frac{\partial q}{\partial t} + \frac{\partial q}{\partial L}\frac{dL}{dt} + \frac{\partial q}{\partial C}\frac{dC}{dt}.$$

(f) From (e),

$$\frac{1}{q}\frac{dq}{dt} = \frac{1}{q}\frac{\partial q}{\partial t} + \frac{1}{q}\frac{\partial q}{\partial L}\frac{dL}{dt} + \frac{1}{q}\frac{\partial q}{\partial C}\frac{dC}{dt}.$$

Evaluating this,

$$\frac{1}{q}\frac{dq}{dt} = r + \frac{1}{q}\alpha A_0 e^{rt}L^{\alpha-1}C^{1-\alpha}\frac{dL}{dt} + \frac{1}{q}(1-\alpha)A_0 e^{rt}L^{\alpha}C^{-\alpha}\frac{dC}{dt}.$$

Substituting for the q's in the denominators of the right-hand side, and simplifying,

$$\frac{1}{q}\frac{dq}{dt} = r + \alpha\frac{1}{L}\frac{dL}{dt} + (1-\alpha)\frac{1}{C}\frac{dC}{dt}$$

$$= r + \alpha n + (1-\alpha)m.$$

Hence output grows at rate r *plus* the rates of growth of inputs, each weighed by its elasticity coefficient.

6 (a)
$$Y_t^1 = Ae^{nt}$$
$$Y_t^2 = Be^{rt}$$

set $Y_t^1 = Y_t^2$ and solve for t.

$$Ae^{nt} = Be^{rt}$$

taking logs to the base e

$$\log A + \log n \log t = \log B + \log r \log t$$
$$\log t (\log n - \log r) = \log B - \log A$$
$$\log t = \frac{\log B - \log A}{\log n - \log r}$$

whence

$$t = \left(\frac{B}{A}\right)^{r/n}.$$

Thus the time taken to catch up depends on how wide is the proportionate gap at the outset and the ratio of the two growth rates.
(b) Inspection shows that a number greater than unity is being raised by an exponent greater than unity.
(c) (i) In country 1 the proportional rate of growth is

$$\frac{dY}{dt}\cdot\frac{1}{Y} = \frac{nAe^{nt}}{Ae^{nt}} = n$$

and in country 2 it is r. Thus the ratio of the two is n/r which is unity by assumption.

(ii)
$$\frac{\mathrm{d}}{\mathrm{d}t}\left(\frac{Ae^{nt}}{Be^{nt}}\right) = \frac{\mathrm{d}}{\mathrm{d}t}\left(\frac{A}{B}\right) = 0.$$

(iii) The absolute discrepancy D is

$$D = Ae^{nt} - Be^{nt}$$

$$\frac{\mathrm{d}D}{\mathrm{d}t} = nAe^{nt} - nBe^{nt}$$

$$= ne^{nt}(A - B).$$

$A - B$ is a constant equal to the initial discrepancy but as t increases this absolute discrepancy increases at a constant rate. (This is consistent with the finding in (ii) that the ratios of the two countries' (growing) incomes were constant.)

INDEX

in income determination models, 83–93, 140–7, 175–8
in monopoly model, 182–7
lump sum, 182
rate, change of, and value of multiplier, 139–40
specific, 68, 172, 182
Tax theorem, 70
Tax yield
  in competitive market model, 137–9
  maximum of, in competitive market model, 172–5
  maximum of, in income model, 176–8
Thompson, Sylvanus P., *Calculus made Easy*, 12
Time, rate of change with respect to, notation, 285
Time lags, 298, 306–7
Time series, 41, 307
Total cost, *see* Costs
Total differential, *see* Differentiation
Total revenue, *see* Revenue
Trade unions, 350–1
Trade-off rate, 88, 89, 91–2, 145, 146, 255

Uncertainty, 7–8, 283
Unemployment
  rate of, and inflation, 286–9

rate of, and money wage rates, 348–57
Utility function, 237, 240, 278, 280, 281

Value judgements, 90
Variable cost, *see* Costs
Variables
  dependent and independent, 42–4
  endogenous and exogenous, 67
  introduced, 30
  relations between, 31 et seq.
Verbal logic, 9
Vertical axis, 32

Wages
  and conditions for efficiency in production, 271
  in marginal productivity theory, 225 et seq.
  rate of change of, and inflation, 355–7
  rate of change of, and unemployment, 348–55
  with imperfect markets, 229–31
Wages policy, 357
Walras' Law, 360
Weak inequalities, 56
Welfare economics, 268 et seq.